Torres Strait

Thursday Is.

Great

CAPE
YORK
PEN.

Coen

Cooktown

Cairns

Barrier

PACIFIC

Camooweal

Townsville

OCEAN

Mount Isa

Mackay

Reef

QLD

Springs

Rockhampton

SIMPSON
DESERT

Birdsville

FRASER ISLAND

STURTS
STONY
DESERT

Gympie

Lake Eyre

BRISBANE

A

Marree

Armidale

Bellingen

Broken
Hill

Port Augusta

Coonabarabran

Port Macquarie

EYRE PEN.

NSW

ADELAIDE

SYDNEY

CANBERRA

Murray River

VIC

MT KOSCIUSKO

Naracoorte

Merimbula

MELBOURNE

Port Campbell

Lakes Entrance

WILSONS PROMONTORY

N

Launceston

TAS

HOBART

AUSTRALIA

THE UNIQUE CONTINENT

AUSTRALIA
THE UNIQUE CONTINENT

JOCELYN BURT

Houghton Mifflin Company
Boston

ACKNOWLEDGEMENTS

I would like to thank Dick Lang of Desert-Trek Australia, Adelaide, for the trips into the Simpson and Sturt's Stony deserts; Doug Fearon of Austrek Safaris, Cairns, for the trip to Lawn Hill Gorge; the National Parks Service in Victoria, and the National Parks & Wildlife Service in New South Wales; and R. & D. Keller/Australasian Nature Transparencies for the aerial view of Green Island reproduced on page 81.

For Dick and Gail

First American edition 1989
Reprinted 1990
First published 1987 by J. M. Dent Pty Limited

Reissued 1989 by Houghton Mifflin Australia
PO Box 289, Ferntree Gully, Victoria 3156
112 Lewis Rd, Knoxfield 3180

For information about permission to reproduce selections from this book, write to Permissions, Houghton Mifflin Company, 2 Park Street, Boston, Massachusetts 02108.

Library of Congress Cataloguing-in-Publication Data

Burt, Jocelyn.
   Australia : the unique continent.

   1. Australia — Description and travel — 1981—
I. Title.
DU105.B84   1989   994   88-34728
ISBN 0-395-50935-1

Designed by Noni Edmunds
Typeset in 12/15 Goudy Old Style by Solo Typesetting, South Australia
Printed in Singapore by Kyodo Printing Co. Ltd

CONTENTS

INTRODUCING AUSTRALIA

AUSTRALIA *is* different. Its fascinating wildlife is unlike that of any other country; it has an abundance of interesting trees and plants; and its ancient topography contains some of the world's most unusual and striking scenery. It also boasts some of the world's greatest natural wonders, such as Ayers Rock, the Olgas, and the Great Barrier Reef.

It is a land full of extremes: there are snow-capped mountains and vast deserts of red sand and gleaming gibber stones; there are deliciously scented eucalypt woodlands, tropical rainforests, and cool myrtle-beech forests that recall the enchanted woods of fairytales. Colourful canyons and gorges contrast with fertile valleys and wide sweeping plains, while ranges of craggy granite dotted with fantastically shaped tors lie near tranquil lakes, splendid waterfalls, and bubbling streams that eventually become sedate rivers slowly carving their wide courses to the sea.

Along the country's 38 000 kilometres of coastline the scenic beauty is no less diverse. Coastal plains and mountains end abruptly at rock-encrusted shores or sheer off into spectacular, sometimes terrifyingly steep cliffs—the Great Australian Bight has the longest line of unbroken cliffs in the world. Remarkable landforms occur in many places, and magnificent beaches of white, gold and even red sand sweep along the coast between imposing headlands. Scores of islands lie offshore, many of them very beautiful and touched with more than a hint of romance.

For centuries Australia lay undisturbed while on other continents empires and civilizations rose and fell. It is extraordinary that this large landmass stayed virtually unknown to the outside world until so recently in history. Yet this has been a blessing for Australia because, although its original inhabitants, the Aborigines, were natural conservationists, the Europeans who eventually settled the country were not. As a result, the fragile environment of the world's flattest, driest and oldest continent has suffered badly in the 200 years since white settlement. Fortunately, there are still wilderness areas that remain practically untouched by outsiders, and such is Australia's vastness that places of astonishing beauty have remained almost unknown until the 1980s—the incredible Bungle Bungle Range in north-western Australia is a classic example, as, to a lesser degree, is Lawn Hill Gorge in western Queensland. The setting aside of large tracts of land as national parks has been of enormous importance to the country. Some of these parks are so significant that they have been placed on the World Heritage List: the Great Barrier Reef and Kakadu National Park are two examples.

It is only since the early 1970s that the rest of the world has been discovering Australia's exciting potential as a tourist destination. Apart from its unusual landscapes and wildlife, it has the added bonus of being a relatively safe place, both politically and environmentally. The natural bushland holds very few dangerous creatures, and bushwalkers need never carry a gun. Certainly there are some poisonous snakes, but people rarely meet these shy reptiles in the wild; and although one of the two species of crocodile in the far north can be very dangerous, it usually attacks only when its territorial rights are infringed—as when someone attempts to swim in its waterhole. There are a few poisonous spiders, but even the most experienced bushman may never meet any, unless he goes looking for them.

Another widely appreciated aspect of this country is the ease with which one can escape from the urban crowds and find solitude in the bush. This is possible simply because Australia is so sparsely populated. It has a land area roughly equal to that of the United States (excluding Alaska), but whereas the population of the United States is around 250 million, Australia's is a little more than 16 million. About 10 million live in the eight major cities—Canberra, Sydney, Melbourne, Brisbane, Adelaide, Perth, Hobart and Darwin—and two-thirds of these urban dwellers are found in Sydney and Melbourne. Settlement is concentrated on the fertile eastern and south-eastern coast, where five of the seven capitals lie and most of the major provincial centres are distributed. Much of the remainder of the country consists of thinly populated 'outback', a term generally used for the land that lies well beyond the coastal cities and towns, the settled rural areas, and the verdant slopes of the Great Dividing Range in the east. This means that the outback covers more than three-quarters of the Australian continent.

It is thus with considerable joy that many Australians make the most of the outdoor life, knowing that whether they are camping in the outback or bushwalking in wilderness areas of the forested Great Divide, they will be relatively safe. Nor will they have the unnerving experience, as so often happens in other parts of the world, of encountering local inhabitants who seem to materialize out of thin air whenever a stop is made in the 'bush'.

In this book I hope to give readers—and prospective travellers—a sampling of what there is to see in Australia, in the hope that they will be inspired to discover its special fascination for themselves. I would also like to share a few of my experiences, and to give motorists a general idea of accessibility and travelling conditions. Obviously, it is not possible for me to show more than a limited number of places: Australia is so huge and so diverse that it would take many volumes to cover it all. However, I have tried to make my selection as representative as possible; and above all, enjoyable.

Share my enjoyment, as we embark on a trip around a truly unique continent.

Jocelyn Burt

Page 2. Sunset in the Australian Alps
Page 6. Mount Sonder at sunrise, central Australia
Pages 10–11. Razorback Ridge and Mount Feathertop, Victoria   *Right.* Karri forest, near Pemberton, WA

ULURU

I T IS ABOUT half an hour before sunset on a cloudless winter day. A line of heavy traffic streams from the Yulara Tourist Village to the parking area known as Sunset Strip, already packed with cars and coaches. Hundreds of people take up positions on the red sandy plain and gaze expectantly at the brooding shape of the huge monolith lying about seven kilometres away. Already its colour is deepening. Innumerable cameras are clutched in readiness to capture that brief moment when it will flare red. These visitors have come to see one of Australia's great spectacles: Ayers Rock at sunset.

The largest piece of exposed rock in the world, Ayers Rock lies in Uluru National Park, south-west of Alice Springs in central Australia. Most people visiting it for the first time are not prepared for its awe-inspiring size, and initially they are perhaps more conscious of its magnitude than of anything else; later comes awareness of the superb detail in its deep gullies and ridges, and in its multitude of holes. Climbing the Rock has become a popular thing to do, in spite of the fact that it is difficult and, if you stray from the white line, dangerous. Everyone seems to want to attempt the climb, regardless of age or suitability of dress. Men and women well into their eighties have made the ascent; and I have seen on the slope women in tight skirts and high heels, and other hopefuls in thongs or wearing medical neck-braces. Most people take a good hour to reach the top, and return in about half the time.

The wonderful colour-effects characteristic of Ayers Rock are caused by vagaries of weather and the play of light. Throughout the day the Rock can change from soft shades of mauve and purple to deeper browns and pinks; and at sunrise and sunset it glows red, the brilliance of the colour determined by the amount of dust in the air and the position of the clouds. In unsettled weather, if a low sun manages to break through cloud the huge monolith may glow a warm gold; in sunshine after rain, it gleams like polished metal.

The other great attraction at Uluru is the Olgas, a collection of extraordinary domes lying in a circle 32 kilometres west of Ayers Rock. They too undergo some beautiful colour-changes. Although the Olgas are geologically distinct from the Rock, both formations are sandstone and each is the revealed surface of a huge parent rock lying under the sandy plain. The fascinating weatherbeaten shapes of the Olgas deserve to be given time—half a day is not enough. There are some lovely walks: Katajuta Lookout, at the top of the only dome that is easy to climb, is at its best in the morning; Mount Olga Gorge is superb in the afternoon; the Valley of the Winds is good at any time. Ayers Rock is encircled by a bitumen road, but the track out to the Olgas is rough and the north-west section of the perimeter track is suitable only for four-wheel-drive vehicles.

Many people find the Olgas more interesting than Ayers Rock. In a way they are; but the Rock is by far the more dramatic, and because of this you *experience* its gigantic presence rather than simply enjoying its beauty.

Ayers Rock
Mount Olga Gorge

KINGS CANYON

ONE OF central Australia's most thrilling places, this incredible canyon is situated in the George Gill Range in Kings Canyon National Park, 370 kilometres south-west of Alice Springs. Visitors travelling to Ayers Rock often include a visit to Kings Canyon, as it is only 170 kilometres from the Ayers Rock road; however, unlike the excellent bitumen road that runs to the Rock, the one leading to the canyon is mostly gravel. En route to the canyon is Wallara Ranch with its motel and camping facilities, a popular base for tour groups and campers.

Kings Canyon is best viewed from the top. To reach the plateau and the head of the canyon you take the marked path that starts at the carpark. Arriving there, you enter a different world. The plateau itself consists of a maze of small valleys topped by domed ridges of rock with a texture so ancient-looking that the overall effect is one of a ruined city. The finest scenery is at the head of the canyon, where the dramatic face of the south wall is so smoothly sheer that it appears to have been sliced by a colossal knife. Down in the canyon, 180 metres below, lie enormous boulders that broke away from the north wall about 2000 years ago. Some cracked sections of the south wall give the impression that it will not be too long before they join the break-away boulders below; indeed, in some cases you feel it would take no more than the weight of one foot to send the thin ledges crashing down. Kings Canyon is the sort of place that makes you feel very jittery when you see people standing close to the cliff edges; on one visit I came across a large group of tourists lying on their stomachs and looking down on the view below them that way.

Tucked behind the head of the canyon is a narrow cleft known as the Garden of Eden, which is full of lush and very beautiful vegetation, including many cycad palms clustered around perfectly still pools of limpid water. The cleft ends at the head of the canyon, where even grander vistas open up: the entire canyon is now visible and there is a breathtaking view of the north wall, which cannot be seen from the top. Access to the Garden of Eden is by way of a small but frightful-looking steep cliff, and the exit is by another route that looks even more hair-raising. An excursion into this spot is only for the fit and the brave, unless you have an experienced guide who knows it well. I was fortunate to have as a guide Jim Cotterill from Wallara Ranch, and he knew every rock and ledge that was safe to step on. Just before we negotiated the difficult exit, I casually asked him about two accidents that had occurred in recent weeks—in one a girl had plunged to her death and in the other a couple had been hurt in a fall. Exactly where had these accidents happened? 'Where we go up the cliff to get out of the garden,' he replied. 'Don't worry, you'll be right. The people who had the accidents didn't know the way.'

So do take care.

North wall, Kings Canyon

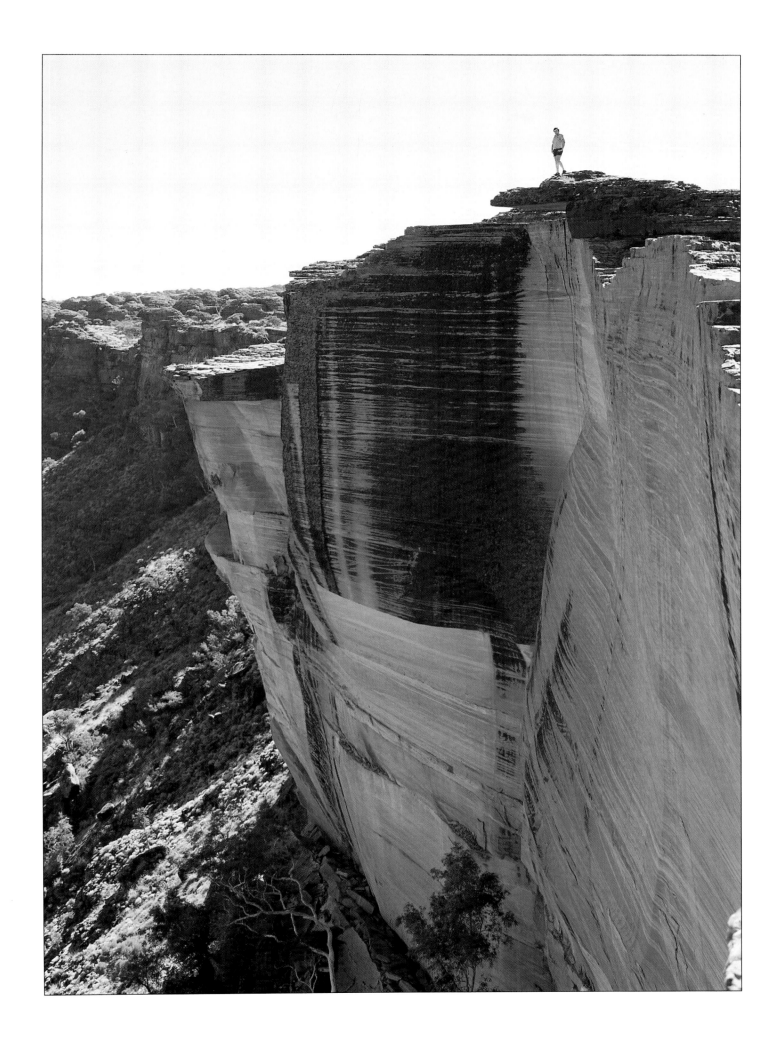

ORMISTON GORGE

THE RUGGED MacDonnell Ranges run for many kilometres both east and west of Alice Springs in central Australia, and are cut with numerous extraordinarily colourful gorges, gaps and chasms. Some are more spectacular than others, but the most dramatic of them all is Ormiston Gorge. Now a national park, it lies 134 kilometres west of Alice Springs and is linked to the town by a good bitumen road that goes to the entrance of the gorge, where the camping ground and ranger's station are situated.

Ormiston Gorge was formed by the action of Ormiston Creek, a tributary of the Finke River, which over millennia eroded lines of weakness in the rocks. Except when it is in flood, the creek is reduced to a few permanent waterholes, and at the gorge's entrance is merely a stretch of dry sand; further inside, the sand gives way to a creekbed studded with rocks. The northern end of the gorge opens out to Ormiston Pound, a natural amphitheatre that makes an ideal catchment for Ormiston Creek. On the pound's north-western side a massive wall rises to form a section of the base of Mount Sonder, one of the highest peaks in the MacDonnell Ranges.

Ormiston's glory is in its wonderfully craggy red-brown walls that rise to heights of 200 metres and are splashed with colours of white, yellow, vermilion, grey and black; but its magnificence is enhanced by its waterholes, which on a still day mirror everything in sight. If there is plenty of water around, the scene can be breathtaking. The best place to see these reflections is the long pool at the entrance to the gorge, only a few minutes' walk from the camping ground and carpark; and the best time to see them is the early morning.

To appreciate the full grandeur of Ormiston you need to walk right through the gorge, a walk that takes about an hour. Many people are deterred by the barrier of rocks on the right, near the end of the first pool, but these are easy enough to scramble over; and although for much of the distance you must pick your way over the stones in the creekbed, this is not difficult. When I walked through, on a mild afternoon with the winter sun low in the sky, much of the gorge was veiled in shadows, but there was still some lovely reflected light on the walls that loomed over the twisting creek. As I approached the end, where the gorge opens out into Ormiston Pound, I was rewarded with the sight of Mount Giles, glowing a soft purplish pink in the distance.

For those interested in plants, Ormiston Gorge is a good place to see Sturt's desert rose, the Northern Territory's floral emblem. There are quite a number of bushes close to the camping ground, and if you are there between June and November you will find them in flower.

Ormiston Gorge
Sturt's desert rose (*Gossypium sturtianum*)

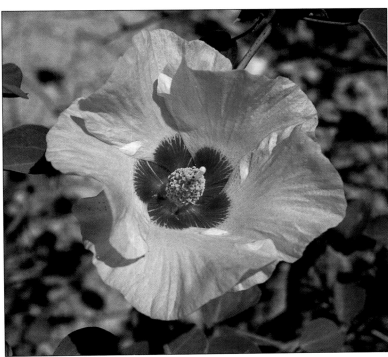

FINKE RIVER

THE FINKE RIVER, central Australia's chief watercourse, is said to be one of the oldest rivers in the world. It rises in the MacDonnell Ranges, near Mount Zeil, and cuts its way through to the plains to follow a generally south-easterly course to South Australia's Simpson Desert, where it joins the Macumba River and flows into Lake Eyre. For much of its 640-kilometre journey it is a wide channel of sand which is dry for months and sometimes years on end, its only permanent water being contained in a string of pools that lie mostly in its upper reaches. However, in seasons of good rains the Finke flows furiously, often spreading its waters over hundreds of square kilometres on the plains of South Australia.

One of the most beautiful stretches of the Finke is in the Glen Helen area, west of Alice Springs. At Glen Helen it flows through a spectacular gorge which at sunrise is one of the great sights of central Australia: the fortress-like walls blaze a fiery red, their glorious colour spilling over into the Finke's long pool in the form of reflections. If the river is low enough to allow you to walk through the gorge, you will discover more good scenery on the other side.

Although thousands of visitors each year see the Finke River at the gorge where the Glen Helen Chalet is situated, few people take the time to explore upstream from the chalet, and this is a pity. For several kilometres along the broad sandy banks of the river there are many lovely stands of river gums and pristine white ghost gums, so called because on moonlit nights their gleaming white trunks give a ghostly quality to the landscape. These trees frame the rugged hills of the MacDonnell Ranges and their dominant landmark, Mount Sonder—the 'Sleeping Lubra'. Depending on the season, you may find a very long pool of shallow water which offers a number of easy crossing-places to enable you to climb some of the rocky outcrops lying on the western side. If you are out early in the morning—always the best time in the outback—you may hear the hauntingly beautiful notes of butcherbirds, the chattering of grey-crowned babblers, and the screeches of cockatoos and brightly coloured galahs. These sounds, and the splendid scenery along the Finke River, epitomize the essential character and uniqueness of central Australia.

Finke River near Glen Helen, with Mount Sonder in the distance

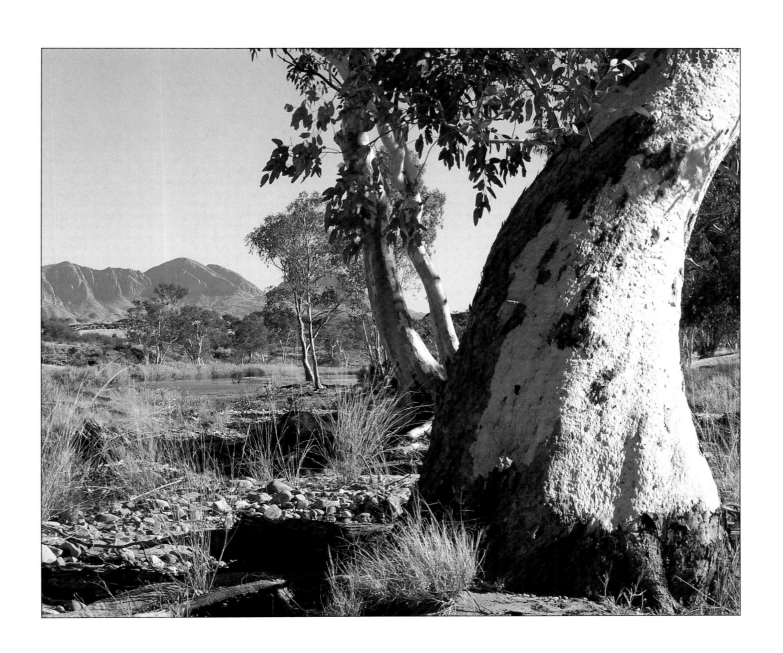

DEVILS MARBLES

SITUATED 100 kilometres south of Tennant Creek, in the Devils Marbles Reserve, these extraordinary rocks lie scattered for many hectares on both sides of the Stuart Highway. They come in a variety of shapes and sizes, some standing alone, others piled on top of each other as if dumped there by a giant tip-truck. All show some degree of roundness, or of softening at the edges, and some are almost spherical, resembling monstrous cannonballs as they balance precariously on larger boulders or nestle in beds of corn-coloured grass. Growing close to some of the boulders are ghost gums, whose snowy-white trunks enhance the beauty of the scene.

Geologists tell us that the Devils Marbles were formed over the ages by sharp changes in temperature and intense weathering that caused erosion along the joints of the original granite masses. The rocks were then rounded to their unusual shapes by the action of wind, rain and sun, which gradually peeled away thin slabs of rock from their surface. The process continues, and many of the rocks look as if their outer layers could flake away at any time. The Aboriginal legend concerning the Marbles' origin is more primordial: they are said to be the eggs of the Rainbow Serpent, a Dreamtime being linked with the source of all life.

Don't hurry past this place—take a walk among these 'eggs of the Rainbow Serpent' at sunrise or sunset and marvel at their glowing rich red-brown colour, which gives the landscape an unreal quality. Your imagination can run riot as you contemplate the marvellous shapes: for photographers, they are irresistible at this time of day. If the moon is full, stay to watch it rise over these giant stones on the plain: the sight is superb.

Such boulders are not unique to this part of Australia. There is a small collection near Halls Creek in north-western Australia; and just north of Tennant Creek masses of them litter some low-lying hills in the Pebbles Reserve—though as the name suggests, these are mere pebbles compared with the huge Devils Marbles.

One of the most famous of the Marbles is the eight-tonne tor taken from the reserve to grace the top of the Reverend John Flynn's grave, situated at the foot of Mount Gillen by the main road, west of Alice Springs. This grand headstone is a fitting memorial to the man who founded the Flying Doctor Service—a service that provides a 'mantle of safety' for thousands of people living in outback Australia.

Moonrise over the Devils Marbles
John Flynn's grave, near Alice Springs

KATHERINE GORGE

MANY PEOPLE feel that a visit to the top of the Territory is not complete unless they take a trip through Katherine Gorge, and this is hardly surprising: it has been one of Australia's most popular tourist attractions for many years. Part of a large national park bearing the same name and situated near the town of Katherine, 312 kilometres south of Darwin, Katherine Gorge extends for about 12 kilometres and consists of thirteen gorges that imprison the Katherine River between spectacular towering cliffs. In many places the sheer walls plunge deeply into the river, and there are only two ways to see the gorges from the ground: by the walking-trails that wind over the clifftops, or by boat. The gorges are separated from each other by shallow rapids, but visitors can easily walk around these to where a boat waits in the next gorge to take them on a further stage of the trip.

Throughout the day there are two-hour boat trips that go as far as the lovely Grand Canyon in the second gorge, but in my opinion the best trip is the all-day safari. This tour is not only more personal, since the group is smaller, but it goes up to the end of the fifth gorge and stops at some interesting spots along the way; however, there is quite a lot of walking on this trip. By the time it returns, in the afternoon, many of the Johnstone's freshwater crocodiles that inhabit the area have come out to sun themselves, and because they have grown used to the boats they will often stay on their rocks and branches while the vessel passes by. These small crocodiles are harmless, and it is quite safe for swimmers to share the river with them.

Those who want to escape the tourist hordes around the busy caravan park and on the equally busy boat tours can enjoy the wonderful peace of the bush on the clifftop walking-trails. When I last visited the gorge I discovered that there seemed to be more people about than during my previous visits, so it was with considerable relief that I set off at first light one clear morning for the clifftop track. At that early hour the tropical woodland was superb, with a delicious freshness that vanished as soon as the sun had climbed high into the sky to bake the countryside in its merciless heat. From the main track I took the Windolf Walk to Pats Lookout. The route was marked only by coloured cans strung in the trees: these were usually easy to follow, but there were times when I had to hunt around for the next one. For the first couple of hours I had the bush to myself, but gradually a few other walkers appeared. However, the majority out walking that day chose to set off in the late morning—which meant that they walked through bushland that was already oven-hot. I did not envy them.

Katherine Gorge from Pats Lookout

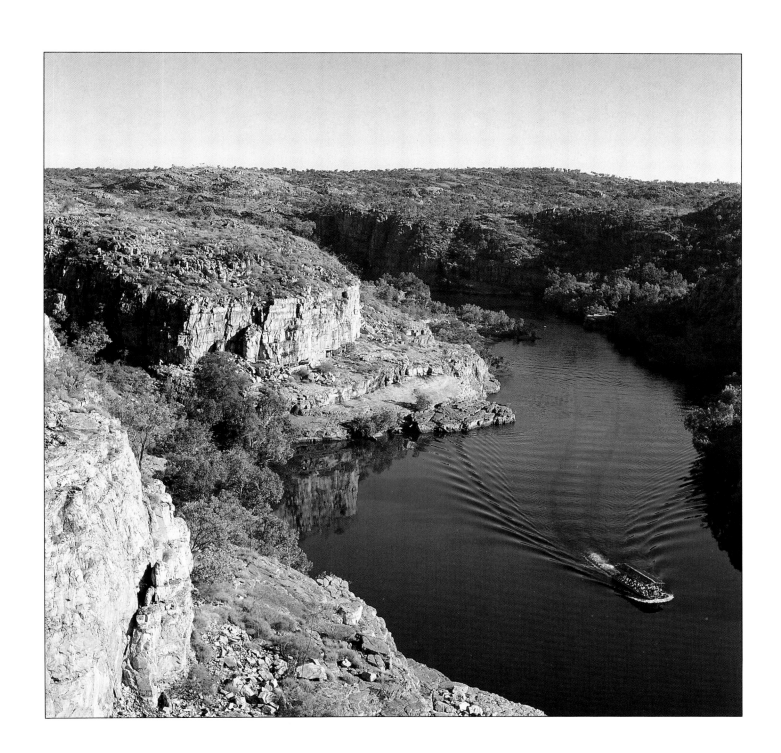

KAKADU

KAKADU is one of Australia's most important and exciting national parks, and has been accepted for inclusion on the prestigious World Heritage List. It is located at the top of the Northern Territory, about 250 kilometres east of Darwin at the edge of Arnhem Land, and covers a large area. Access is via the bitumen Jabiru Highway from Darwin and the mostly gravel road that runs from Pine Creek in the south. Roads within the park are improving all the time, and conventional vehicles can reach most of the major attractions that are open to the public. Accommodation in and around the park ranges from bush camps to comfortable motels.

Kakadu National Park is special because it preserves not only a wealth of wildlife and natural beauty but also a rich heritage of Aboriginal culture. Much of its beauty lies in its tropical wetlands, a wonderful world comprising vast floodplains and sedgelands, rivers, backwaters and channels lined with paperbarks and pandanus, and lily-studded lagoons and billabongs. All are fed by the heavy monsoonal rains that drench the region between November and April. This area abounds in wildlife and is comparable to the world's great wildlife reserves.

In dramatic contrast to the wetlands is the worn and craggy Arnhem Land escarpment, a dominant feature in the north and east of the park. In many places the escarpment's sandstone cliffs are notched with deep, narrow gorges that are at their most beautiful during the wet season ('the Wet', as it is known), when the rains cause spectacular waterfalls to thunder over their sheer rocky walls. At these times, the only way to see the gorges is by air. The edge of the escarpment has also been eroded by streams, with the result that a variety of rocky outliers were left isolated on the plains—features such as Nourlangie Rock, Jabiru Dreaming and Ubirr.

In the overhanging shelters of the outliers lie galleries of Aboriginal rock art, recognized as being the finest of their type in the world. Because they present a vital record of human occupation of the area, these galleries are extremely important to the present-day owners of the land, many of whom still have a traditional association with the paintings. Some of the best galleries open to the public are at Ubirr and Nourlangie Rock. All the paintings are very fragile. Water dripping over them during the Wet has been a big problem, although this has been overcome to a large extent by diverting it through silicone drip-lines placed above the paintings. By far the greatest potential damage to the paintings is from visitors who want to touch them.

The rock art is not the only aspect of Kakadu that faces damage. Because the region's wealth of natural assets lies not only above ground but beneath it, in the form of rich deposits of uranium, gold and other minerals, there has been the inevitable battle between various groups over the mining issue. One thing must be remembered: when a place is accepted for the World Heritage List, the nation that has ownership must do everything in its power to protect it.

Ubirr
Rock paintings, Nangaloar

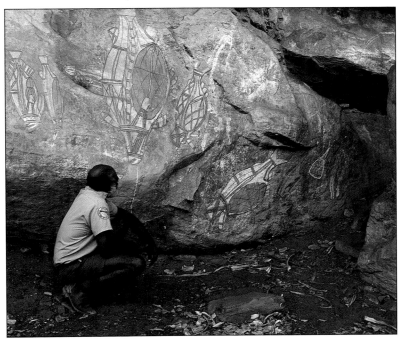

TROPICAL WETLANDS

STAND QUIETLY at the edge of a tropical billabong and absorb the fascinating beauty of your surroundings: maybe the billabong is in Kakadu National Park, or somewhere closer to Darwin. It is a late afternoon in August and the hot air is still and balmy, but there is little sting left in the heat. Already the low sun is splashing a golden pathway over the glassy sections of water not taken up by sedges, waterlilies and graceful melaleuca trees; the reflections are beautiful. You notice that a few wallabies have nervously distanced themselves from you but are content enough to continue their grazing in the area.

Birdcalls fill the air, the loudest coming from the cloud of restless white corellas that have settled noisily in some dead trees at the far end of the billabong. Small groups of magpie geese dotted here and there over the water also make their presence felt by their incessant honking. A short distance away from where you are standing, two stately jabirus strut purposefully through the water, their solid beaks clapping together on juicy morsels found in the shallows. The white egret they pass takes no notice of them but stands like an elegant statue, poised ready to spear a small fish with its long beak.

Further down the lagoon, on the shore of a small island, a colony of water whistle-ducks is clustered so densely that it looks like a slab of mud lining the water; some of the ducks whistle quietly to themselves. There are many other birds around, and you raise your binoculars in order to see them better. Beyond the ducks there is another island, and through the binoculars you see a large saltwater crocodile lying on the bank. Unfortunately the sighting is brief, for suddenly the magnificent reptile slips into the water as some buffalo come down to the edge of the billabong. Showing little regard for the billabong's vegetation, especially the lovely waterlily pads where many lilies are in bloom, these lumbering beasts plunge into the water. The crocodile is not the only creature to be disturbed by the buffalo: the water whistle-ducks rise from the ground in a flurry of brown feathers and anguished whistling that doesn't stop for the entire five minutes they spend circling the lagoon before they settle down again.

By now the sun is about to set and its last rays cast a gloriously warm glow over the billabong. A deep tranquillity descends over the place. After sunset a new sound is heard: the droning of armadas of hungry mosquitoes. It is time to go back to your vehicle, and to leave.

Sunset in the wetlands
Corellas

UMBRAWARRA GORGE

THIS NARROW but very picturesque gorge lies 25 kilometres west of Pine Creek, at the top end of the Northern Territory, in a declared nature park. A dusty, unsealed track leads to the park's camping area, which is situated near the creek that flows through the gorge. There is some delightful walking here, but progress is slow because much time must be spent rock-hopping over the creek's tumbled rocks and boulders. The path starts by the small carpark near the creek, a couple of hundred metres away from the camping ground, and it takes about ten minutes to reach the beginning of the gorge, which runs for some 10 kilometres through the range. Just before you reach the gorge, the path gives way to the rocky creekbed, but it is easy enough to make your way to the splendid cliff that guards the first long pool at the gorge's entrance.

If you are at the first pool at sunrise and there are no annoying breezes to disturb the glassy surface of the water, the cliff's craggy walls, glowing orange in the first rays of the sun, will reflect superbly in the pool. Don't stop here, but continue past the pool and over the stone-studded creekbed to the narrow but even lovelier second gorge, only about five minutes away. Here, another long pool lies at the base of a high, colourful and astonishingly sheer wall that gives the place a special character of its own. After you leave this pool you will find that the rocks in the creek have become huge chunky tors, and that in places the creek is so deep that you will have to swim—which is no hardship in the 30°C heat of northern Australia.

I have always found Umbrawarra Gorge a peaceful place, simply because there are usually very few people around. This certainly makes it a pleasant change from the better-known and often overcrowded beauty spots of the tropical Top End. As long as the road leading to the park remains unsealed, the place will probably retain its atmosphere of peace.

The dusty road may deter tourists who like to travel only on bitumen; but it does seem that, even once they have arrived, some visitors cannot be bothered to look for the beauty of Umbrawarra Gorge. One afternoon when I had the place to myself and was parked at the start of the walking-track, a four-wheel-drive vehicle with four young people on board pulled up. The driver got out, announced to the others that he would 'take a look', and set off down the path while the others waited in the vehicle. About ten minutes later he was back, and as he resumed the driver's seat he declared, 'There's nothing much to see.' Then off they roared in a cloud of dust. I suspect the fellow had got no further than the section where the path disappears into the rocks, just before the first pool with the lovely cliff. To think what they missed!

The second gorge, Umbrawarra Gorge

VICTORIA RIVER VALLEY

T HE LOVELY scenery of the Victoria River Valley in the far north-west of the Northern Territory is a refreshing sight for motorists who have made the journey from Katherine through 195 kilometres of
open and rather uninteresting tropical woodland. Although a sign on the Victoria Highway at the valley's
entrance tells you that you are entering the Gregory National Park, this reserve was still only at the proposal
stage in the late 1980s; it would be some time before it was officially declared. When its development is
complete, the Victoria River Valley will be part of one of Australia's most exciting parks—an area of 10 500
square kilometres incorporating some incredibly spectacular country.

This area has been virtually unknown since the Victoria River was first explored by John Lort Stokes in
1839. Towards the end of the nineteenth century pastoralists began grazing cattle in the district, and some of
the largest properties in Australia were established there. When a growing number of tourists started to pass
through the valley on their way to the west in the early 1970s, few stopped for any length of time; but that
changed in 1980, when a motel and caravan park were opened next to the highway. Today most travellers
consider it a 'must' to stop here in order to take the excellent boat tour that passes through a breathtaking
section of the Victoria River Gorge.

The boat leaves three times a day—just before sunrise and sunset, and during the morning—and travels
for 12 kilometres along the Victoria River as it cuts through the Stokes Range. Red sandstone cliffs up to
200 metres high rise over the river and the lush vegetation that lines its steep banks, and on still days
everything is beautifully mirrored in the water. As the gorge narrows, the reflections become more
impressive, and the colour spilling over the water from the craggy red cliffs is of such richness that those
sitting in the slowly gliding boat feel as if they are part of an enchanted oil-painting.

The river is home for the harmless Johnstone's freshwater crocodile. These creatures can usually be seen
on the morning tour, and in one particular spot the boat-operator stops to feed them—a rare sight, for they
are normally very timid. Occasionally a wild scrub-bull is sighted near the banks. Until the 1980s this area
had not been mustered for about twenty-five years, and although helicopters were used for the job, some
animals were missed—which is hardly surprising in such rugged country.

The most important river in the Northern Territory, the Victoria rises in the spinifex plains of the Great
Sandy Desert and flows for about 640 kilometres before it empties its waters into the Joseph Bonaparte Gulf
on the north coast: at its mouth it is 26 kilometres wide. Like all rivers in northern Australia, the Victoria
changes dramatically in the wet season, when it becomes a swollen, slow-moving mass of muddy water. In its
gorge it may rise up to eleven metres above its usual dry-season level, leaving logs and other debris stranded
in the trees that grow high above the riverbanks.

Victoria River
Johnstone's freshwater crocodile

BUNGLE BUNGLE RANGE

FEW PLACES have stirred such interest in recent times as the 'discovery' in 1983 of the Bungle Bungle Range in northern Western Australia. It is amazing that such a remarkable landform could remain virtually unknown for so long. However, the magnificently wild and rugged Kimberley region is ideal for keeping secrets, and it is quite possible that there are further scenic treasures hidden in other remote and inaccessible parts of this area. Until 1983 only some Aborigines and a handful of pastoralists knew of this extraordinary triangular massif that rises from vast plains in a multitude of eroded, banded domes like beehives, marked with steep, narrow gorges and high cliffs. Today it is a national park and is seen by thousands of tourists every year.

'The Bungles', as the locals call the range, lie around 200 kilometres south of Kununurra. Before 1983 there were no access roads of any sort, but since then the inevitable four-wheel-drive track has been pushed through from Turkey Creek to the edge of the domes. According to one couple, it took nine hours of hard, rough driving to get there. 'And when we arrived,' they told me, 'heaps of people were there—and even a commercial tour!'

Many people see the Bungles only from the air. The two-hour flight from Kununurra has become so popular that during the winter tourist season around twenty flights run daily from the town's airport. Quite a few of the tourists I spoke to had not even heard of the Bungles until other tourists told them to take the flight: such is the importance of the travellers' grapevine. I joined four other people on a flight that left at sunrise. As we approached the range, we decided that the Bungles resembled nothing so much as the ruins of a city lying at the edge of the plain, but once we were flying over the top of it we could see marvellous detail in the steep and narrow gullies. Coloured bands and whorls patterned the domes' worn, ancient-looking sedimentary sandstone; Livistona palms appeared to grow out of sheer rock, and dry riverbeds coursed through the maze of extraordinary formations. Afterwards we found it hard to locate the right superlative to describe the experience; 'fantastic' was the word most resorted to by our party.

Considerable publicity was given to a photographer and bushwalker who were lowered into the Bungles by helicopter shortly after the world was informed of the range's existence, and their account of the experience was an exciting one. However, few knew that some months after that dramatic entry a young man from Perth, used to hiking solo in wilderness areas, quietly walked in alone, taking four days to get there from Turkey Creek and three days to return. I met him in Kununurra, when he was on his way—on foot—to 'have a look at the Carr Boyd Ranges'. He didn't think there was anything remarkable about his hike into the Bungles, although he admitted that it had been hard going in places. He had found that the sandstone of the domes was very fragile: sections broke off easily, and this had made climbing extremely difficult and dangerous.

KIMBERLEY BOABS

BOAB TREES, with their strange swollen trunks and ungainly limbs, are a distinct and fascinating feature of the Kimberley region in the north of Western Australia. The tree grows solely on the sandy plains and stony hills of this corner of the continent, and is one of only two species, the other originating in Africa. Its more formal common name on both continents is baobab, but Australians find this rather a mouthful and have shortened it. In Africa the tree has collected a string of colourful names, such as dead-rat tree, calabash, sour-gourd and monkey bread tree. The botanical name for the Australian species is *Adansonia gregorii*. Some people call the boab a bottle-tree, but it is not to be confused with the bottle-shaped trees in Queensland that belong to the genus *Brachychiton*.

Motorists travelling to the Kimberleys from Katherine in the Northern Territory will have their first glimpse of boabs around Timber Creek, near the Western Australian border. Most people visit the north in the winter dry season, when the deciduous boabs have shed their leaves, and it is at this time that they are at their most intriguing. The young trees are relatively slender and quite graceful, but the older ones, with their huge trunks and distorted gouty-looking limbs, are full of marvellous character. 'Double-bungers'—trees with split trunks that have continued to grow separately into obese shapes—are quite common, as are boabs with fat low boles that squat on the ground like dumpy old gnomes. The older the tree, the more gnarled and interesting it becomes; but age also brings a high risk that the tree will be desecrated by idiot name-carvers. Just about every old boab that stands close to the road between Timber Creek and Kununurra has been vandalized, and the sight is enough to make you weep. The most famous boab—and the most covered in graffiti—is the Prison Tree at Derby. Its enormous trunk has a hollow inside which is reputed to have been used as an overnight cell for a group of prisoners.

Boabs are ideal subjects for photography—especially at sunrise and sunset, when their fantastic shapes make splendid silhouettes against the sky. At these times they are best seen on a wide plain where few other trees are growing, and where young and old boabs often huddle gregariously in groups: with the rising or setting sun behind them, they resemble a collection of curious vases each holding an intricate arrangement of sticks. However, nothing can compare with the sight of their dark shapes standing against a sky filled with clouds that have been dyed rich crimson and soft pink in the afterglow of sunset.

During the wet season, when they are respectably clothed in their leafy summer attire and are no longer naked figures of fun, boabs lose much of their character. But at the start of the Wet, just as their new leaves appear, the trees burst into flower and their large fragrant creamy blooms create a lovely display.

Sunset near Derby
An old boab
Flower of the boab (*Adansonia gregorii*)

GEIKIE GORGE

FEW VISITORS to the Kimberleys miss seeing Geikie Gorge. It is one of the most colourful gorges in Australia and is easily accessible—an important consideration for motorists in a region that is known for its wild, rough terrain. Situated 20 kilometres from Fitzroy Crossing in a small national park, the gorge flanks the Fitzroy River for eight kilometres. It is worth noting, however, that the gravel road from Fitzroy Crossing to the park's camping ground is suitable for conventional vehicles and caravans only during the dry months of the year. An increasing number of caravanners are finding it easier to stay at Fitzroy Crossing and make a day trip to the gorge, because the camping ground at the park tends to get very crowded and dusty.

Geikie's origins are prehistoric. Over countless centuries the thundering floodwaters of the Fitzroy River have cut through the remains of an ancient coral reef that formed in an earlier era and is known today as the Devonian 'Great Barrier Reef'. The waters wore down the fossil cliffs to their present height of about twelve metres, and the action still continues during each wet season, when the limestone walls are washed by the floodwaters that race through the gorge. During the dry season rangers run boat tours twice daily from the camping ground, and at such times the use of private boats is restricted. These tours are made aboard a series of flat-bottomed boats strung together, and the ranger skilfully guides this strange craft close to the walls of the gorge, enabling you to appreciate fully the detail of the incredible markings, indentations and holes that riddle sections of the cliffs. The walls' other outstanding feature is their brilliant colouring: in many places the shades of orange, rusty red, pink, white, grey and black seem to have been splashed on with a paintbrush.

The degree of beauty at Geikie at any given time depends on the weather: if there is no wind at all, the sight of the coloured cliffs reflected in the river is stunning. Often the breezes drop just before sunset, and that is the time to take a walk along the western bank of the river. Some of the best places from which to see the cliffs lie a couple of kilometres from the camping ground, and walking to them can sometimes be very hard going because there is plenty of loose sand. If the day is still and the cliffs are mirrored in the water, this section of the gorge is a photographer's paradise—provided other tourists don't choose the same spot to do some fishing. The first time I took this walk, shortly before sunset on a day when the reflections were perfect, a man in a boat decided to hunt for a good fishing spot. I was in the process of setting up my camera to capture the scene when he started to drive his boat in circles right across my entire picture area—and continued to do so until the sun set. To my chagrin, the glorious reflections were reduced to a coloured smudge on the ruffled surface of the river.

Fitzroy River in Geikie Gorge

WINDJANA GORGE AND TUNNEL CREEK

WINDJANA GORGE and Tunnel Creek lie between Derby and Fitzroy Crossing, in the Kimberleys. Both places are national parks, and both were used in the last century as a hideout for the Aboriginal outlaw Sandamara, also known as Pigeon. Motorists with caravans will find that access is easiest from Derby, because the road between Leopold Downs and Fairfield stations is twisty and rough in places. Camping is permitted only at Windjana Gorge; by the mid-1980s the old burr-ridden camping ground by the riverbank had been moved to a more developed spot on higher ground.

For sheer grandeur Windjana is the most impressive of all the well-known gorges in the Kimberleys. Situated about 150 kilometres from Derby and not far from the Gibb River Road turnoff, the gorge cuts through the Napier Range, one of the rugged limestone ranges that once formed part of the ancient Devonian 'Great Barrier Reef'. Its orange-splashed grey walls rise to a height of up to 90 metres as it shelters the Lennard River for a distance of about five kilometres. By the time the tourists start arriving in the winter months, the once-swollen river has ceased to flow, leaving only a string of pools. In the gorge there is good walking—although in places the loose river sand is everywhere. However, most people go no further than the permanent pool by the large white rock, about ten minutes' walk from the camping ground. If you wait quietly by the pool, some Johnstone's freshwater crocodiles will probably appear, looking remarkably like a collection of knobbly sticks floating on the surface of the water.

Further east, 37 kilometres from Windjana, is Tunnel Creek, a 750-metre-long cave that pierces through the Oscar Range from one side to the other. In the wet season water flows swiftly through the tunnel, but during the Dry it is possible to walk right through it, provided you don't mind meeting the odd snake or doing a bit of wading in cold water. The later it is in the dry season the easier it is, because the water-level drops considerably, allowing you to walk around or step over the pools. On my first visit I attempted to walk through the tunnel alone, but after a close encounter with an olive python, followed by an unexpected stumble into an extremely cold and deep pool of water that my weak torch had failed to illuminate in the heavy blackness of the tunnel, I fled to the entrance. On my next visit I went through with three adventurous companions—and better torches. Not all of the twenty-minute walk is undertaken in utter darkness; about halfway through, where part of the roof has collapsed, rocks and roof are reflected in a long pool and tree-roots dangle like streamers, festooning a scene of unusual beauty

The entrance to Tunnel Creek alone is worth seeing. The huge cavern situated close to the carpark is almost blocked by a jumbled pile of boulders, many of them a musk-pink intricately laced with white. It is easy enough to scramble over the boulders to reach the dimly lit cave, where a deepening of the blackness before you indicates the beginning of the tunnel walk.

Windjana Gorge
Tunnel Creek

MANNING GORGE

IT IS HARDLY surprising that many people consider the Kimberley region, with its worn and colourful ranges, splendid gorges and lush waterholes, and its strange boab trees, to be one of the most exciting regions in Australia: I know I do! Somehow one has here a heightened expectation of adventure, largely because this inhospitable yet wildly beautiful corner of the continent is still very much 'last frontier' country. However, much potential enjoyment is lost if you choose to be in the Kimberley inland between mid-September and the start of the wet season in November–December, for during this period temperatures can climb to 40°C and more. Because of the effects of this heat on human beings, October is known as 'suicide month'.

One of the joys of exploring the Kimberley gorges is that each is so different from every other—and the last one visited is always the best. Manning Gorge is one of several beautiful gorges lying off the Gibb River Road in the west Kimberleys. Situated on Mount Barnett Station, about 320 kilometres from Derby, this gorge has become a popular resting-place for travellers exploring the area. The station provides a camping ground, a small store, petrol, and, on occasions, helicopter rides over the gorge. The Gibb River Road links Wyndham and Derby. Sometimes the entire road is upgraded and conventional cars can get through if driven with care, but usually the upper section near Wyndham is fit only for four-wheel-drive vehicles.

I had heard a great deal about Manning Gorge before my first visit. One tour-operator told me that when he had taken a group of tourists there they had become 'drunk' with its beauty. Stories like that can leave you with unrealistic expectations, but most people who explore this gorge properly will not be disappointed: it *is* superb. There are two main walks. The first, a track marked with cans and leading from the top camping ground to the main pool and falls, is, according to the notice, a three-hour return journey, but a good walker can do it in about half that time. Although this is the easiest way to the pool, the trail runs over the hills and shows you little of the gorge.

The second walk—and the one better enabling you to appreciate Manning's beauty—leads you through the gorge itself to the pool. This is a challenging walk and it takes most of the day. Large boulders litter the floor for part of the way, and you will find that you have to cross fairly often from one side to the other. In many places the boulders give way to beautiful rockpools that are fed by Manning Creek. By the middle of the dry season the flowing creek is reduced to a trickle but the pools still hold enough to reflect the surrounding vegetation and the chunky orange walls.

Those who don't want to tackle the long hike through the gorge can take a fifteen-minute walk from the top camping ground and follow the water's edge to the entrance of the gorge. The scenes from here, particularly at sunrise, are glorious.

In Manning Gorge

BROOME

SITUATED in the far north-west of Western Australia, 2213 kilometres from Perth, the Kimberley town of Broome is spread over a finger of land that separates the wide expanse of Roebuck Bay from the Indian Ocean. Although it is a long journey from anywhere to reach Broome, people show more enthusiasm for this town than for any other in the north, and a growing number of visitors from all States have discovered it to be a holiday haven. For Western Australians it has become the Cairns of the West: each winter thousands head for this northern spot in order to escape the lower temperatures of the south. Ever since the last link of the road from Perth was sealed, the number of winter visitors from the south has grown from a steady flow to a flood. Many other tourists cut across from the Northern Territory through the Kimberleys, a road that is now sealed.

All visitors to Broome—whether winter sun-seekers, tourists passing through or workers from the hot dusty inland—tend to forget, as soon as they reach their destination, that any other world exists. Although this is partly because of Broome's isolation and pleasant climate (it is much cooler here than inland), much of its charm and relaxed atmosphere can be attributed to the strong oriental character it has retained from the great pearling days. At the turn of the century Broome, then known as the 'Port of Pearls', had a fleet of around 300 vessels, many of whose crewmen were Japanese and Malays. But since the Second World War the pearling industry has declined, and today luggers are no longer seen moored at the jetty that used to lie just beyond the town's main shopping centre.

Broome has another drawcard: its beaches. On the ocean side of the town lies Cable Beach, which extends for about 22 kilometres over fine white sand and is bordered by dunes varying in colour from white to red. At an average low tide, this superb beach stretches a good 150 metres from dunes to sea: its sheer vastness is balm to the spirit. In the winter months, the clear brilliant water has a temperature of around 26°C and the gentle surf provides safe swimming—unlike the waters of Roebuck Bay, which are dangerous because of sharks.

Roebuck Bay may be unsuitable for swimming but it is stunning in its colourful beauty. At the jetty end of the beach a heap of fantastically shaped red and black rocks engraved by weathering with swirling patterns gives way to a series of red dunes and a ribbon of red sand sweeping along the bay; this, together with the intensely bright turquoise blue sea gently lapping the red beach and the few green mangroves that have colonized the shore here and there, gives the place an extraordinary air of unreality. At Gantheaume Point, a few kilometres from Broome, there are further splashes of vivid colour as a profusion of rich-red rocks sprawls into the sea.

Roebuck Bay

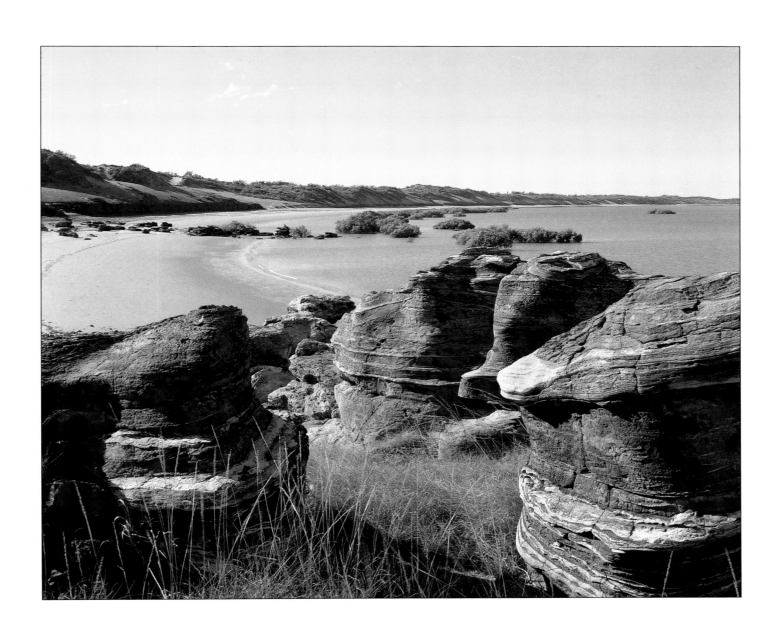

HAMERSLEY RANGE

WESTERN AUSTRALIA covers one-third of the Australian continent, and to motorists travelling to the Hamersley Range in the hot dry Pilbara region it must seem that, regardless of the direction from which they approach it, the distances are never-ending. Situated 300 kilometres from Port Hedland on the coast, the Hamersley Range lies some 900 kilometres south-west of the Kimberleys and around 1450 kilometres north of Perth. In addition to the problem of distance, the iron-ore-rich range and the surrounding ironstone country have some of the stoniest roads in Australia; and although the major routes are much better than they used to be, they are still rough. One motorist reckoned that he could feel through the steering-wheel the stones ripping his tyres to pieces. Strong tyres and adequate spares are a must for this area!

The Hamersley Range stretches for nearly 400 kilometres across the Pilbara. It is Western Australia's highest landmass, its loftiest point reaching 1245 metres. Part of the range is a national park that preserves a series of deep and colourful gorges fissuring the plateau that tops it. Long before you arrive in Wittenoom, the small town nestling at the foot of the range, the massive Hamersleys look promising. If it is late afternoon when you reach the road that runs alongside the range, you will see the folded rugged hillsides standing out boldly in relief as they are lit by the low sun; and if you are there in springtime, great candelabras of mauve mulla-mullas in flower rise over the golden spinifex to decorate the landscape.

From Wittenoom, roads lead up to the plateau and to the camping grounds in the national park. Once on the plateau the scene is different again, for this vast area is agape with extraordinarily sheer gorges that reveal terraced walls of rich chocolate and rusty browns and reds, their vivid colours accentuated by the golden beefwood blooms and lush green vegetation beside pools lying deep in the gorges. Although it is possible to go down into a few of the gorges, most people prefer to view them from the top. Even this can be a terrifying experience for those who don't like heights, for in some places the walls plummet to 150 metres. Paths enable you to walk easily to good vantage-points; but when you wander away from these, loose stones can become quite treacherous underfoot.

Probably the most popular of all the gorges, and one of the loveliest, is Dales Gorge. From the carpark above the gorge there is easy access to the falls and the large pool at their foot. When I was there the pool was full of people swimming, so I sought a quieter environment by exploring some very attractive rockpools that lay further up the gorge. The debris from past floods which littered the gorge floor occasionally made the walking difficult, and at other times I had to wade through water—although this was rather hazardous, as the rocks beneath were very slimy. I had hoped to reach Circular Pool, which lies at the end of a small arm off the main gorge, but there was not enough time left that afternoon: a full day is needed for a walk through Dales Gorge.

Near Wittenoom
Dales Gorge

KALBARRI

THE COASTAL town of Kalbarri, which lies around the mouth of the Murchison River 590 kilometres north of Perth, has become one of the most popular resorts in Western Australia. Although its beaches, its safe waters for boating, and the good fishing in the river estuary are enough to attract holidaymakers, the town has another important attraction: it is bordered by the large Kalbarri National Park, one of the State's major national parks.

Kalbarri National Park is renowned for its superb coastal gorges and cliffs, for the winding gullies of the Murchison Gorge, and for the vast sandplains that in spring blaze with an astonishing variety of wildflowers. From Red Bluff, just a few kilometres south of the town, high cliffs indented with unusual multicoloured gullies drop to the strong surf of the Indian Ocean. The names of many of these gullies are equally colourful: Rainbow Valley, Goat Gulch, Layer Cake Gorge and Madmans Rock are just a few. The greatest panorama—a long wall of warm-yellow cliffs—is at Castle Cove, a few minutes' walk from the last carpark on the 16-kilo-metre coastal drive from the town (the last seven kilometres are rough). At Castle Cove, don't miss seeing the Natural Bridge: it is not visible from the main viewing area but lies further around to the left.

The Murchison River cuts its way through sandstone for about 80 kilometres before spilling into its wide estuary at Kalbarri. The national park has various lookout points that can be reached by good firm sandy roads. Those closest to the township are along the Loop, 26 kilometres away. One of the most scenic spots on the Loop is around Nature's Window, a five-minute walk from the carpark. From this large weathered arch of rock that frames the view of the river and gorge, you can find a relatively easy place to scramble down the steep slope to the river below, where there is some good walking. The Murchison River Gorge responds particularly well to the low light of early morning and late afternoon; at other times of day photographers may be disappointed, as the lighting tends to be very flat from the clifftops.

Spring, when the wildflowers are in bloom, is the best time to see the national park. Well over 300 species have been recorded here, and a number of them are endemic to the area. Two of the showiest plants of the sandplains are the grey-blue common smokebush and the tall white-plumed grevillea with its pale-yellow, sweet-smelling blooms. If you want to find Western Australia's intriguing floral emblem, the red-and-green or Mangles kangaroo-paw, there are always plenty growing beside the main Kalbarri–Ajana road that runs through the park.

Murchison River Gorge
Red-and-green kangaroo-paw (*Anigozanthos manglesii*)

PINNACLES DESERT

ONE OF THE JOYS of exploring Australia is the constant element of surprise. Occasionally you will find a place that doesn't seem to fit the Australian scene at all: one such place is the Pinnacles Desert. The Pinnacles are situated in the Nambung National Park, about 250 kilometres north of Perth, and comprise an astonishing collection of limestone spires that rise from the desolate coastal plain like the ruins of an ancient and forgotten city. Some of them are grey, but most are as golden as the surrounding sand, and they range from the size of a man's hand to five metres in height. It is thought that each pinnacle extends deep into the ground, showing only its tip.

These odd formations developed thousands of years ago, when the climate in this part of Australia was much wetter. Limestone formed around the roots of trees and plants, and then erosion gradually exposed the solid spires, leaving the surrounding sand held together by a crust of what appear to be tiny petrified roots only a few centimetres long, some lying on the ground, others valiantly erect, like minute icicles of sand. They are so fragile that they will disintegrate at the slightest touch.

Up until 1986 the last section of the road leading in to the Pinnacles Desert from the small fishing village of Cervantes was terrible, and the huge rocks that studded it stopped most conventional vehicles. I made my first trip to the place in 1975 in a Kombi, but even with that vehicle's good clearance I felt as though I was navigating a boat through a dangerous coral reef, and it took me an hour and a half to travel the last five kilometres. So when I was in the West in 1986, it was with considerable relief that I learnt that a new road replacing the last horror section had just been opened.

Once in the desert, you follow the original but now better-marked one-way track that loops for about four kilometres through the Pinnacles. Those making their first visit are certain to experience a thrill at being in this unique environment, but anyone who knew the place before it was made easily accessible will be saddened to find that it no longer has the wilderness atmosphere it used to have. Admittedly, my second visit was on a weekend; but the streams of traffic driving around the loop, the coaches stacked into the main carpark (they are not allowed on the loop), the large groups of people noisily posing for photographs among the spires, and the sight of masses of footprints covering sand that was once a sea of beautiful undisturbed ripples fashioned by the wind, did nothing to enhance the sense of wilderness. Considering the enormous inroads tourism has made into wilderness areas in recent decades, it is almost a miracle that the incredible Pinnacles Desert remained in relative isolation for as long as it did.

In the Pinnacles Desert

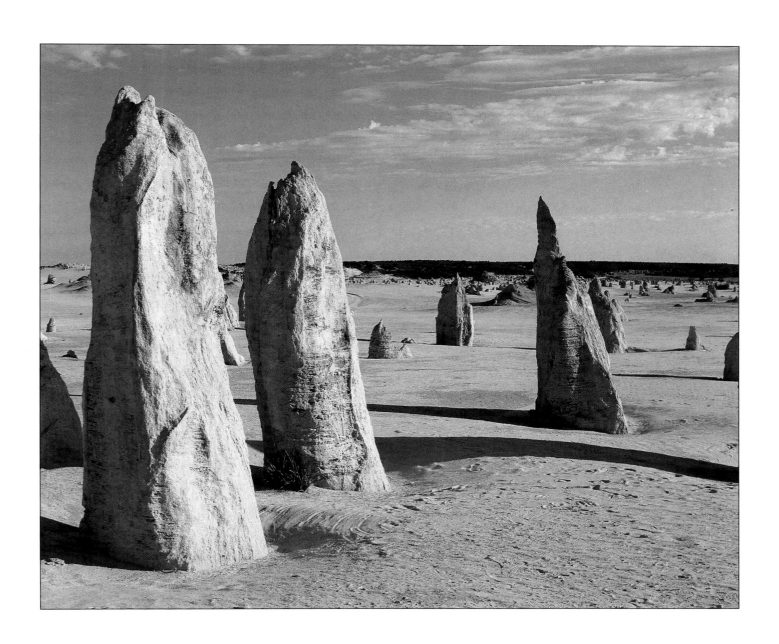

STIRLING RANGE

WESTERN AUSTRALIA is known as the Wildflower State—even some of the registration plates on Western Australian vehicles remind you of that. Indeed, Australia as a whole, with approximately 15 000 species of flora, contains more plants unique to its area than any other country. About half of the continent's total number of species are found in Western Australia, with many being endemic of that State; and, as elsewhere in the country, new species are being discovered there each year. The richness of the West's flora is perhaps best illustrated by its banksias: by the 1980s there were 58 named species, of which 46 were found in Western Australia. Only one of these was also native to two other States, and most of the other 45 were confined to very small areas of Western Australia. The remaining twelve species originated in the eastern half of the continent.

A popular and botanically interesting place to see wildflowers in Western Australia is Stirling Range National Park in the south-west. Because of its floral wealth, it has become one of Australia's most important reserves; more than 800 species have been recorded here, and this figure is expected to rise. Such abundance is thought to have occurred because the south-west corner of Australia is geologically one of the most undisturbed landmasses on the earth's surface. It was isolated millions of years ago by sea on one side and desert on the other, and the remarkably specialized flora found there today was able to develop in peace.

The Stirling Range, situated about 80 kilometres north of Albany, rises abruptly over the vast agricultural plains of the south-west. The park protects the range's entire system of rugged hills, bold outcrops and craggy peaks that in a number of places rise to over 1000 metres; Bluff Knoll, at 1109 metres the highest peak, occasionally wears a mantle of snow in winter. The park also includes an area of plains, where heaths and woodlands occur. The green vegetation that covers the slopes of the ranges is mostly thick scrub.

If the weather is drearily overcast with no interesting cloud-effects, people visiting the Stirling Range for the first time may be disappointed, for under these conditions the hills can appear almost devoid of character. However, once they have been seen in the superb light of early morning or late afternoon and some time has been given to exploring the area—either by driving around on the good gravel roads or by taking some of the walks—that first impression will certainly change. As for the flowers, they are so interesting and varied that I always find that the longer I spend 'botanizing' among them the more difficult it is to leave. Although the spring flowers are in bloom from August to November, the best time to see them is usually from around the end of September to mid-October.

Spring in the Stirling Range
Scarlet banksia (*Banksia coccinea*)
A petrophile (*Petrophile divaricata*)

CAPE LE GRAND

CAPE LE GRAND National Park, which covers a stretch of magnificently wild coastline facing the Archipelago of the Recherche, lies about 45 kilometres east of Esperance on Western Australia's southern seaboard. One of the park's best features is the massive outcrops of craggy granite that dominate much of its scenery. Headlands walled in grey granite fall boldly to the brilliant blue of the Southern Ocean, and oddly shaped weatherworn rocks litter the coastal slopes as if carelessly flung down by a giant hand. At Thistle Cove there is the tall Whistling Rock, which emits a distinct and eerie moan when the wind blows from a certain direction. Gently curving bays are lined with unbelievably white sand, so fine that it squeaks underfoot and, when pressed into the hand, feels like talcum powder. One of the most prominent landmarks is the deceptively steep Frenchman Peak, so named because of its resemblance to a Frenchman's beret; under its summit runs a huge rocky cavern.

When I first visited Cape Le Grand in the 1970s it was a national park in name only. Few signposts marked the awful roads, no information was available, and there was no evidence of any rangers. When I returned a decade later I was delighted to find an exceptionally well-run park where I could obtain plenty of information about both the place itself and the excellent walking-trails that had been established. The roads were in good condition, and the ranger was particularly helpful.

There are two camping grounds in the park: Cape Le Grand Beach and Lucky Bay. Apparently, visitors from the eastern States prefer to camp at Cape Le Grand Beach, where individual camping areas afford a high degree of privacy, whereas Western Australians prefer the more open Lucky Bay, which, if crowded, offers cheek-by-jowl camping. 'Our State is not as populated as the eastern ones,' the ranger told me when he visited my carefully chosen secluded camp at Cape Le Grand Beach. 'West Aussies like to be with people — not to get away from them!'

All is not perfect at Cape Le Grand: the dreaded disease of dieback has been a serious problem in the park, and has led to the death of many species of plants. Dieback, which is caused by a fungus introduced from the tropics, can reduce whole tracts of bushland to botanic graveyards. Although there is no cure, we do know how the disease is transmitted, and an all-out effort is being made both at Cape Le Grand and elsewhere to control it. One of the main ways in which it spreads is through infected soil picked up by vehicles, and certain areas must therefore be quarantined by restricting vehicle access. Most people are willing to cooperate with the rangers; but according to one ranger that I met, there are visitors who take no notice of the quarantine areas because they have no understanding of the disease and think the authorities are 'carrying on about nothing'.

Hellfire Bay
Creeping banksia (*Banksia repens*)

POINT LABATT

Point Labatt lies on the west coast of Eyre Peninsula, about 50 kilometres south of Streaky Bay in South Australia. The area is renowned for its spectacular cliffs, which march for many kilometres at the edge of the bays and chunky headlands that push into the powerful swells of the Southern Ocean. The cliffs, 100 metres high in places, sometimes drop perpendicularly or tumble like massive landslides to the sea below. At Cape Blanche in Sceale Bay, just north of Point Labatt, the sheer creamy-white rockfaces display strata with strange patterns rather like the smocking on a child's dress. At sunset all the cliffs are tinted with rich shades of gold, in dramatic contrast to the inky sea flecked with white waves rolling towards the shore.

The turnoff to Point Labatt is near Calca. After you have travelled about 16 kilometres, the road ends at the clifftop; from here the scenery literally makes you gasp. On both sides of the point a craggy line of high cliffs, worn and eroded by the elements, falls to the surf below. On a sandy beach at the bottom of the cliffs there is a permanent colony of sea lions, the largest on the South Australian mainland. Unfortunately, they are considerably fewer in number than in earlier years because the colony was frequently raided by sealers.

There is a track down to the beach and its seals, but most sensible people balk at the initial hair-raising scramble over the cliff edge to reach the narrow ledge tucked under the clifftop from which the path starts. Once the main slope is reached care must be taken, as the ground is loose, crumbly and steep. When I reached the clifftop I took one look at the cliff and said to my companion, 'Forget it!' However, my longing to photograph the seals at close quarters got the better of me, and after speaking with a young couple who had been down and lived to tell the tale I decided to go. The descent, and the subsequent ascent, were nothing short of a nightmare.

Seals were everywhere on the beach. They littered the sand in great mounds of snoring flesh, wearing expressions of utter contentment as they slept the time away. The only signs of activity were the odd yawn, a passing scratch, or an affectionate nudge to a nearby mate. I had been warned to stay clear of the bulls, because when aroused they can be dangerous. When I nearly fell over one bull, having vaguely registered his form in my mind as a rock, he opened an eye and glared at me in a most chilling way that certainly belied his docile, slothful appearance. I spent most of the time photographing a nursery of pups supervised by a few mother seals, who showed more signs of being alert than the others. As I approached them they sat up and put their noses in the air in that typical seal pose that makes them look almost snooty. Far too soon, it was time to climb that terrible cliff.

Cliffs at Point Labatt

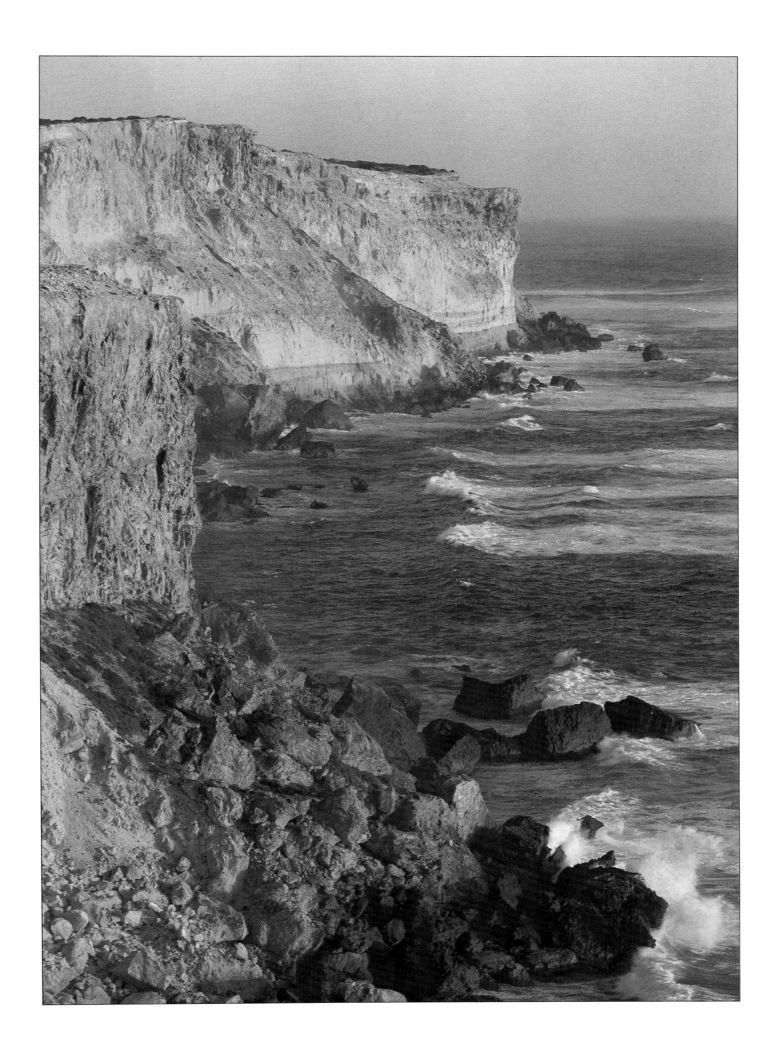

FLINDERS RANGES

T HE FLINDERS RANGES rise in low hills around Crystal Brook, north of Adelaide, and extend for nearly 400 kilometres to just south of Lake Eyre. For most tourists the gateway to the Flinders is Quorn, near Port Augusta. Although considered 'outback', these ranges are relatively close to the densely populated south-eastern portion of Australia; the southern Flinders are only a few hours' drive from Adelaide, and less than two days from Melbourne.

Most people will tell you that the Flinders Ranges have a unique character—a quality unlike anywhere else in the country; somehow they are so essentially *Australian*. It is therefore hardly surprising that they are much loved by visitors, who come in their thousands, often returning to favourite camping sites every year. Artists and photographers are particularly sensitive to the beauty of the area, with its magnificent river gums, its carpets of spring wildflowers, and the colour and dramatic contours of the rugged hills, peaks and mountains, all of which is enhanced by the superb light-conditions at dawn and dusk. There are two major national parks: the Flinders Ranges National Park, which includes Wilpena Pound, and the Gammon Ranges National Park further north.

Excellent roads link the Flinders with civilization, and within the ranges themselves several of the tracks that wind through the gorges are suitable for conventional vehicles—although in places only just! Nearly every road, major or minor, is a scenic route. I have many favourites, but one I return to again and again is the Moralana track, which links the Leigh Creek road in the west and the Wilpena–Hawker road in the east. This beautiful route runs for 28 kilometres, passing the superbly contoured Elder Range and the spectacular south-western walls of Wilpena Pound. In spring, if the winter rains have been good, the profusion of red wild hops, purple salvation jane and yellow daisy bushes adds a touch of brilliance. However, heavy winter rains frequently continue into spring, with the result that all unsealed routes—including sections of the good gravel roads—are potential quagmires. At these times a delightful day's drive can turn into an ordeal.

Some of the most impressive scenery in the Flinders Ranges lies to the north, in the Mount Painter–Arkaroola Sanctuary. The character of the country is quite different here: wild rugged mountains edged with razorlike ridges plummet to rocky valleys; there are narrow spurs and boulder-studded creekbeds; and splendid panoramas reveal tier after tier of folded stony slopes falling away to the vast northern plains. The area is a paradise for rockhounds, and for the keen botanist a good spring season will provide more diversity of species here than in any other part of the Flinders. The drive to Arkaroola via Copley is particularly scenic, but the highlight of a trip to this area is the Ridgetops Tour, which runs for a tortuous 30 kilometres along the mountain ridges around Arkaroola.

Elder Range from the Moralana track
Sturt's desert pea (*Clianthus formosus*)

BAROSSA VALLEY

AUSTRALIA'S most famous winegrowing area is the Barossa Valley, just north-east of Adelaide in South Australia. It is not only that top-quality wines are produced here; the district has a special atmosphere not found in any other winegrowing region in Australia. This atmosphere is present partly because all the wineries in the 32-kilometre-long valley are physically close to each other, but also because of the rich heritage bequeathed by the pioneers. The unique heritage is reflected in the wineries themselves, many of them fine examples of traditional European or Australian colonial architecture: indeed, a number of the wineries have become nearly as famous as their wines.

Some of the Barossa Valley's first settlers emigrated from Germany, many of them to escape religious persecution, and settled near Tanunda. Because they were so numerous, it was easy for them to retain their customs and language. Initially twenty-eight families arrived from Silesia in 1842, and during later years more followed. Conditions in the Barossa were ideal for viticulture and it was natural that some of the settlers should turn to winemaking, using the same methods that their forefathers had used in Germany. In some of the wineries the old traditions have been passed on from father to son for five generations right down to the present day. In recent times quite a few new wineries have opened in the valley. Some of these have been started by grapegrowers whose forebears were already in the district a century ago; others have been built by families new to the area.

Tourism in the Barossa Valley has been growing at a very fast rate, and no doubt part of the reason for this is the warm hospitality that comes so naturally to the local people. In the smaller wineries it is sometimes the winemaker himself who acts as host in the tasting-rooms—that is, provided you are not visiting during the busy vintage (the term used for the season's grape-picking and winemaking activities). Because the valley lies only 56 kilometres from Adelaide, it is ideal for a day trip. But don't expect to cover all the wineries in one day, even if you don't drink wine; there are just too many of them.

There is more to the Barossa than picturesque villages and charming wineries. Take the Angaston–Tanunda scenic drive to Menglers Hill Lookout and see the vineyards blanketing the valley. In the late-afternoon light the panorama is superb.

From Menglers Hill, near Tanunda

NARACOORTE CAVES

EXTENSIVE areas of Australia are honeycombed with limestone caves, many of which contain exquisitely beautiful formations. Quite a few of these caves have been opened to the public; and in every State, and in the Northern Territory, there is at least one series of caves illuminated with electric lights and made suitable for conducted tours. Hundreds more caves are open only to cavers, whilst a host of others have yet to be explored. Because of the growing popularity of caving and the fragility of some of the formations, certain areas in most States have had restrictions placed on them. Most of the important caves are located in national parks.

The Naracoorte Caves lie about 14 kilometres from the town of Naracoorte, in the far south-east of South Australia. This conservation park has twenty-six known caves, which are part of a larger group of ninety-six documented caverns. Although speleologists can obtain permits to enter many of them, only three are open to the general public for inspection: the Alexandra, the Blanche, and the Victoria Fossil caves. For sheer beauty, the Alexandra Cave—a wet or 'live' cave—is the best: one of its appealing features is the fine display of straw stalagmites and stalactites, which in a couple of chambers are reflected magically in pools of still water.

Although the caves were discovered in the middle of the nineteenth century, properly organized guided tours did not get under way until the early 1970s. The first to be discovered was Blanche Cave, which was explored in 1843 after the bones of an Aboriginal had been found close by. It was recorded in those early years that on one occasion a dray and a team of bullocks fell into a cave when their weight proved too much for its thin roof. In 1894 a series of interconnected chambers full of superb live formations was found, and this was named the Victoria Cave; its most exciting chamber, however, had to wait for discovery until 1969, when a group of exploring South Australian speleologists squeezed through a 25-centimetre-high passage into a cave that contained an extraordinarily rich bed of fossils. Gradually they unearthed the bones of many extinct marsupials and other animals, many of them quite large, along with the remains of species still in existence. Some scientists believe that this site holds the greatest accumulation of Pleistocene fossil vertebrates yet found in any cave in Australia. After such a significant find, it was fitting that the cave's name should be changed to Victoria Fossil Cave. When you visit the caves today, it is easy to wonder what other treasures they may be concealing.

Alexandra Cave

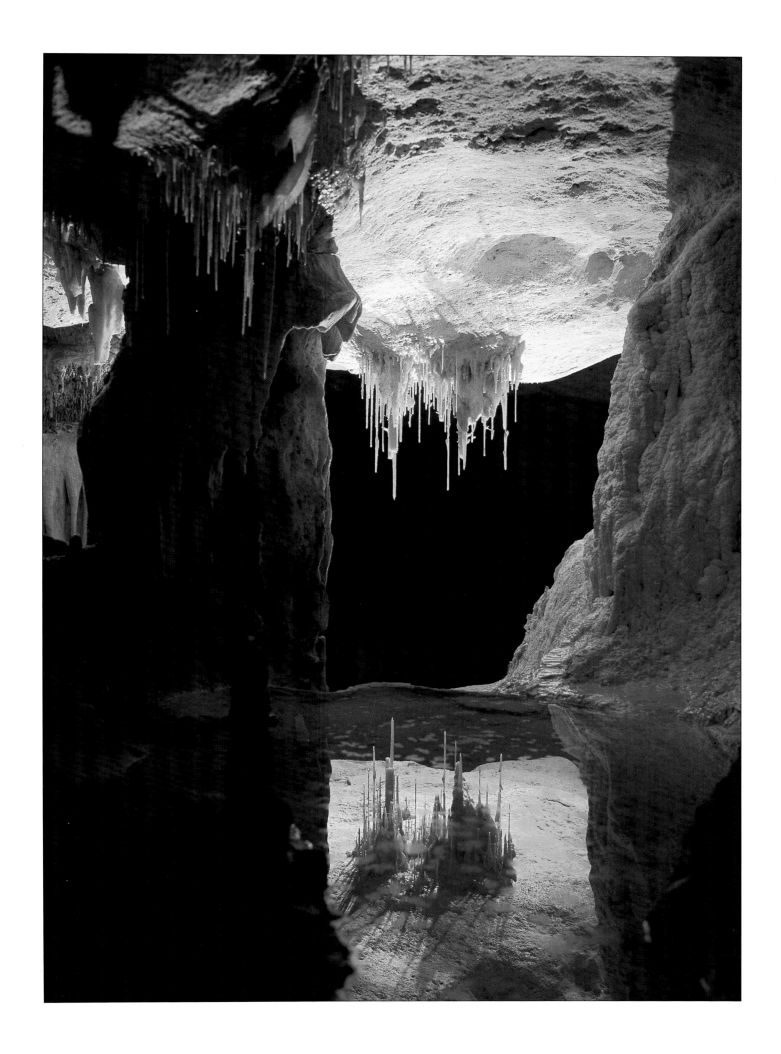

LAKE BONNEY

WITH THE TOWN of Barmera sprawling around its southern shore, Lake Bonney lies 225 kilometres from Adelaide in the Riverland district of south-eastern South Australia. The lake is fed by the Murray River through Chambers Creek; consequently, when the Murray is in flood Lake Bonney spills over its banks to threaten the town. However, since the 1930s the river's flow has been controlled by the great Hume Reservoir, situated hundreds of kilometres upstream in Victoria and New South Wales, and the floods are no longer nearly as frequent or as serious as they used to be.

Seen from the air, Lake Bonney is egg-shaped. With a circumference of around 15 kilometres and a water-depth of between three and four metres, it is an ideal place for watersports, and over the years it has been the venue for many State and national sporting events. There is another lake by the same name in the far south-east of the State, and when, after the Ash Wednesday bushfires of 1983, it was announced that many of the logs salvaged from the ravaged pine forests were to be stored in Lake Bonney, there was considerable alarm among the watersports enthusiasts—especially among the speedboaters, who were reluctant to hold races on a lake brimming with logs. As it turned out, the lake intended for this storage was not the Lake Bonney of the Riverland but the other much smaller one. It took some time for the misunderstanding to be cleared up.

Although Lake Bonney is a freshwater lake, it has some salination problems, as do many parts of the Murray River system; large numbers of trees around its shores have died. One local woman I met recalled childhood picnics held by the lake, when the family went to well-timbered spots that offered plenty of cool shade along the water's edge. Today many of these trees are dead. But salination is not the only culprit: heavy floods have also taken their toll of many of the trees, and (according to the woman with whom I was speaking) in recent years vandals have contributed to the destruction.

I found the sight of all the dead trees around Lake Bonney quite depressing; certainly the fact that the day was overcast did not enhance the scene in any way. However, towards sunset I took a stroll along the water's edge, taking my camera just in case the scene should change. And change it surely did: the last rays of the setting sun quite unexpectedly tinted part of the clouds a glorious pink, transforming the simple scene of bare trees and water into one of warm beauty.

Lake Bonney, Barmera

THE MOUND SPRINGS

THE UNIQUE mound springs are a series of artesian springs that occur from Dalhousie at the south-western edge of the Simpson Desert in South Australia to near Marree and into Queensland. They all lie at the southern rim of the Great Artesian Basin, and are fed by the basin's underground flow of water. As their name suggests, they are mounds of earth with springs of water at the top, formed by drifting sand and the action of artesian springs, which deposit heavy mineral salts as the water evaporates. As the mounds built up over the ages, water collected at the top, spilling over the side in one or more places before it eventually dried up.

The size of the mounds varies greatly; some of the older ones rise to about 40 metres from the plain, others are only a few metres high. The classic is Blanche Cup, situated north-west of Marree. Resembling a miniature volcano, it rises about ten metres above the plain and is topped by a lovely circular pool edged with grasses. At irregular intervals thousands of tiny bubbles rise to the surface and the pond looks like a pot of water just starting to simmer.

Another active mound spring is the Bubbler, a very small pool on slightly elevated ground about a kilometre north-east of Blanche Cup. The first time I saw this delightful entertainer it performed well: at intervals of about ten minutes the placid pool suddenly began to swirl frantically and a growing bubble of mud struggled to escape. Sometimes it burst with great aplomb, but at other times it just disappeared slowly as the water settled down. I had a mad desire to poke the bubble with a stick, but as there were no sticks on this bare landscape my impulse remained unfulfilled. Five years later I made another visit to the Bubbler and was saddened to see that there was very little water left. It was still active, however, and when I thrust my hand into the warm mud the sensation was similar to that of a gentle massage. Many of the mound springs are gradually drying up and becoming extinct—probably because of the massive siphoning-off of artesian water through bores during this century.

At Dalhousie a number of active springs feed large and deliciously warm thermal pools, which, with their deep water edged by luxuriant vegetation, are like the proverbial oases in the desert. Many in this area are also close to extinction. Some of the smaller springs lie near the large pools, others appear on the vast plains as low hills crowned with tufts of vegetation. A few are topped with very old date-palms. I explored one such mound near the ruins of the old Dalhousie homestead. After battling my way through a tangled mess of snapping and crackling palm fronds, I eventually found it. The pool was very small, barely a metre across, and lay at the foot of a gnarled old palm trunk; there was no sign of a fresh spring replenishing it. I dipped my hand into the stagnant-looking water and found it to be barely lukewarm.

Dalhousie landscape
The Bubbler, north-west of Marree

SIMPSON AND STURT'S STONY DESERTS

THE SIMPSON DESERT covers a vast area that spreads into parts of South Australia, the Northern Territory and Queensland. On its south-eastern side the red dunes gradually give way to vast seas of gibber stones, and this section is known as Sturt's Stony Desert. The Birdsville Track, which runs from Marree in the south to the small settlement of Birdsville just over the Queensland border, is the unofficial dividing-line between the two deserts.

The lines of unbroken dunes that lie like great ribs across the dry plain of the Simpson Desert are not of the constantly shifting type, as for example in the Sahara Desert, but are fixed in longitudinal ridges that rise to heights of up to 45 metres. Because the western aspect of each dune slopes gently to the crest before dropping steeply on the other side, vehicular crossings must be made from west to east. Even though there are more than a thousand dunes to be crossed, the current popularity of four-wheel-drive vehicles has made it very fashionable to cross the Simpson. Clubs will spend many months planning a journey — and rightly so, because this forbidding desert is not to be taken lightly. It is necessary to carry a good radio transmitter and enough provisions, water and petrol for the entire three-to-five-day crossing.

I first crossed the Simpson in 1979 with one of the Desert-Trek Australia safaris, and we had the entire desert to ourselves; six years later, when I went again with this company during a school-holiday period, the sandy track looked more like Melbourne's Bourke Street than like a route through one of the world's wildest places. Sadly, some of the travellers gave me the impression that they were not really interested in the desert's wildlife and wildflowers, or in the fascinating beauty of the dunes' ever-changing colours, ranging from pinks to spectacular blood-red: their only aim seemed to be to rip through the area as quickly as possible in order to say that they had 'done' it.

Sturt's Stony Desert remains a wilderness. Crossings must be made with the aid of a compass — and even then navigation can be difficult because of the nature of the terrain. It is probably the grimmest of Australia's six deserts, and one is not surprised to hear that when the explorer Charles Sturt made the first crossing of this inhospitable area in 1845 he commented that it was 'A country such as I firmly believe has no parallel on the earth's surface'. Its vast seas of gibbers lie chiefly between Cooper Creek and the Diamantina River in the north-east of South Australia, their monotony broken in places by areas of spinifex and red sand-dunes. There is a strange beauty in the landscape's desolation, for the play of light on the harsh stones stretching to the far horizon can change their colours from hard steel-greys to deep warm-reds. In a year of exceptional rains, you can be offered the astonishing sight of green plants growing among the stones; however, despite the hard gibbers, rain makes the ground treacherous for vehicles.

Simpson Desert
Sturt's Stony Desert
Sturt's Stony Desert after rain

LAWN HILL GORGE

LAWN HILL GORGE lies in remote country north of Camooweal and the Barkly Tableland in far-western Queensland, near the Northern Territory border. Once part of a large cattle station by the same name, this spectacular natural wonder was not declared a national park until 1982. Before an ABC television programme featured the naturalist Harry Butler looking for the Lawn Hill water-rat at Lawn Hill Gorge in the late 1970s, few Australians knew that the place existed. Its stunning beauty equals that of Australia's two best-known gorges: Katherine Gorge in the Northern Territory and Geikie Gorge in the Kimberleys. Most people visiting Lawn Hill Gorge for the first time wonder how it managed for so long to remain undiscovered by today's insatiable world of tourism.

Of the five gorges that imprison Lawn Hill Creek, the second, with its sheer red-brown craggy walls rising from the green water to heights of 60 metres in places, is the most beautiful. In areas where the splendid walls fall back far enough from the creek to allow vegetation to grow on the banks, there is a lush world of paperbarks, wild-passionfruit vines, pandanus palms and ancient Livistona palms. The water close to the banks is frequently decorated with lovely pads of waterlilies. The second gorge, which extends for about two kilometres, is also the longest; and it is very deep, even in the dry season—as some men from Mount Isa discovered when they dropped a weighted 60-metre-long rope and found that it did not touch the bottom. During the wet season the level of the water usually rises by only about two metres, although in one exceptionally big Wet it rose by twelve metres.

Lawn Hill Creek is fed by streams that drain the Barkly Tableland, and about 100 kilometres north-east of Lawn Hill Station it flows into one of the Gulf Country's biggest rivers, the Nicholson. There are many fish in the gorge, including barramundi, black bream and yabbies, and the waters are also home for tortoises and freshwater crocodiles.

The only way to see Lawn Hill Gorge properly is by boat—and this means by canoe or rowing-boat because motorboats are now banned. (Tenders submitted to the national park for operating boat tours similar to those in Geikie and Katherine gorges were refused.) However, it is possible to walk over the clifftops near the camping ground to the top of the second gorge: the views from the cliffs here are magnificent. Whether you choose to take the hot walk over the clifftops or go by boat, you will find when you arrive at the end of the second gorge that you are more than ready for a swim around the small waterfalls that separate this gorge from the third one. Although to swim against the currents created by the falls is rather strenuous work, once you have anchored yourself to one of the rocks near the tumbling water you will feel as though you are in a giant spa bath—or inside a washing machine.

The second gorge, Lawn Hill Gorge

CHILLAGOE

CHILLAGOE National Park lies near the old mining town of Chillagoe at the southern end of Cape York Peninsula, about 200 kilometres west of Cairns in north Queensland. The park protects an outcrop of limestone about 60 kilometres long and six kilometres wide, its extraordinary appearance the result of long weathering which has worn and chiselled the rock into a series of jagged towers, spires and peaks. These weird formations rise over the surrounding flat country, giving a strange, dramatic beauty to the otherwise monotonous tropical woodland which is the main characteristic of this region.

The remarkable scenery is more than merely on the surface: inside the towers there is an apparently endless series of caves and passages containing some truly superb formations. These caves are unusual in that all of them are above ground-level, although a few may extend a short distance underground. In some of the chambers a partial collapse of the roof has created natural skylights, which allow for an eerie illumination of the formations. The Royal Arch Cave has some impressive examples of naturally lit chambers, and at the Archways there is a fascinating series of open caves that are coloured here and there with mosses and lichens. Park rangers conduct daily tours into the Royal Arch Cave and the Donna Cave. The Donna is the prettier of the two, but the Royal Arch Cave is the more spectacular. In both caves you can see figtree roots which in their search for moisture have penetrated through cracks in the limestone, and grown to fantastic lengths in the process.

I visited Chillagoe National Park in June, when the days were still very warm and the nights surprisingly cold, dropping to 5°C. The ranger suggested that I might like to climb to the top of the Royal Arch Tower in the cool of the early morning, but I decided against this when he told me that after his one and only climb he had had to have his boots resoled. The sharp edges and striations covering every surface of the tower had made him feel that he was walking on knives—but the view, he said, was marvellous. Instead of climbing the tower and ruining my shoes, I spent the last few hours of the day wandering around its base. It was very peaceful, and a deep sense of timelessness settled over the land as the shadows grew longer. The only other person to come by was a young man who stopped for a while to play his flute in one of the caves.

Royal Arch Tower
Balancing Rock

CAPE YORK PENINSULA

CAPE YORK PENINSULA is the long finger of land that extends for about 780 kilometres from just south of Cairns to the Torres Strait in the north. Much of this region is true wilderness and quite inaccessible, particularly in the far north, where the land is laced by a network of watercourses, swamps and lagoons, and where the rugged slopes of the Great Dividing Range, clothed either in eucalypt woodland or dense rainforest, present formidable barriers. Even the coastline is wild, with its seemingly endless lines of tangled mangroves broken intermittently by magnificent but lonely beaches.

Until the 1970s few people ventured past Coen—if they did, they were in what Queenslanders called 'broken-vehicle country'. Although this name still applies to many parts of Cape York Peninsula, each year in the dry season thousands of four-wheel-drive enthusiasts and many commercial safari units follow the Bamaga–Thursday Island telegraph line on a track that is only moderately rough. Their goal is Cape York, the most northerly point of the peninsula—and of Australia. If you don't mind a crowded wilderness, the trip is a fascinating one.

It may be satisfying, after the rough journey, to stand on the rocks at the tip of Cape York; but by far the most interesting place at the top of the peninsula is Somerset, which lies just to the east. Somerset is one of Australia's most historic localities and its story is one of the strangest in the annals of the country's colonial history. Thursday Island was made the government headquarters for the Torres Strait islands in 1877, but before that time Somerset was the site chosen by Britain for development into a 'second Singapore' of the Empire. Unhappily, however, this was no more than a glorious dream, doomed to fail right from the start. What chance did such a settlement have in this remote place, where the Aborigines, the local soil and the climatic conditions alike fiercely rejected the settlers? For twelve years Somerset struggled for survival under the leadership of John Jardine, the first appointed Resident Magistrate. Today the only reminders of its much-hoped-for glory are two shabby guns standing on the hilltop where Jardine's palatial Government House once stood, a few remaining stumps of what was once the jetty, and the derelict graves of the Jardine family. Only the colonies of mangroves growing at both ends of the small but charming beach appear to be thriving.

As I walked over the sands of the beach, past tourist litter and other rubbish, my mind was full of memories of a previous visit I had made from Thursday Island, when Somerset was unspoiled and rarely visited. The oppressive December air had then been hot and still; a large king brown snake had slithered uncomfortably close to my feet; and I could hear a wild bull moving noisily through the undergrowth. It was easy to imagine how the settlers must have despaired.

Mangroves at Somerset, Cape York

CAIRNS

C AIRNS, at the foot of the Atherton Tableland on the coast of tropical north-eastern Queensland and about 1860 kilometres from Brisbane, has one of the most beautiful natural settings in Australia. High forested mountains dominate the city and its sheltered harbour at the western side of Trinity Inlet, so that as you approach from the azure Coral Sea the buildings and the myriad pleasure craft that dot the harbour appear dwarfed. Rustling palms edge the shoreline and streets; parks and gardens are full of lush plants and heavy tropical scents; bougainvillea grows everywhere in a riot of colour. Like the rest of northern Australia, Cairns has only two seasons: the Wet (summer) and the Dry (winter). The wet season's cyclonic storms and monsoonal rains occur mostly between mid-December and the end of April, but the north coast of Queensland and the eastern slopes of the Great Dividing Range receive some rain during the pleasantly warm Dry—often to the annoyance of tourists, who come to Queensland expecting it to live up to its reputation as the 'Sunshine State'.

Cairns is now no longer the sleepy, rather weatherworn sugar town it was up until the end of the 1960s—tourism has changed that image. Although it still serves the sugar industry and the surrounding sugar plantations, it has become one of Queensland's leading growth areas and one of its most popular tourist centres. People flock to Cairns in their thousands to escape the cold southern winters and to enjoy the attractions for which it is famous: the pleasant winter climate; the tropical charm of the city, its outer suburbs and the settlements with their lovely beaches along the coast; the excellent fishing, including big-game fishing; the district's superb scenery; and the nearby wonders of the Great Barrier Reef.

I have known Cairns since the 1960s and with every visit have noticed the increasing signs of 'progress': a little more sophistication in the shops, restaurants and hotels; a proliferation of new buildings, including highrise ones; more and more people on the beaches and visiting popular tourist attractions such as Green Island, Port Douglas and the national parks on the Atherton Tableland. But not everything has changed. Underneath much of the activity in Cairns you can still sense the old *mañana* attitude, and a local may well say to a southern tourist, 'Slow down, mate—you're in the FNQ now!'

And indeed, Far North Queensland to a southerner is almost like a different world.

The harbour, Cairns
Palm Cove

THE BOULDERS, BABINDA

T HE BOULDERS are located close to Babinda, a small town on the Bruce Highway, 58 kilometres south of Cairns. During my various visits to Cairns I had several times passed the signpost to the Boulders but had never had enough spare time to investigate them. I knew nothing about this feature, nor had I met anyone who had been there. When I finally made the effort, I was more than a little astonished.

The six-kilometre bitumen road that runs from Babinda to·the Boulders ends at a beautiful picnic ground nestling into the rainforested slopes of the Great Dividing Range and the nearby Mount Bartle Frere. Through the picnic ground flows Babinda Creek—and it is here, in the creek, that the Boulders are to be found. Sculptured into fantastic shapes, the great granite stones lie higgledy-piggledy in the creekbed, leaving the swift-moving stream to flow through them as best it can, so that sometimes it must find its way noisily through subterranean tunnels and holes. These underwater tunnels, and the strong currents, have made the water very treacherous: if you had the misfortune to slip off the rocks and fall in, you would have enormous difficulty pulling yourself to safety. When I went exploring with the camera I soon discovered that it would be easy to fall in because in places the surface of the rocks was wet, making them as slippery as ice. A notice nearby warned grimly that a number of people had lost their lives among the Boulders. An Aboriginal legend has it that only young men are drowned; and so far, at least in recent years, only young European men have lost their lives here.

Before leaving the picnic ground I followed a narrow walking-path through serene rainforest to the lookout over the Devils Pool, a large waterhole enclosed by massive walls of granite a short distance downstream from the Boulders and a marvellous sight in the early-afternoon sunlight. I left this fascinating place with reluctance.

At the Boulders

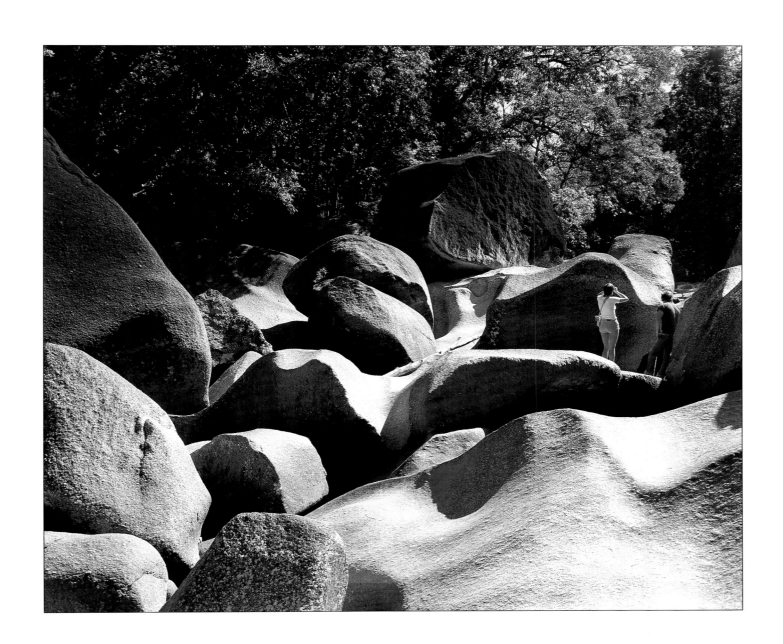

ATHERTON TABLELAND

T HE ATHERTON TABLELAND in north Queensland is the most fertile plateau in Australia. A part of the Great Dividing Range, it extends from the Palmer River on Cape York Peninsula to around the head-waters of the Burdekin River beyond Ingham, and reaches inland for several hundred kilometres. Much of the region, particularly in the west, consists of open eucalypt woodland, with rainforest edging the higher eastern side. Since the middle of the nineteenth century most of the rainforest has been progressively cleared, and what is left is unfortunately still being eaten away by land-developers, much to the alarm of conservationists. Only small sections have been set aside as national parks.

That the Atherton Tableland covers such a wide area may come as a surprise: many tend to think of it only as the stretch of rainforest and agricultural country lying high in the mountains behind Cairns. This is the part that tourists come to see, as there are many scenic attractions near the towns of Malanda, Atherton and Kuranda. Some of these sights, including the beautiful crater lakes of Eacham and Barrine and the Hypipamee volcanic crater, lie in national parks.

The Palmerston National Park, famous for its waterfalls, protects a narrow strip of rainforest along the Palmerston Highway, which runs from Millaa Millaa on the tableland to Innisfail on the Bruce Highway. Visitors driving south from Cairns may take the excellent alternative route from the Atherton Tableland via the Palmerston Highway. Parking bays make it possible for travellers to stop and explore some of the marked walking-paths that meander through the forest's luxuriant vegetation to various waterfalls. One such lovely spot is the Tchuppalla Falls, a series of waterfalls spilling over steep rockfaces; another is the Wallacha Falls, situated off the main walking-path from the Tchuppalla Falls carpark. The best time for visitors to see all the waterfalls on the Atherton Tableland is around May and June, after the summer's wet season. At this time there is plenty of water cascading over the falls, and the weather is usually more clement for sightseeing.

One spectacular inhabitant of the Atherton Tableland's tropical rainforests is the cassowary. Despite its size—it can grow to two metres in height—and the brilliant blue-and-red colouring of its neck, this black-feathered flightless bird is very difficult to see in the forest's dim light. It is more than likely that your first inkling of its presence will be a low rumbling, which has been likened to the sound of an approaching truck, and this is rather unnerving if the bird cannot be seen. Cassowaries can be extremely dangerous if they feel threatened: a kick from one of their powerful legs—each equipped with a long, knifelike inner toe—could be lethal. They have been known to attack humans, and even to kill.

Tchuppalla Falls
Cassowary

GREAT BARRIER REEF

ONE OF THE WORLD'S greatest natural wonders, the Great Barrier Reef stretches for 2000 kilometres from Torres Strait, north of Australia, to just south of the Tropic of Capricorn, near Gladstone. The largest structure created by any living thing (including humans), it was built by a multitude of species of coral polyps. The reef is much more than its name suggests. It is a complex of innumerable coral reefs, cays, deepwater channels, bays, lagoons and rocky islands, all covering some 160 000 square kilometres. The inner side fringes an abundance of beautiful tropical islands that were once the peaks of mountains on the mainland, while the outer side has massive coral ramparts that rear up to 180 metres from the floor of the continental shelf. This formidable barrier gives the north-eastern coast a large degree of protection from the heavy seas of the Pacific Ocean. The reef's magnificence is enhanced by the profusion of creatures whose habitat it is: around 1500 species of fish, six species of turtle and some 40 species of birds are sustained by this unique environment.

The most popular place from which to view the coral is Green Island, a coral cay off Cairns, where there is an underwater observatory and a marine museum. The island is the base for a fleet of glass-bottomed boats that take visitors out over the reef, giving them virtually a fish-eye view. Hook Island, in the Whitsunday Passage off Mackay and Proserpine, also has an underwater observatory. For those who want an even closer look, Heron Island, a coral cay lying off Gladstone, is one of the best places to study marine life and coral at low tide. Although the shores of all the holiday-resort islands are fringed with sections of coral, these cannot compare with the coral on the outer Barrier Reef. All resorts, and some places on the mainland, arrange visits to various parts of the outer reef, about 80 kilometres offshore, but visits can be made only when the weather is stable and when it is low tide at the reef itself.

A day on the outer reef is an unforgettable experience. Most tour-operators have snorkelling equipment for hire and the expense is worthwhile: you can't really appreciate the beauty of the reef until you have snorkelled in one of the lagoons—or better still, dived to deeper waters. At first I found snorkelling rather strange. Even in a small lagoon I had the feeling of being completely detached from reality as I gazed down on the silent and almost eerie underworld, where everything is magnified by one-third through the glass of the goggles. Schools of small bright-coloured fish paused only centimetres away from my face before darting away, and I discovered fat sea-slugs, a wonderful variety of starfish and many interesting shells. Best of all was the coral, so exquisite in formation and colour that I never grew tired of looking at it.

Aerial view of Green Island and its coral reef (*Photo: R. & D. Keller*)

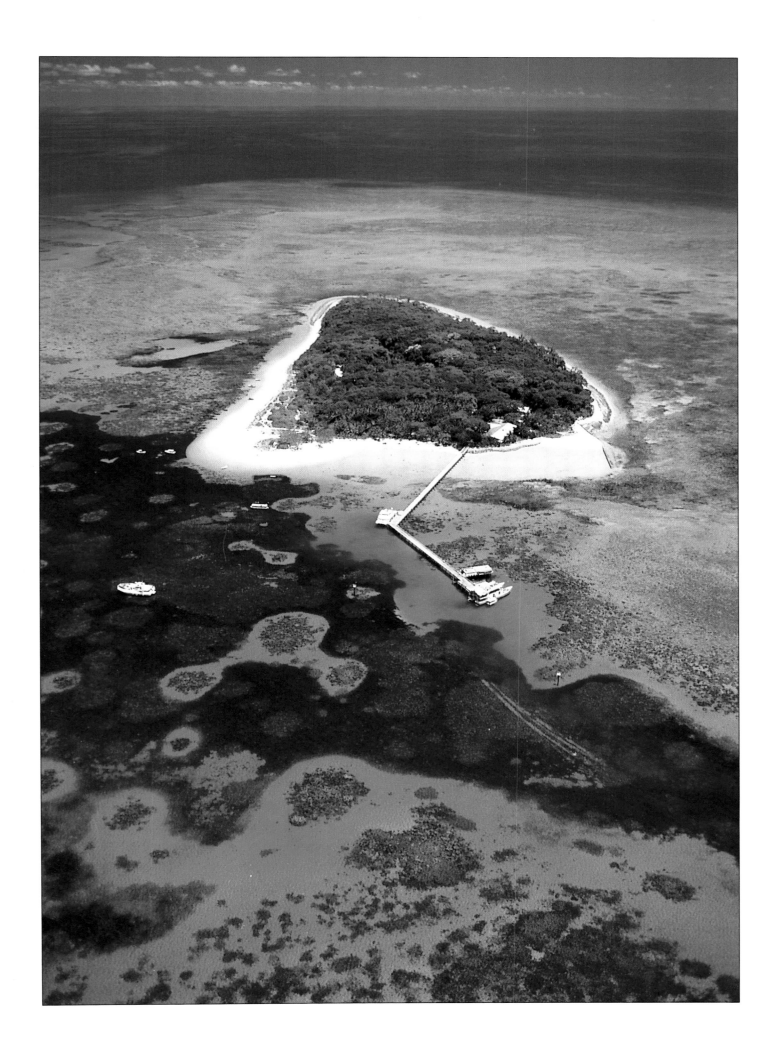

RAINBOW BEACH

RAINBOW BEACH is at the northern end of the Cooloola National Park, which covers part of a section of the Queensland coast known as the Great Sandy Region, lying between Noosa Heads in the south and Hervey Bay in the north. Included in this region is the world's largest sand island, Fraser Island. The Great Sandy Region has dunes that rise to 250 metres, the result of thousands of years' accumulation of sand carried from southern waters by the prevailing wave action. In some places on the ocean side of the dunes there are high walls of beautiful multicoloured sands, relics of a system of iron-stained dunes that were deposited during an era when the sea-level was much lower. Rainbow Beach is one of these places.

Curving into the southern part of Wide Bay, this colourful beach lies three kilometres north-east of Gympie and can be reached via the Tin Can Bay bitumen road. At the edge of the bay is the small settlement of Rainbow Beach, which offers a variety of accommodation for the growing numbers of people who come to fish for bream and taylor from its shore, and to see the coloured sands. The best colours in the clifflike dunes can be found towards Double Island Point, which is about two hours away along the beach to the south from the village. From the moment you set foot on the beach, it is a lovely walk.

I set off in the cool of the day, just after sunrise. The outgoing tide had exposed rocks that were just as colourful as the nearby dunes, and in the soft morning light of the rising sun their chunky shapes of black and warm-yellow, with others wearing green seaweed, were beautifully accentuated. It was a relief to find that the sand was hard, for this made walking easy—if you had to plough through soft sand for that distance, the walk would turn into something worse than a marathon. I stayed fairly close to the dunes that rose sharply from the flat beach, as they were full of interesting formations that had been fashioned by the weather. The sands—white, mingled with varying shades of yellow, red and orange—were covered with a fine crust that gave the appearance of hardness, though in fact the dunes were quite fragile and crumbled easily. In some areas small waterfalls of sand poured down to create miniature landslides, and even a small stone tumbling down the slope tended to start off a new one.

Beyond Double Island Point and lying some distance south are the famous Cooloola Sands at Teewah Beach, which can be reached only by four-wheel-drive vehicle from Tewantin. The cliffs and formations are more spectacular at Teewah Beach, but Rainbow Beach is prettier and more easily accessible.

Rainbow Beach

GLASSHOUSE MOUNTAINS

QUEENSLAND'S Glasshouse Mountains, about 100 kilometres north of Brisbane, have one of the strangest names given to any landform in Australia. They bear no resemblance to horticultural glasshouses — or to any other kind of glass building for that matter. The origin of the name is much more prosaic. When Captain Cook first sighted their strange shapes looming above the horizon as he was making his epic voyage along the east coast in 1770, he was reminded of the glass furnaces of industrial Yorkshire, his home. The mountains are, in fact, the cores of volcanoes that once dominated this corner of south-east Queensland. As the volcanic vents cooled, the molten material inside them solidified to form plugs, and although the exteriors of the volcanoes gradually eroded away over the centuries, the hard plugs remained.

The Glasshouse Mountains tower over rich farmland and forests. There are eleven formations, ranging from narrow skyward-rearing spires to massive bluffs with sheer sides: Mount Beerwah (an Aboriginal word meaning 'up in the sky') is the highest at 556 metres. Some of the peaks lie in small national parks. Although they are clearly visible from the Bruce Highway in the vicinity of the small village of Glasshouse Mountains, the views are better from the back roads in this area, and from the official lookout and picnic ground situated on one such road between Beerburrum and Glasshouse Mountains. One of the loveliest panoramas is from the Mary Cairncross Park, a delightful picnic ground set at the edge of the rainforest near Maleny, high in the ranges further north towards Nambour.

I discovered that you need to be careful when exploring the back roads around Beerburrum and Glasshouse Mountains, because many of them fork off in various directions and few are signposted. On several occasions I ended up in a newly created pineapple plantation that had been hewn out of the surrounding forest. Some of the roads are rough too. When I followed signposts to the Tibrogargan National Park the road soon became a track, so narrow and rugged that even before I reached the national park I had no choice but to back the campervan out.

Glasshouse Mountains, from Mary Cairncross Park

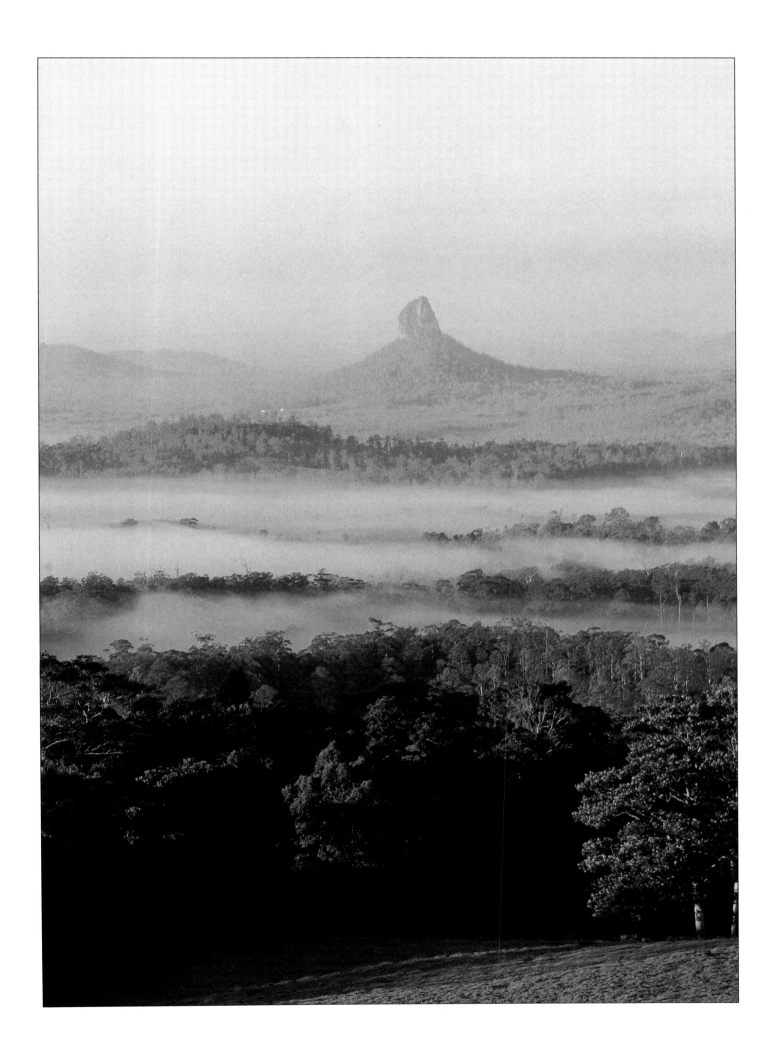

LAMINGTON PLATEAU

T HE LAMINGTON PLATEAU is part of the magnificent Scenic Rim—the portion of the Great Dividing Range that lies along the border of Queensland and New South Wales. Bounded by escarpments rising to 900 metres and covering much of the plateau, the Lamington National Park in Queensland is a glorious world of lush rainforests, peaks, bluffs and gorges, cascading waterfalls and high mountain streams. From the edges of the plateau there are panoramic views of the coast and ranges, and from the eastern side, on a clear day, you can see the Pacific Ocean and the highrise buildings of the Gold Coast. A good bitumen road leads to the resort of Binna Burra on the north-eastern side of the plateau; and to the west lies O'Reillys, which can be reached via the long, greatly improved but still mostly gravel road that winds up the mountain from Canungra. My favourite place is O'Reillys, despite the muddy, steep-sloping camping ground, which is a nightmare for campervan owners. During my most recent visit, the ranger assured me that he would bring the tractor to pull out my van if I bogged it. Needless to say, the comfortable guesthouse nearby looked much more inviting.

From the O'Reillys guesthouse a network of well-kept walking-paths radiate into the wilderness of the plateau, the main one of these being the 21-kilometre Border Track that links O'Reillys to Binna Burra. The track, particularly at the O'Reillys end, is one of the loveliest forest walks in Australia. Apart from the breathtaking views from the various lookout points, there are the Antarctic beech trees, some of the finest and oldest in the Southern Hemisphere. These methuselahs of the forest, found only in the higher reaches of the plateau, seem incredibly old in their robes of green moss. Nobody has been able to say with certainty just how old many of them are, but some forestry experts think that the more ancient ones at Lamington could be around 3000 years. They are believed to be relics of an ice age, and are now dying out—the ones in this national park no longer regenerate from seeds, although shoots and suckers do grow from the bases of old stems.

Most people would prefer to walk through the rainforest on a nice sunny day, yet somehow the beauty of the Border Track, where the old beeches stand, is more appealing when the clouds roll in—and because of the high altitude this type of weather is common. When fog envelops the forest, you feel as if you are entering another world, full of mood and mystery. The large beeches, many of them with a number of misshapen trunks rising from one base, loom eerily out of the mist, their outlines softened by the moist greyness of the fog. Heavy rain is never far away on days like this. On one occasion when I was walking along the Border Track, it started to pour and I took cover in the cavernous trunk of a huge old beech near the path. The floor of this rather unusual shelter was covered with deep, soft mulch which seemed to consist mostly of rotted wood turned to soil; it felt almost spongy underfoot.

Antarctic beeches (*Nothofagus moorei*)

WARRUMBUNGLE RANGE

'To the east a most stupendous range of mountains, lifting their blue heads above the horizon, came into view,' wrote the explorer John Oxley when he first saw the Warrumbungles in 1818. Lying about 500 kilometres north-west of Sydney, near the township of Coonabarabran in New South Wales, this remarkable range topped with intriguing spires and domes continues to attract and impress travellers today. The main access to the Warrumbungle National Park is by way of a bitumen road from Coonabarabran. There is also access via the Coonamble road, which enters the park on its western side, but this route includes some very rough gravel sections. Within the park there is a number of camping grounds.

The extraordinary spires and domes that characterize the Warrumbungles are plugs of lava that formed in the cores of volcanoes during violent geophysical action in ages past. Of these, the most unusual is the Breadknife, a straight wall of rock nearly 100 metres high and only one metre thick. The formations, particularly Belougery Spire and Crater Bluff, are popular with rock-climbers—there is even a visitors' book to sign at the top of Belougery Spire! However, climbing of the Breadknife is banned because the rock, fractured by frequent severe frosts, breaks away very easily and poses dangers not only for climbers but for those walking below. It seems that not all people heed this regulation: shortly before I was there, members of an interstate rock-climbing club made the rather daft decision to climb the Breadknife at night when nobody was around. They were sighted by hikers returning late from a walk.

There are many wonderful walks in the park but without doubt the most popular is the one that leads to the Grand High Tops, passing the base of the Breadknife before it reaches the top ridge with its breathtaking views. On my first visit, some years ago, I set off after breakfast for this four-to-five-hour return walk, but by the time I had reached the top the light for photographing the Breadknife and the other spires was disappointing because I was shooting slightly into the sun. On my next visit, therefore, I decided that the only thing to do was to be on the Grand High Tops at sunrise—which meant walking for more than an hour in the dark through the forest. Not only was that an interesting experience but the scenery was quite magnificent in the early light. Another walk I found rewarding at that time of day was the Alex Gould Circuit track: from the top of Macha Tor, I took in the glorious sight of the first rays of sun lighting up Belougery Spire and the Breadknife.

Crater Bluff
Grasstrees (*Xanthorrhoea*)
The Breadknife

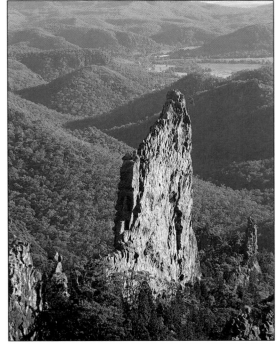

BELLINGER RIVER VALLEY

THE BEAUTIFUL Bellinger River Valley lies close to the coast, just off the Pacific Highway between Nambucca Heads and Coffs Harbour, in north-eastern New South Wales. The hub of the valley is Bellingen, a prosperous little town set by the Bellinger River.

I first discovered this very scenic valley when I was travelling over the Great Dividing Range to the coast from the New England Highway in northern New South Wales. I decided not to take the Oxley, Gwydir or Bruxner highway, and drove instead along the road from Armidale, on the eastern side of the Divide, to Dorrigo. It is a gentle enough climb, as Armidale is only 975 metres above sea-level, but once you have passed the Dorrigo National Park the road drops very steeply indeed, and in an extraordinarily short time you are almost at sea-level. Of all the good bitumen roads that cross the mountains to the coast in New South Wales, this one is the steepest; so if you want to see the marvellous scenery, it is best to travel down from Dorrigo to Bellingen rather than taking the hard climb up.

The Bellinger River Valley starts around Thora in the cleared foothills of Mount Dorrigo, and for about the next 30 kilometres the road stays fairly close to the river on the south side as it passes through lush rural land. There is a distinct air of fecundity in this valley. Cattle and horses graze the fertile flats flanking the Bellinger; banana plantations thrive on the lower slopes of the hills; and in the spots where the land has not been cleared, pockets of superb native forest stand as a reminder of the rich vegetation that once covered the valley. The best view is from the Rotary Lookout, a few kilometres out of Bellingen on the road to Kalang. The short final section of the dirt track to the lookout is steep, but at the top there is a flat area for parking. From here a splendid vista stretches over banana plantations, Bellingen township, and the undulating farmlands that sweep to the mountains.

Another scenic drive in the valley takes you along the North River Road, which, true to its name, runs on the north side of the river to the Pacific Highway. I prefer to take this narrow, winding bitumen road from the Pacific Highway end to Bellingen, as the pastoral scenes are enhanced by the lovely backdrop of Mount Dorrigo, which dominates the entire Bellinger Valley.

From the Rotary Lookout, near Bellingen

CAPERTEE VALLEY

Situated about 120 kilometres north of Lithgow in New South Wales, the Capertee Valley is believed to be one of the largest enclosed valleys in the world. There are only two entrances to it: from Capertee on the highway and from Rylstone near Mudgee. The main settlement in the valley is Glen Davis, a small village that flourished for a few years in the 1940s, when shale-mining for synthetic oil was considered economically viable. By 1952, because of the small output of shale and the high cost of production, the town had closed and its plant had been removed. It did not become a ghost town, however, for many of the vacated buildings were made available at low rentals and people returned to live there. The tiny village set beside the ruins of the mining complex now serves local farmers, craftspeople living in and around the settlement, and an increasing number of tourists; there is a general store, a post office and a camping ground with just the basic amenities.

At present the valley is a peaceful place, but this air of tranquillity may not last for much longer: subdivision of the properties has started and unsightly shacks are beginning to appear. A local farmer told me that one of the worst aspects of subdivision for the established property-owners is that the city people who buy the land for 'weekenders' tend not to look after their lots, and then, in the hot summer months, are generally not around to help take responsibility for firefighting in the district.

Much of the Capertee Valley is pastoral land. With the magnificent backdrop of high vertical sandstone cliffs that edge the Wollemi National Park to the east, the picturesque Capertee and Nile rivers, and the superb stands of river gums, its beauty is a landscape-artist's dream. I was told that most of the major art galleries in Sydney regularly feature paintings of this area.

As a Victorian, I was not at all familiar with the Capertee Valley until recently, when, on my way back from a trip further north, I called into the tourist office at Mudgee for some information on the district. When I enquired about the scenery in the Glen Davis area, the attendant informed me rather unenthusiastically that it was 'quite nice'. I can only say that this was the most understated piece of tourist information I have ever received!

Near Glen Davis

BLUE MOUNTAINS

ONE OF Australia's most spectacular and best-loved panoramas is that from Katoomba's clifftop lookout at Echo Point in the Blue Mountains, 100 kilometres west of Sydney. Dominating the majestic view over Jamison Valley are the three great crags of sandstone known as the Three Sisters, rising 450 metres above forested slopes that plunge a further 200 metres to the valley floor. The best time to be at Echo Point—which is only a minute's drive from the Katoomba shopping centre—is at sunset, when the Three Sisters and the surrounding cliff-faces that edge the walls of the valley flare a warm gold in the last rays of the setting sun.

A spur of the eastern highlands of the Great Dividing Range, the Blue Mountains consist of a plateau dissected by canyonlike gorges that rise to around 1080 metres. The mountains are named for the distinctive hue they take on when viewed from a distance, a colour caused by particles of vaporized eucalyptus oil scattering blue light.

In the early days of colonization the massive ramparts presented such a formidable barrier to any expansion west of Sydney that it was twenty-five years before the first settlers were able to find a way over them. Today, the towns lying along the busy Great Western Highway that crosses the plateau seem virtually an extension of suburban Sydney—yet only minutes away from the heavy traffic it is possible to escape to peace and tranquillity on the forested walking-trails of the Blue Mountains National Park. The park covers more than 200 000 hectares and stretches from Newnes in the north to the Wombeyan Caves in the south; it is bordered by two other parks, the Wollemi and the Kanangra-Boyd national parks.

Although there are many easy walks in the Blue Mountains National Park, most of the tracks winding down to the valley floor are not the sort you would tackle on an afternoon stroll—unless you were a fit and experienced bushwalker. The track down to the Grose Valley from Govetts Leap at Blackheath, 10 kilometres west of Katoomba, almost seems to have been gouged into the side of the mountain, which is knife-sheer in places: for much of the way it consists of a long series of steep steps, and in one spot you must negotiate a metal stairway that gives the distinct impression of being suspended in midair. The descent to the valley floor is fine—but then there is always the journey back to the top.

The Three Sisters, from Echo Point

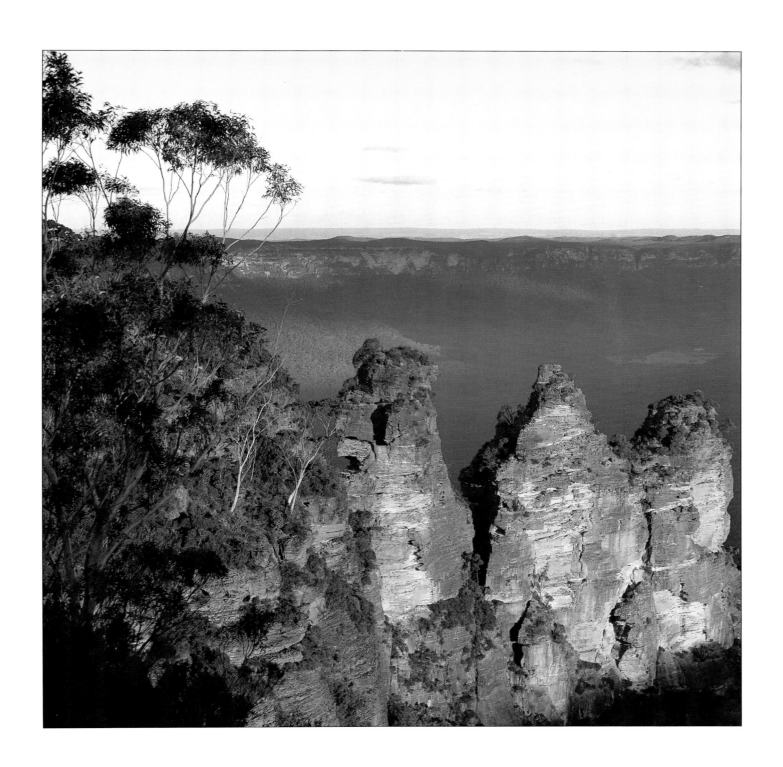

DARLING RIVER AND LAKE MENINDEE

PART OF Australia's greatest river system, and the country's longest river, the Darling rises in the form of numerous streams on the slopes of the Great Dividing Range in Queensland and eventually becomes the Darling just east of Bourke, in outback New South Wales. After travelling for some 3750 kilometres, it empties into the Murray River at Wentworth. Its waters are dammed as it passes through the Menindee Lakes, about 110 kilometres east of Broken Hill.

When I first saw the Darling River between Wentworth and Pooncarie I wondered how the riverboats of last century could possibly have managed to navigate it, because the river, which is extremely narrow in places, twists and turns like a writhing snake. I was there after a long spell of dry weather, and the level of the water revealed astonishingly deep banks of grey mud that dropped quite steeply in places to the equally muddy water. Debris from previous floods lay in the water and along the banks, giving the river an untidy air, yet to my eyes it had a depth of character and beauty unrivalled by any other Australian river. The Darling's flow has been much more reliable since it was dammed at Menindee. Before this, the river would cease to run altogether in times of drought, often leaving paddle-steamers stranded for months in a bed of mud.

Another notable feature of this river is its many magnificent stands of river red gums, some of them amazingly old with enormous trunks and massively thick branches—the girth of one grand old tree measured five spans of my outstretched arms. While I was busily wrapping my arms around it, an old fisherman wandered along the bank and stopped for a chat. He said that at one time there were many more of these big old trees, but over the years they had been cut down. 'That's progress for you,' he said sadly. 'It's the same with the river—the days of good cod-fishing have gone—most of the catch now is the useless European carp.'

A section of the Darling River lies within the Kinchega National Park (originally Kinchega Station), near Menindee. This national park is a good place to see not only the Darling but also Lake Menindee, the largest of a string of lakes fed by the Darling River. Lake Menindee now holds the Darling's storage water, and the many dead trees drowned by the rising waters have given it a rather forlorn look. However, the lake and the stark outlines of the drowned trees took on a special charm for me at sunset, when the water mirrored a brilliant sky streaked with golden and orange clouds. Unfortuantely, the lovely sunset heralded a storm that night; by morning the rain had transformed the dusty roads into quagmires of treacherous, slippery mud.

Lake Menindee
River gum, Darling River

JUGIONG

NORTH OF Gundagai, in south-eastern New South Wales, the small settlement of Jugiong on the busy Hume Highway nestles by the lovely Murrumbidgee River, the second-longest river in the State. Some very attractive pastoral country lies in this foothill region of the Great Dividing Range, and countless scenes between here and Gundagai depict the classic Australian rural landscape of sheep and cattle beneath splendid gumtrees or beside flowing streams, with sunburnt hills and forested mountains in the background. Many Hume Highway travellers are familiar with the panorama over the Murrumbidgee Valley which can be enjoyed from the rest area at the side of the road on the hill just above Jugiong. Most people only have time to stop and take a quick look before continuing their journey, but if you leave the highway and explore a few of the minor roads that lead to the river, you will find some delightful spots.

On one occasion, when I drove away from the noisy highway to find a quiet place in which to have lunch, I discovered an idyllic pastoral scene near a local quarry. A mob of sheep had wandered down to drink from a nearby billabong, and the animals showed only a little nervousness when I stepped quietly out of the van to take a photograph. I expected them to run off immediately in alarm, but instead they continued slowly along the path that ran close to the vehicle.

The characteristically peaceful scene of sheep grazing is one of the most common sights in rural Australia — for the good reason that there are around 165 million of them. According to many farmers in outback Queensland and New South Wales, there would be many more if it wasn't for the high population of kangaroos, who enjoy the same pastures as sheep. Once upon a time it used to be said that, economically, 'Australia rides the sheep's back'. To a certain extent it still does, as wool is the country's most important export after coal; today, however, that ride is not quite as smooth as it used to be.

By the Murrumbidgee River

MINNAMURRA FALLS RESERVE

MINNAMURRA Falls Reserve protects a small but important pocket of rainforest within the Illawarra Escarpment, part of the Southern Highlands in the Great Dividing Range, behind Kiama on the south coast of New South Wales. The reserve is situated five kilometres from Jamberoo and can be reached by a bitumen road. Parking inside the reserve is limited, so all groups, buses and mini-buses must book ahead. The best time to see the area is early in the morning on a weekday, though not during holiday periods.

A good walking-track leaves the carpark and follows the Minnamurra River to the 50-metre-high gossamer-like waterfall that hides in a narrow chasm set back from the main rockface at the end of the track. Although a sign at the start of the walk advises that it will take half an hour to reach the falls, most fit people can do it in half that time, provided they don't stop too often to admire the superb forest—mostly warm temperate rainforest, with some pockets of subtropical rainforest. In one spot there is a large and very old Illawarra figtree, full of character and beauty.

Anyone familiar with the forests of New South Wales will appreciate the importance of this rainforest, as there are precious few left in the State. But Minnamurra Falls Reserve, as one of the last stands of rainforest in the Illawarra region, is significant not only for its ecological value but for reasons of science and education as well. It is believed that the world's rainforests contain more than a million as yet unidentified plant species. While these virgin forests worldwide are gradually being destroyed, scientists continue the search for new botanical 'miracle drugs' and new food crops that may well be waiting to be discovered amid the forests' astonishing diversity.

I arrived at the Minnamurra Falls Reserve early in the day, when few people were around; by mid-morning the carpark was swarming with children from several bus tours. As one teacher shepherded his charges for the walk, he loudly informed them that there was to be no littering, no kicking (did he mean the vegetation or other children?) and no throwing. It was a pity the other groups were not given similar reminders: that morning I had stones thrown at me while I was photographing a particularly appealing scene by the boulder-strewn river, and the previously clean path was littered with lolly-papers and cans.

Rainforest, Minnamurra Falls Reserve

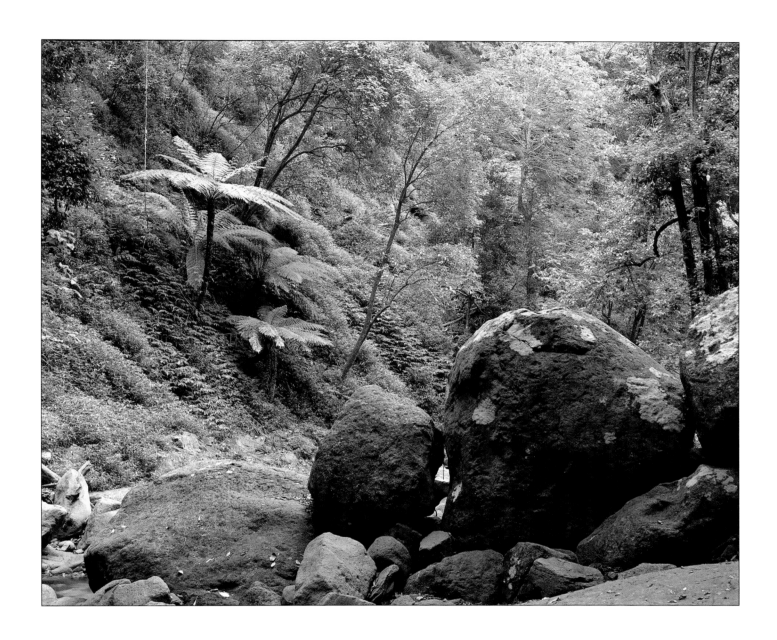

MERIMBULA

ALONG THE south coast of New South Wales there are many towns and villages set around picturesque inlets, estuaries and lagoons. One of the loveliest of these settlements is Merimbula, situated 470 kilometres from Sydney and only about 80 kilometres from the Victorian border. The town spreads over wooded hills and along the shores of a beautiful inlet known as Merimbula Lake. The trees that line the roads and paths meandering along the hillsides reveal tantalizing glimpses of golden sand and blue water, and occasionally you may spot an armada of pelicans; more commonly, you will see fishing boats or pleasure craft pass by.

Some of the prettiest views lie along the road that leads to the site of the old wharf. Just beyond this site, rocks of an unusual red colour stretch for some distance, and in the late afternoon they glow richly in the light of the sinking sun. For many years the old wharf was a favourite spot for fishing, and even when it was condemned and on the verge of collapse, fishermen and tourists risked using it. It has now been replaced by a platform for the use of those who want to fish the waters. Some historic sheds still stand nearby, bearing silent testimony to the busy days when the wharf served the steamships that used to ply the south coast from Sydney. Merimbula's history dates back to 1855, when a port opened to serve the rural community and the gold-diggers bound for Kiandra in the Snowy Mountains.

Merimbula has become an extremely popular tourist resort and retirement centre. This is hardly surprising, for apart from its scenic beauty the south coast of New South Wales has the most equable climate in Australia: the summers are never too hot and the winters are mild (I have even swum in the sea at Batemans Bay in June, and I am no stoic fond of cold-water swimming). The entire south coast, from Narooma in the north to the Victorian border, is known as the Sapphire Coast. Its delights are endless: the many lakes and quiet inlets, the pleasant sandy beaches and prominent headlands washed by the glittering blue sea, and the magnificent backdrop of forest-clad mountains, rolling green hills and quiet valleys laced with streams and rivers.

Whenever I visit the Sapphire Coast I feel like packing my bags and moving there to live — it's that sort of place. Perhaps it is becoming too popular for some of the locals: one oldtimer grumbled to me that Merimbula was not the place it used to be. 'There are too many people here, and they are spoiling its serenity,' he said. He may be right, but then many of us do not know what the area was like thirty or so years ago, and what we see today is delightful anyway.

Merimbula Lake

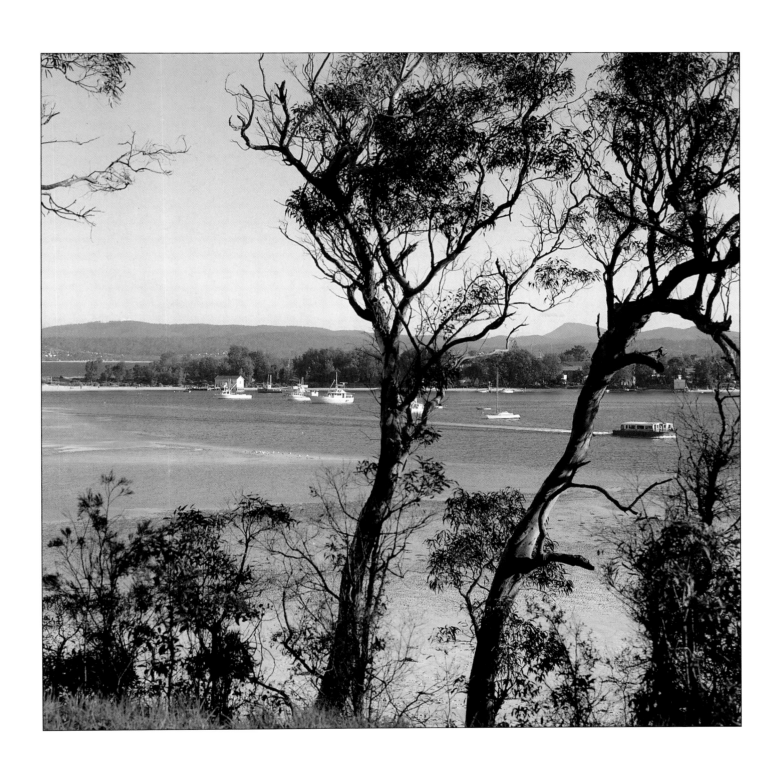

SNOWY MOUNTAINS

I N SOUTH-EASTERN New South Wales the Great Dividing Range rises in wild splendour to form Australia's highest landmass, the Snowy Mountains. This region, known as the Australian Alps, also extends into the north-eastern corner of Victoria. Like so much of Australia's terrain, the mountains are old and worn, and no longer show the great craggy massifs, the sharp towering peaks or the volcanic activity seen in other countries. Yet although the Australian Alps are less dramatic in formation than the other great alpine areas of the world, they have their own characteristic beauty of weathered granite, fantastic tors, high grassy plains, steep escarpments, rugged gorges and forested ridges. Fortunately, a good portion of the Snowy Mountains lies within the important Kosciusko National Park. The largest park in New South Wales, it extends south from Tumut and the national capital, Canberra, to the Victorian border. Although the Snowy Mountains Hydro-electric Scheme and a number of popular ski resorts intrude into the national park, at least half the area is true wilderness, where landscapes and vegetation are virtually in their natural state.

One of the major features of the park is Mount Kosciusko, at 2228 metres Australia's highest mountain. In the winter months it is heavily blanketed in snow, but in late spring and early summer the slopes below its summit are transformed into carpets of colourful alpine wildflowers that attract thousands of visitors each year. Apart from the flowers, the deliciously cool weather lures many people wishing to escape the summer heat and humidity of the coastal regions.

Until about the mid-1970s it was possible to drive up to the summit, but since then the increase in traffic has made it necessary to close the road eight kilometres away at Charlotte Pass. Like many people, I was at first rather annoyed at this, and it wasn't until I walked the area one sunny Saturday in early January that I understood the wisdom of closing the road. Instead of walking up the old road to the summit, most people take the shorter five-kilometre route from Thredbo, first taking the Crackenback chairlift to the top and walking across from there. This was the route I took on that Saturday. By mid-morning there was a constant flow of people on the track, and by early afternoon it resembled a corridor inside Flinders Street railway station. Just imagine if all those people had driven to the summit via the old road!

Another necessary conservation measure taken here to combat the erosion caused by constant use is the placing of a metal walkway over the original path at the Thredbo end of the route. I suspect that many seasoned bushwalkers will now prefer the longer trek by the old road from Charlotte Pass.

Winter at Perisher Valley
Tors, Mount Kosciusko

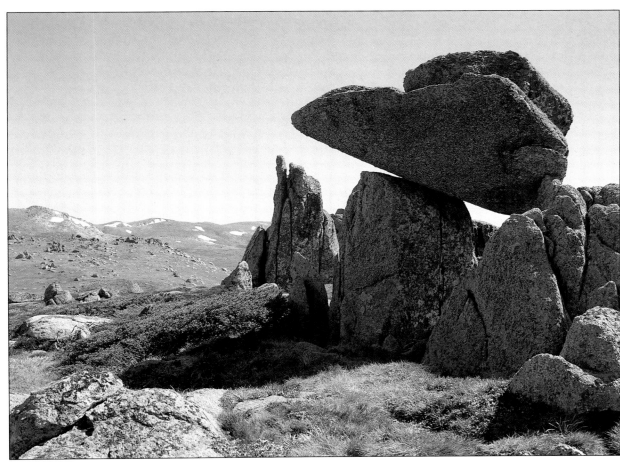

VICTORIAN ALPS

VICTORIA'S high country, an extension of the Australian Alps, lies in the north-east of the State and is known as the Victorian Alps. Mount Bogong, at 1986 metres the highest peak, dominates the Kiewa Valley; and not far behind is its relatively close neighbour, Mount Feathertop, which rises to 1922 metres over the top end of the Ovens Valley. The Victorian Alps have a gentler beauty than the wilder and higher Snowy Mountains region to the north in New South Wales; in fact, many Victorians will happily tell you that their Alps contain the most beautiful mountain country in mainland Australia. They will point out that the glorious scenery is not confined to the high altitudes but extends as well to many of the valleys that lie within the mountains: the Kiewa, Ovens, King and Buckland valleys, and, further south, the valleys of the Wonnangatta, Macalister and Tambo. All are guaranteed to delight artists and photographers.

The high country means different things to different people. For some the mountain streams provide the ultimate in trout-fishing; for others the slopes are a hiker's paradise, particularly in the wilderness areas. However, for a growing number of people the high country means winter sports. While the relatively short season lasts, the peaks and high plains are blanketed in snow, and every weekend between June and September streams of cars topped with skis fill the highways leading to various ski resorts.

Like many people, I have caught the skiing bug; but it is not so much the skiing as the pristine beauty of the snow which thrills me. No other environment gives me such joy with the camera as the snow country. For landscapes of sheer grandeur, there are the spectacular views of the Razorback Ridge and Mount Feathertop seen from Hotham Heights. Falls Creek and Mount Buller, too, offer photogenic if less dramatic scenes of mountains blanketed in snow: on some days, after particularly cold conditions, the silence of their slopes is broken by the wind moving through a multitude of frozen gumleaves that tinkle like bells. Best of all are the sights on the Bogong High Plains around Falls Creek when, after blizzards, the windward side of every branch, twig or marker-pole is laden with driven ice, sometimes formed into fantastic shapes of exquisite beauty.

In summer it is time for the wildflowers. Although many alpine roads have unquestionably improved over the past decade, it is much easier to drive on them in the summer months, and as a result many more people are visiting the Alps between December and February to see the flowers. At that time the mountain air is refreshingly cool—often around ten degrees cooler than in the valleys.

Falls Creek
Mount Feathertop from Hotham Heights
Crimson rosella

SUGGAN BUGGAN

SOME OF Victoria's wildest mountain scenery lies tucked away in the far south-east corner of the continent, in eastern Gippsland. Access is often limited to riders on horseback, hikers (who need to be equipped with reliable maps), and motorists with four-wheel-drive vehicles. However, some roads in the region are suitable for conventional vehicles. Of these, two of the most scenic are the Wulgulmerang–Bonang road, which passes over the spectacular McKillops Bridge, and the Buchan–Jindabyne road, which runs from Buchan in the south through Suggan Buggan (pronounced 'Sooggan Booggan') and on to Jindabyne in the Snowy Mountains. A growing number of people come to this area to take in the scenery that lies along the Snowy River as it flows through three national parks: the Tingaringy and Snowy River national parks in Gippsland, and the Kosciusko National Park in New South Wales.

Some breathtaking panoramas can be seen from the road that leads from Wulgulmerang to McKillops Bridge, but in places the road clings to the sheer sides of the mountain and is hair-raisingly narrow. A notice at the top warns that it is unsuitable for caravans and semitrailers. The Buchan–Jindabyne road is kinder on the nerves. The only petrol available on this route is at Wulgulmerang's Seldom Seen Petrol Station (yes, that's its official name; and the first time I was in the area I nearly missed it because of thick fog). About 65 kilometres from Buchan, shortly after you have reached the Benambra turnoff, the Jindabyne road descends dramatically to what the locals call 'the gorge', which in fact is an escarpment of the Rocky Range and plunges to around 610 metres. The views from here are magnificent. Below the road, mountains stretch back, fold on fold, to the distant horizon, each fold bathed in misty blues and mauves, and each ridge a slightly different shade. To watch the sun rising over them is a memorable experience.

Sunrise in Victoria's mountains is often heralded by kookaburras, whose laughing call rings loudly through the valleys at the break of day. Of all the sounds in the bush, the joyful call of the kookaburra, the continent's largest kingfisher, is surely the most uniquely Australian. Early settlers named the bird the laughing jackass, and were quite unnerved by its call; but today it can be the most welcoming sound to an Australian returned from overseas. Nowadays it is not even necessary to go into the bush to hear it, for kookaburras inhabit quite a few suburban areas of the big cities. Their home is eastern Australia, but around the turn of the century they were introduced into Western Australia, and later into Tasmania.

From Rocky Range
Kookaburra

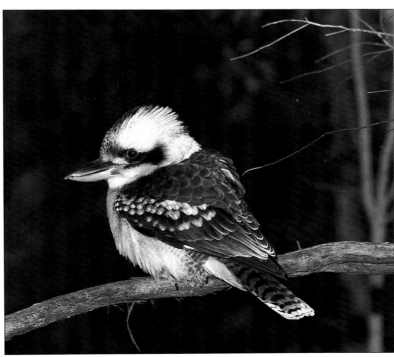

OVENS VALLEY

THE SUN is rising over the Ovens Valley in north-eastern Victoria. The April morning is crisply cold, and although the sun has lit the surrounding mountaintops and the blanket of mist lying above the towns and farms, the valley is still curtained in shadows. The calls of kookaburras and currawongs proclaim the start of the new day. As the sun rises higher in the sky the shadows gradually disappear and the mist begins to break up into gossamer wisps that drift lazily against the hills. The lifting mist reveals a lovely pageant of autumn colours throughout the valley.

One of the most scenic regions in Victoria, the Ovens Valley extends from Wangaratta to the rising slopes of Mount Feathertop. Much of the valley is dominated by Mount Buffalo, which provides a superb backdrop for farms, orchards, and the fast-flowing Ovens River. Myrtleford, the largest town in the valley, is the commercial centre for the district's primary industry, and the town of Bright is the tourist 'capital'.

The seasons are marked here with a clarity not often seen in Australia, and this gives the valley much of its charm. In winter, snow mantles the mountain-peaks and ridges, and the valley becomes a gateway to various ski resorts; in spring, there is much beauty in the profusion of golden wattles and blossoming fruit-trees; in summer, the melting snow on the high plains gives way to alpine wildflowers; in autumn, the dying leaves present a kaleidoscope of colour.

The Ovens Valley is the best place in Australia to see autumn colours. Although many other localities have brilliant displays of deciduous trees, no other area has such a wide variety of scenes dominated by autumn tones. Most of Bright's major avenues are lined with well-established trees dressed in glorious hues; Centenary Park becomes a poem of green and gold; and everywhere in the town falling leaves cover the ground in thick carpets of gold, burnt orange, bronze and red. When the early-morning sun shines through the trees, the play of light on the leaves makes them glow like jewels. Myrtleford and all the smaller villages radiate colour too, and there is yet more along the banks of the Ovens River. Away from the towns and villages, stately golden poplars grow beside sheds, tobacco kilns and pine plantations, and lines of them brighten paddocks, hop farms and roads. The long double-row of poplars at Wandiligong, a small village near Bright, is deservedly famous.

The Ovens Valley has long been one of my favourite places in Australia; whenever I visited it in the past, I made fresh scenic discoveries. Now it is my home, and, like most people who live here, I find that it constantly presents different moods that never fail to delight.

Mount Buffalo, from Porepunkah
Bright

LAKE MOKOAN

LAKE MOKOAN lies nine kilometres from Glenrowan in north-eastern Victoria. It is clearly visible from the Hume Highway on the western side, where its most notable feature is the depressing line of dead trees that stand like a skeletal army at its edge; these trees died when the waters of an inlet channel from the Broken River were trapped to form the lake. The stored water is used for irrigation purposes within the Murray River system.

The lake provides a good venue for watersports and is a favourite with many people in the summer months. It is also a bonus attraction for tourists who visit Glenrowan to see the Ned Kelly memorabilia and 'living history' presentations. The latter include a spectacular if somewhat spooky re-enactment of the notorious bushranger's last hours and of the final dramatic shootout, which occurred at the Glenrowan railway station in June 1880. After you have experienced that, a drive out to Lake Mokoan makes a very pleasant diversion!

The scene on the page opposite shows Lake Mokoan at sunset, during a time in autumn when the Forests Commission was having a major burning-off spree in the mountain-eucalypt forests of north-eastern Victoria. For days the air in the district was thick with heavy smoke because a large high-pressure system was reluctant to move from its position over south-eastern Australia. As a result, palls of smoke drifted well into New South Wales and as far south as Melbourne. However, at a time like this, landscape photographers happily reach for their cameras because sunrises and sunsets can be stunning in the smoky conditions.

Standing at the edge of Lake Mokoan in the late afternoon, I watched with joy while the sun changed from a bright golden to a fiery red as it gradually slipped to the horizon in a film of haze. The vibrant colours spilled over the still surface of the lake, which reflected the warm smoky hues of the sky. The dead trees were transformed into ghostly silhouettes, and as the tracery of their stark limbs accentuated the soft evening light, the scene took on a magical quality. It was like being in another world.

Lake Mokoan

MURRAY RIVER

ONE OF Australia's greatest blessings is the Murray River. Fed by a vast network of tributaries—including the mighty Darling and Murrumbidgee rivers—it is the lifeblood of many cities, towns and villages, and of thousands of fertile farms lying like green jewels in an area that before irrigation was largely arid wasteland. It is Australia's most important river, draining more than one-fifth of the continent in four States; it is also a river full of character and interest, and contains along its length a wealth of beautiful scenery.

The Murray rises in the Snowy Mountains and travels 2570 kilometres before its muddy waters flow into the clean surf of the Southern Ocean near Goolwa in South Australia. For the first part of its journey it is a fast-running stream of clear icy water bubbling through mountain forests, but after it has reached the Upper Murray Valley it becomes a wide mature river. Once out on the plains, where its most noticeable feature is the majestic river gums that line its banks, the Murray's meanderings create large numbers of billabongs, swamps and marshes that teem with wildlife. By the time it enters South Australia the swollen river is a major waterway, sedately making its way past the great limestone cliffs that are such an outstanding feature of the river in this State. After passing through shallow Lake Alexandrina and Lake Albert, it pours its waters into the sea through a small mouth.

No other river in Australia has greater importance as a recreational playground than the Murray. On weekends and holidays during the warmer months, the river is alive with a variety of boats, many of them speedboats towing waterskiers. In recent years too, there has been a dramatic increase in the number of houseboats: at just about every Murray town, you can find them clustered around the riverbanks. For a family or a small group of congenial friends, a houseboat must surely provide one of the most idyllic ways of exploring the river. The quiet *put-put* of its engine does not disturb the environment the way the penetrating whine of a speedboat does, and there is the special delight of being able to find a quiet mooring at night, away from other people and settlements.

River traffic is not new to the Murray. During the nineteenth century paddle-steamers churned through the water, carrying wool, wheat and other produce to and from towns and properties along the river. No modern craft can match the character and charm of these marvellous old vessels, and some have fortunately come back to the river to carry tourists on sightseeing trips and help them relive a little history. Mildura and Echuca are good places from which to take day trips, and for extended cruises there are paddle-steamers operating from Murray Bridge in South Australia.

Murray River, Echuca

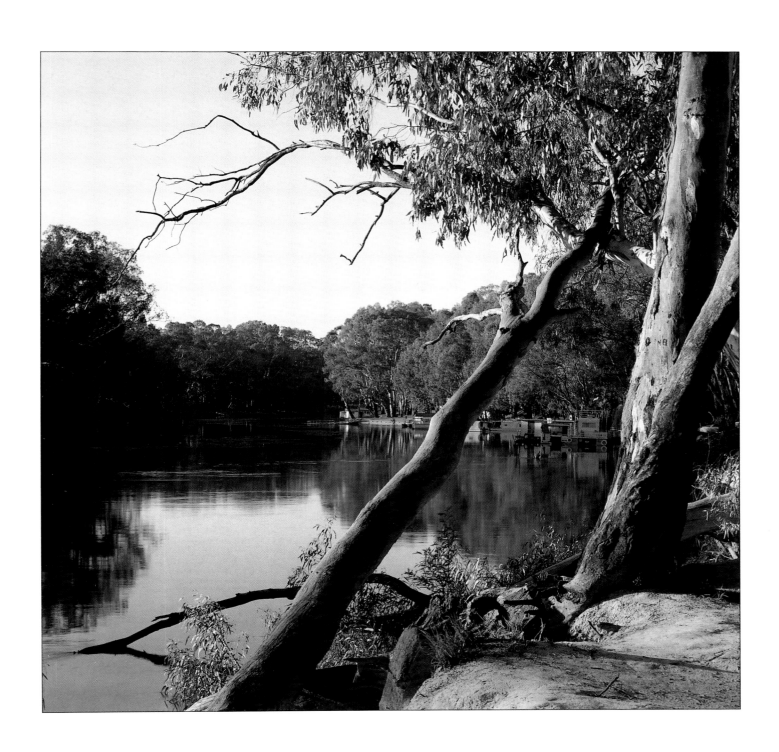

GIPPSLAND LAKES

T HIS UNIQUE system of coastal lagoons covers an area of nearly 400 square kilometres just east of Sale in Victoria's east Gippsland. The lakes have become so popular with holidaymakers and boating enthusiasts that Gippslanders have declared the area to be the Victorian Riviera. Their opinion could well be confirmed by the current local boom in real estate, with land values that may soon match those of Australia's wealthiest resorts. At Paynesville, on the south-western side of Lake King, canal blocks (homes sharing canal waterways) similar to those on the Gold Coast are being built. Paynesville has become an important centre for the yachting fraternity, and Metung, the jewel of all the settlements around the lakes, is sought after for its superb natural beauty and sheltered waters. Lakes Entrance, 313 kilometres from Melbourne and situated at the eastern end of the lake system, has long been a popular holiday resort as well as an important base for a large fishing fleet.

Long ago the entire area was a huge bay, which gradually became closed by a barrrier of sand deposited by the action of the waves. Later, another outer sand-barrier developed, forming narrow Lake Reeve and the Ninety Mile Beach. Eventually the present maze of lakes, swamps and deltas was built up as silt and clay were carried by numerous rivers and streams into the water behind the barrier. By the time the first Europeans came to the area in the 1840s, the lakes were virtually landlocked, with only an occasional outlet occurring in one of the weak spots along the great sandbar after heavy floods or storms — most commonly at the present site of Lakes Entrance. In 1889 a channel was cut through the Ninety Mile Beach at Lakes Entrance to enable steamers to enter the lakes from the sea. Today this channel is used by the locally based fishing boats. .

Two national parks protect some of the natural bushland left around the shores. The Lakes National Park covers Rotamah Island and Sperm Whale Head, the tip of the long finger of land that separates Lake Victoria and Lake Reeve. Access is via Loch Sport, 65 kilometres from Sale, or via Paynesville, just five kilometres across the water. The Gippsland Lakes Coastal Park takes in most of the golden sands of the Ninety Mile Beach from Seaspray to Lakes Entrance, and includes other parts of the lake system.

The Gippsland Lakes are at their most beautiful in early morning and late afternoon, particularly in summer and autumn when the days are more likely to be still and balmy and the water lies like a vast sheet of glass, perfectly reflecting everything on its shores. When the sun balances on the horizon at either sunrise or sunset, the lakes are bathed in warm glowing colours highlighted by the brilliant pathway splashed by the sun on the water. At such times a deep and wonderful calm settles over the place.

Lakes Entrance at sunset
Metung

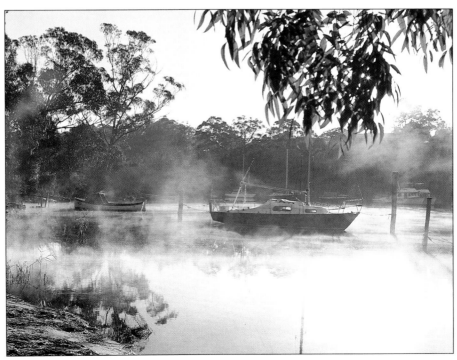

STRZELECKI RANGES

THE BEAUTIFUL Strzelecki Ranges lie south of the Princes Highway in eastern Victoria and dominate the southern part of Gippsland. The steep hills, high ridges and deep gullies that characterize the Strzeleckis are watered by good rains throughout the year, and this makes for a vibrant lushness seen in few other areas of Australia. At the western end of the ranges, where the topography is gentler, most of the land has been cleared for farming and the tightly folded emerald-green hills are dotted with dairy herds, sheep, dams and farm buildings. In the eastern Strzeleckis the slopes are steeper and more rugged; they used to be called the 'heartbreak hills', because the land cleared for agriculture during the last century proved to be quite unsuitable for that purpose and the struggling farmers faced enormous difficulties.

For Melburnians the Strzelecki Ranges are only a few hours away by car, and for those living in the well-populated Latrobe Valley they are virtually next door. Several national parks, including the renowned Tarra Valley National Park, are located in the area, and nearly every road among the network winding through the ranges could be called a scenic route. Many of the roads are sealed, or have good gravel surfaces; others are forest tracks suitable only for four-wheel-drive vehicles. The most famous route is the Grand Ridge Road, one of the loveliest scenic drives in the State. The signposts start at the western end, at the Warragul–Korumburra road, which, after winding along the tops of the Strzeleckis' main ridge for about 140 kilometres, finishes at the far-eastern end at the Traralgon–Yarram road. If you travel along the Grand Ridge Road you will discover something of the Strzeleckis' superb character and beauty, for it brings together all the main features of the area: majestic mountain-ash forests, silent pockets of ancient rainforest, commercial pine plantations, picturesque rural land and grand panoramas that stretch in places to the sea.

Some years ago I had travelled on sections of the Grand Ridge Road, but I had never driven along its entire route. I was interested to see how much time the complete journey would take, so on a rainy day (when I would not be tempted to stop for photographs) I started at the eastern end and drove straight through to the Korumburra–Warragul road. It took around six and a half hours, including a stop for lunch. I was grateful for my map, because several times the Grand Ridge Road joined other roads only to turn off a few kilometres further on, and in places there were no signposts. Although the road surface was more gravel than bitumen, the only hair-raising stretch was near Rytons Corner, which was horribly muddy and very narrow. A sign advised that log trucks used this section, but on that occasion I luckily had the road to myself.

Near Korumburra

WILSONS PROMONTORY

THE PROM, as Wilsons Promontory is affectionately known by Victorians, is one of the most important and popular national parks in Australia: for me, as for countless others caught in its spell, it has been a firm favourite since my first visit. Situated in Gippsland, 225 kilometres south-east of Melbourne, this splendid peninsula juts deep into the cold waters of Bass Strait to form the most southerly point of the Australian continent. It is a world of exceptional beauty, a marvellous combination of mountain and sea. Forest-clad slopes drop to meet wide sweeping beaches of fine white or golden sand lying between bold granite headlands; and sparkling streams sheltered by lush vegetation and moss-covered rocks bubble through deep gullies, some of them canopied by huge sprays of tree-ferns, others graced by tall eucalypts. There are wild heathlands, sweet-scented woodlands and an abundance of wildlife.

If the beaches and the blue sea are major contributors to the Prom's beauty, the granite is its strength and character. Hills, peaks and headlands are strewn with tors of astonishing proportions or studded with massive slabs that fall away as sheer cliffs to the sea, where powerful swells send white-plumed waves crashing against the hard granite. Even the weather, which can often be wild and stormy—to the despair of many visitors—adds to the beauty and character of the place.

The base for visitors is Tidal River at Norman Bay, where a holiday resort provides camping facilities, flats and lodges. There is also an excellent information centre run by the staff of the national park, and a general store. The resort is ideally situated close to Norman Beach. The sea is not always visible from the resort, but all day and all night you can hear the dull boom of the surf rolling over the spacious white sands of the bay. Its sound is never loud enough to intrude, yet it creates an ever-present awareness, a sense of pleasure in the knowledge that the ocean is so near.

Most of the Prom's scenic spots are accessible by walking-tracks, and one of the joys of this national park is that there are plenty of short walks, as well as longer and more challenging hikes. Of all the long walks, that to Sealers Cove—an ideal day trip—is probably the general favourite. This track starts and ends at Mount Oberon carpark and is part of the magnificent circuit trail that links Sealers and Refuge coves and Waterloo Bay to the lighthouse track. Those who wish to continue on from Sealers Cove generally take two to three days to complete the walk, camping at the outstation camping grounds; but there are fitness fanatics who complete this mountainous 37-kilometre round trip in a day. One wonders if they have had time to enjoy any of the glorious scenery.

Whisky Bay
Lilly Pilly Gully
Koala

PORT CAMPBELL COASTLINE

SOME OF the most dramatic coastal scenery in the world can be found along the Victorian coast in the Port Campbell National Park, east of Warrnambool. The park lies off the western end of the Great Ocean Road and covers about 32 kilometres of coastline where the plains of the Western District end abruptly at rugged limestone cliffs that plunge into the ocean. These cliffs are riddled with caves, tunnels, blowholes and gorges. In places, some of the vertically walled headlands have been fashioned over the ages into archways and natural bridges by the powerful waves of the stormy Southern Ocean, and occasionally whole sections have broken off to form islands. The eroding action of the pounding waves has also left rocky stacks standing isolated from the mainland cliffs. Seen from the air, this coastline is so indented that it resembles a portion of an unfinished jigsaw puzzle. Whether they view it from an aircraft or from the clifftops, few people leave this area without being stirred by the sheer drama of its scenery.

One of the best-known sights in the national park is the group of residual rocky stacks known as the Twelve Apostles: with Ayers Rock and the Three Sisters, this is one of the three most frequently photographed landscapes in the country. Towering above the sea, the Apostles are easily viewed from a walking-path that meanders over the clifftops from a nearby carpark. A question often asked, however, is 'Where are all the Twelve Apostles?' The park's brochure states that only eight can be seen from the lookout; tourists have claimed thirteen. My count is eleven, and includes the stump of a crumbled stack and the two formations on the other side of the headland. However, I was told that the latter are not 'official' Apostles — which seems rather odd, since they are part of the whole scene from the lookout. No one is even sure of who named the Twelve Apostles. The locals will tell you that they were once called, of all things, the Sow and Piglets — the sow being Mutton Bird Island off Loch Ard Gorge.

Other interesting places in the national park include London Bridge, Island Archway, and the Loch Ard Gorge. It was in this gorge that a clipper, the *Loch Ard*, foundered in 1878 with the loss of fifty lives. As you walk along the clifftops around the gorge on a stormy day and look down at the sea crashing against the cliffs, it is easy to understand why seamen the world over fear this section of coast, which has claimed many vessels and lives. It is not only in wild and blustery weather that the sea demonstrates its power. One pleasant summer day I walked around the cliffs at London Bridge and watched in fascination as huge, creaming, curling waves borne on a monstrous swell slid along the cliff walls, licking into crevices and splashing great fountains of spray into the air. The swell subsided momentarily, leaving dozens of miniature waterfalls streaming over the seaweed-encrusted rocky ledges, but within seconds more waves had burst into the narrow opening of London Bridge, booming and crashing against the walls and spreading foam everywhere. Such extraordinary power was both awesome and humbling.

Several of the Twelve Apostles

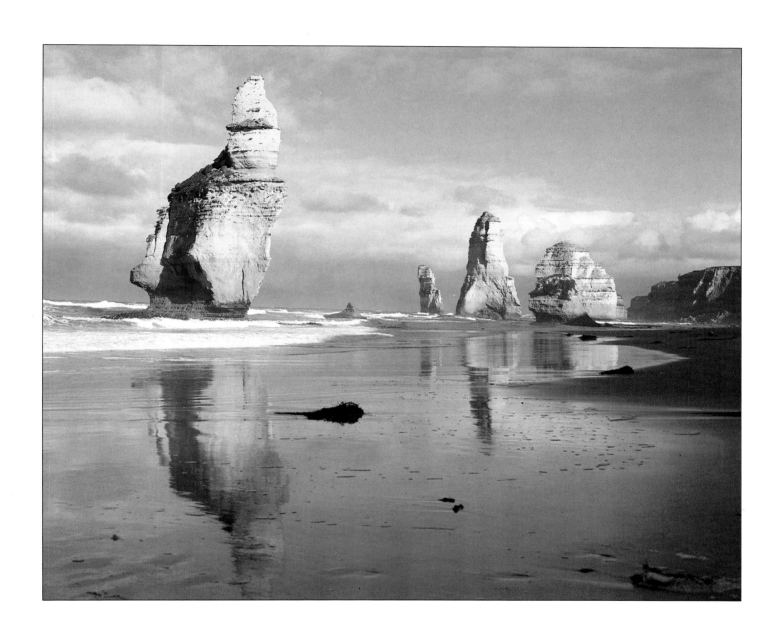

CRADLE MOUNTAIN

OF ALL Australia's mountains, it is those in Tasmania which most closely resemble classic alpine scenery. Serrated ridges and jagged peaks, frequently shrouded in mist and polar-borne snow, rear above glacial lakes and rugged plateaux to form part of an extensive and beautiful wilderness. Cradle Mountain, one of the scenic gems in this wilderness, is also a most exciting place for bushwalkers, and is high on the list of my favourite places in Australia.

Situated in the central Tasmanian highlands, 80 kilometres from Devonport, Cradle Mountain is part of a large national park that extends as far as Lake St Clair in the south; the two places are linked by the Overland Track hiking route. There is also a network of tracks that wind around Cradle Mountain and the numerous lakes and tarns, starting from Waldheim Chalet and the Dove Lake carpark. The distinctive shape of Cradle Mountain rises over Dove and Wilks lakes to dominate most of the walking-trails, and gives the area an awesome atmosphere. Once you start exploring here it is very hard to stop, even when the weather is inclement—which is more often than not. Even in summer, snow and severe storms can suddenly envelop the land, presenting a major hazard for hikers. It is essential that even day walkers register their routes with the ranger.

With the exception of the easy, well-formed paths around Dove Lake in the vicinity of the carpark, the tracks are rough and in places quite steep; there are also sections that have become rather boggy as a result of heavy use by hikers. Much of the terrain resembles a giant sponge. On one occasion, after I discovered I had taken a wrong track on the plateau near Kitchen Hut, I cut across country to pick up the right one and found the ground so spongy that water oozed out at every step.

The deterioration of the tracks is a major concern for the park's management and for the hikers who regularly come here. Although some sections have been bridged, the cost of repairing all the boggy areas— including the considerable sections on the 80 kilometres of Overland Track—would be well beyond the budget of any national park.

Before they reach the plateau region, some of the walking-tracks pass through myrtle-beech forests, the most popular being Weindorfers Forest near the chalet and the delightfully named Ballroom Forest, which lies between Dove Lake and the Face Track. As you walk through these superb woods you enter a different dimension: the overall effect of the moss, the twisted roots and the lacy canopy of tiny leaves is more European than Australian, and makes a refreshing change from the country's ubiquitous eucalypt forests.

Cradle Mountain and Dove Lake
Weindorfers myrtle-beech forest
Bennett's wallaby

LAKE ST CLAIR

MOST VISITORS travelling to Queenstown from Hobart call in to Cynthia Bay on Lake St Clair, which lies five kilometres off the Lyell Highway in the central Tasmanian highlands. Part of the Cradle Mountain–Lake St Clair National Park, this large and beautiful lake with its boulder-studded shores is surrounded by dense forests and the spectacular peaks of Mount Ida, Mount Olympus and Mount Rufus. Cynthia Bay is the starting- and finishing-point for hikers walking the Overland Track — Australia's answer to the famous Milford Track in New Zealand, although the Overland Track does not have the range of accommodation facilities that the Milford offers. Once they have reached the top end of Lake St Clair, many hikers nowadays prefer to take the boat rather than continue along the 17 kilometres of trail that follow the lake through the forest to the camping ground. It takes four days to walk from the top of the lake to Cradle Mountain, but most people take longer to explore the many interesting sidetracks. On the main track, alpine huts are located at intervals to provide accommodation after each day's walking.

Numerous day walks allow visitors to take in areas surrounding the picnic and camping grounds at Cynthia Bay. Among the most enjoyable is the walk to Shadow Lake, one of several charming mountain tarns that lie on a high alpine moorland. It takes about two hours to reach the lake from the camping ground, and the track passes through some superb myrtle-beech forest before making the easy ascent to the buttongrass plain and the snow-gum woodlands. During my visit the weather was kind, and the lake was a glorious sight as it mirrored Mount Rufus and Mount Hugel, the beauty of the peaks enhanced by a dusting of snow.

This national park is one place where visitors are able to see at close range the endearing Bennett's wallaby. At both the Cradle Mountain and the Lake St Clair camping grounds these animals are quite tame. They will stand shyly a little distance away from your camp, peering at you with hopeful eyes that just beg for something to eat. Most tourists cannot resist them and will offer some kind of titbit, usually bread, which the animals gobble up as if it were manna from a macropod heaven. This may be a pleasant pastime for tourists but it is less beneficial for the wallabies: a few years ago the rangers were very concerned because the Lake St Clair wallabies were showing signs of dietary deficiency — they were eating so much white bread that they had lost interest in grazing.

Cynthia Bay, Lake St Clair

LAKE PEDDER

SOUTH-WEST Tasmania has regions of incomparable scenery, and the large South West National Park, together with Cradle Mountain–Lake St Clair and the Franklin–Lower Gordon Wild Rivers national parks, forms part of Tasmania's World Heritage area. Access to much of the south-west's natural beauty is difficult because it is a wilderness of rugged mountains, thick vegetation, glacial lakes and high buttongrass plains. Only those who are prepared to walk—often for days—manage to see it. However, there is one spectacular area open to all: Lake Pedder. This has been the case only since the early 1970s; before that, it was a two-day walk over the mountains to see the original lake, which was flooded by the Serpentine River as part of the Gordon River Development Scheme. The one positive result from that tragedy is that now thousands of people instead of just a few can enjoy the area's splendour. The new Lake Pedder itself is not part of the South West National Park, but most of the country bordering its shores south of the Strathgordon area is part of the park's 403 240 hectares, which extend to the coast.

Lake Pedder is only 170 kilometres from Hobart, so tourists today can reach it with ease. However, to see it at its best in fine weather is another matter: Tasmania's south-west has probably the most unstable climate in Australia. Locals will tell you not to bother about official weather forecasts because it rains on most days anyway. However, there are some splendid sights to be seen even when the weather is bad, as I discovered while I sat in my campervan for a week waiting for it to clear. It was April and I was at the south-eastern end of the lake, in one of the national park's bush camps. The character of the scenery changed constantly: one minute clouds swirled over the mountains around the lake, shrouding them in grey; the next they lifted to reveal the high rugged peaks, now lightly powdered with snow. Sometimes the sun broke briefly through billowing grey-black clouds to cast a dazzling silver path on the windswept water, only to disappear in a heavy curtain of rain. It grew colder and colder. Fat raindrops burst as ice on the van's windscreen, and soon afterwards flurries of sleet whirled through the nearby trees. Then, quite suddenly, the sleet stopped. Patches of blue sky appeared, and within half an hour the sun had chased away the clouds blanketing the Western Arthurs, leaving a breathtaking sight: the entire range was covered in a heavy mantle of snow. At a time like this, photographers are inclined to go mad with their cameras—I certainly did! It was just as well, for within two hours the clouds had returned and it had begun to rain. When the clouds lifted again several days later, most of the snow had disappeared.

Lake Pedder and the Western Arthur Range

MOUNT FIELD

MOUNT FIELD National Park lies about 85 kilometres north-west of Hobart, and the entrance to the park is only one kilometre off the main Strathgordon–Lake Pedder road. Because it is both close to Hobart and strategically placed to allow an easy diversion for visitors travelling to Lake Pedder, the 17 000-hectare park is extremely popular. Its most famous attraction is the Russell Falls; indeed, for many people Mount Field National Park *is* Russell Falls, and it has been estimated that some seventy-five percent of visitors do no more than use the picnic facilities and take the ten-minute walk along the bitumen path through the forest to the base of the falls.

With its generous curtain of water tumbling over three tiers of rock, Russell Falls after rain is certainly one of Australia's grandest waterfalls, but it is nonetheless a pity that visitors do not see more of this national park. If they were just to continue on past the falls (where fortunately the bitumen ends) to see tree-ferns even more magnificent than those lining the main walking-path, they would be well rewarded, for this section of the forest is truly superb. Here the tree-ferns—known as manferns—stand in primeval grandeur, their trunks rising to four metres and topped by fountains of green fronds that form the forest canopy. Beneath, in the cool damp atmosphere of their shade, velvety green moss cloaks tree-fern trunks, fallen branches, stones and boulders, leaving barely enough space for an assortment of lichens and fascinating fungi.

From the picnic grounds the road continues for 16 kilometres through some extremely beautiful forest up to Lake Dobson, one of several tarns in the alpine area of the park. It is from Lake Dobson that skiers in winter have access to the park's ski fields, the only developed skiing area in southern Tasmania. At other times of the year a good variety of walks lead hikers through eucalypt woodland and rainforest, over alpine heaths which in summer are ablaze with wildflowers, to areas of high, craggy mountain ridges.

Mount Field's beauty was first recognized during the nineteenth century, and in 1885 the Russell Falls, with a very small surrounding area, was declared a reserve. By 1916 the reserve had been considerably enlarged and was officially declared a national park, although its present-day name of Mount Field was not adopted until 1947. Tasmania was the first State in Australia to enact legislation for the protection of scenery (in fact, it was one of the first places in the world to do so); but if today's conservationists had been around then, one wonders what they would have made of the title given to the Act which embodied the legislation: the Wastelands Act.

Manferns (*Dicksonia antarctica*)
Russell Falls

TASMANIA

COLES BAY

O NE OF Tasmania's most popular coastal holiday resorts is Coles Bay, which is situated off Great Oyster Bay, about halfway up the east coast and some 200 kilometres from Hobart. Although the mild climate, white sandy beaches and good fishing have long lured local holidaymakers to this small inlet, it is the surrounding spectacular scenery which draws most people—particularly interstate visitors. Nestling around Coles Bay, the little town of the same name is dominated by a series of towering red granite peaks known collectively as the Hazards, after a Captain Hazard whose ship the *Promise* was wrecked in the bay last century. However, Coles Bay is only the start of the good scenery. One kilometre from the town is the Freycinet National Park, which covers the remainder of Freycinet Peninsula—a slender finger of land jutting into the Tasman Sea—and all of Schouten Island, situated off the peninsula's southern tip. Freycinet was declared a national park as far back as 1916, and shares with Mount Field the distinction of being the oldest park in the State.

Beyond the Hazards is a very narrow isthmus that forms part of Wineglass Bay; one of the most popular walks in the park takes visitors to the saddle between two of the Hazards' peaks, Mount Amos and Mount Mayson, to view this spacious bay. The rest of the peninsula comprises areas of thick scrub and eucalypt woodland, and a massive backbone of rugged granite mountains. The interesting eastern shore is notched with small bays dotted with chunky rocks and inlets sheltered by craggy cliffs, and grand bluffs of red granite that glow warmly in the early-morning sun. Sleepy Bay is a good place to see these cliffs—the earlier in the morning the better. Access to this spot is easy, as it lies close to the road that runs to the lighthouse. From the Sleepy Bay carpark a fifteen-minute walk runs along the clifftops and down to a delightful little bay. A 'must', even for the visitor who has time only to breeze in and out of the area, is to drive up to the lighthouse situated just outside the north-eastern boundary of the national park, about eight kilometres from Coles Bay. From here there is a marvellous view of Freycinet's grand and colourful coastline.

The Hazards, Coles Bay

Three Mughal Poets

Three Mughal Poets

MIR · SAUDA · MIR HASAN

by Khurshidul Islam and Ralph Russell

OXFORD
UNIVERSITY PRESS

OXFORD
UNIVERSITY PRESS

Oxford University Press is a department of the University of Oxford.
It furthers the University's objective of excellence in research, scholarship,
and education by publishing worldwide. Oxford is a registered trademark of
Oxford University Press in the UK and in certain other countries

Published in India by
Oxford University Press

2/11 Ground Floor, Ansari Road, Daryaganj, New Delhi 110 002, India

First published 1969
First Indian impression 1991
Oxford India Paperbacks 1994

ISBN-13: 978-0-19-563391-7
ISBN-10: 0-19-563391-1

Printed in India by Replika Press Pvt. Ltd

CONTENTS

PREFACE

Some sixty years ago an Oxford don is reported to have said that the mention of India was enough to empty the smallest lecture hall in Oxford.[1] His statement was perhaps exaggerated, but that relatively few people in the West felt any great interest in India and its culture was certainly true in those days. This is no longer the case. In recent years the desire to know more about the South Asian subcontinent has markedly increased and is still increasing. This book is addressed to those who share that desire. It is an attempt, which so far as we know has not been made before, to introduce to the English-speaking reader the work of three great poets of one of the major modern languages of the Indian subcontinent—namely, Urdu. We have not assumed in the reader any previous knowledge of the subject. All that we have assumed is a readiness to make that minimum mental effort which is required of anyone who wants to understand and appreciate the literature of another people and another age.

Urdu is one of the most developed of the dozen or so major modern languages of the Indo-Pakistan subcontinent, but it differs from most of the others in that it is not the language of a single, continuous, well-defined geographical area, as, for example, Bengali is the language of Bengal. Its real homeland is the western part of the state of Uttar Pradesh[2] and the country round Delhi, for it is on the native speech of the people of this region that literary Urdu is based; but its speakers are to be found all over India and Pakistan, and are particularly numerous in the area comprising Pakistan and the great northern Indian plains

---

[1] The dictum of the Oxford don was often quoted by the late Edward Thompson. It stands at the head of his sketch *A History of India* (London, 1927).

[2] Its name before independence was United Provinces. The initials of the old and the new names conveniently coincide, and the state is still commonly called 'U.P.,' as it was long before it received its present name.

up to the western border of Bengal. It is spoken especially by Muslims—though
by no means exclusively by them—and its literature has for the most part a
Muslim background. We do not mean by this that it is primarily a religious
literature, but simply that, like the Arabian Nights, it portrays the life of a people
who profess the religion of Islam. The language developed to approximately its
present literary form early in the eighteenth century, and the three poets with
whom this book deals were among the first to write it in this form. During
the greater part of their lifetime the acknowledged centre of Urdu was Delhi,
though in later years the city lost its exclusive importance as the one great
centre of the literature. Urdu is today one of the major languages listed in the
Indian Constitution, and is the national language of Pakistan.

Urdu is thus one of the most important languages of the subcontinent. But
it does not necessarily follow that its literature is worth the attention of English-
speaking readers. If it is, they may ask, why have they not heard of it before?

To this very natural question there is no simple answer. But the explanation lies mainly in the history of Britain's relationship with India. The beginning
of British rule in India is often dated from the Battle of Plassey in 1757, which
made the British the real rulers of Bengal. By this date the fame of Mir and
Sauda, the first of the great poets of modern Urdu, was already established;
but until nearly half a century later the great centres of Urdu literature still
lay outside the area of British rule, and it is not surprising that only a very
few Englishmen should have been acquainted with it. When at the beginning
of the nineteenth century the British extended their power as far as Delhi, it
might have been expected that a knowledge and appreciation of Urdu literature
would have become more widespread; but an attitude was now rapidly becoming dominant which was to prevent this even more effectively than geographical
remoteness had done—that of the early Victorian age, when Englishmen were
profoundly convinced that in contemporary England human civilisation had
reached its highest development, and that while further progress would continue along the lines which English had laid down, Englishmen now had little
to learn from the past or from other nations less favoured by God than Victorian
England. It was Macaulay who gave classic expression to this outlook. In his
view a knowledge of English sufficed to provide for every important cultural
need. 'Whoever knows that language,' he wrote, 'has ready access to all the
vast intellectual wealth, which all the wisest nations of the earth have created.'
Certainly the literature of India and other Asian countries had in comparison
nothing to contribute—'no books on any subject which deserves to be compared

to our own.' 'A single shelf of a good European library...[is] worth the whole native literature of India and Arabia.' The quotations are taken from his Minute on India and Arabia.' The quotations are taken from his Minute on Indian Education, written in 1835.[3] In it he is mainly concerned to belittle the value of Arabic and Sanskrit, the classical languages respectively of the Muslims and the Hindus. It is interesting that Persian, the language of Omar Khayyam and of other poets greater than he, which had for centuries been the language of diplomacy and culture not only in India but throughout a large part of the Muslim world, is not even referred to, while the modern languages of India ('the dialects commonly spoken among the natives') are dismissed as being 'poor and rude'. This is not the place to assess Macaulay's Minute as a whole, but there can be no doubt that the attitude it expresses is one which precludes any sympathetic interest in Indian literature. And that attitude did not die with the Victorian age; it has continued up to our own day to influence English opinion deeply. This is not our view alone; it is also that of the Scarbrough Commission appointed by the British Foreign Office in 1944 to investigate the state of Oriental and other studies. Its report, published in 1947, quotes from Macaulay's Minute as the expression of 'a traditional exclusiveness which tends to disregard and even look down upon culture which has little in common with our own,' and   considers this exclusiveness to be 'the chief reason why these studies have not prospered'.[4]

So far as India is concerned, direct subjection to British rule and the rise of a movement for national independence led to a tension which also limited the development of British interest in Indian culture and reinforced the effect of the Macaulay outlook. The result has been that while the British, throughout the period, recognised the importance of the Urdu language for administrative purposes—for example, Urdu in the Roman script was, until independence, the official language of the Indian Army—the literature of Urdu aroused very little interest. Only relations of equality and mutual respect between nations enable them to appreciate truly one another's culture, and it is only recently that such relations have been established between Britain and the Indo-Pakistan subcontinent. Now that they have been, work can begin in earnest to introduce to

---

[3] Macaulay's Minute is included in the volume *Selected Speeches*, ed. G.M. Young (London, 1935). The extracts quoted here are to be found on pp. 350, 351, 349, and 348, in that order.

[4] Para. 25, in *Report of the Interdepartmental Commission of Enquiry on Oriental, Slavonic, East European and African Studies* (London, 1947).

English-speaking readers literatures which, if hitherto little known, are all the same worth their reading.

Those who attempt this task may draw encouragement from the fact that they are not breaking entirely fresh ground. The literatures of India are Oriental literatures, and differ in many ways from those of the West. But experience has already shown that the differences are not too great to prevent the English-speaking reader appreciating them. The Bible, the Arabian Nights, and the Rubaiyat of Omar Khayyam are all works of Oriental literature, and successive generations of English-speaking readers have been moved, inspired and entertained by them. It is worth stressing that the chief reason for this has been that they have approached these works with respect, knowing of the power they have exercised over millions of readers before them and expecting to experience something of this power themselves. There are things in them which they do not understand or appreciate, but they generally assume (and for the most part correctly) that this is because of an insufficient knowledge of their background, and they do not allow these things to stand in the way of their enjoyment. All of which is only another way of saying that the Macaulay spirit is dormant when they approach these books.

Unfortunately it is not only the Macaulay spirit which hinders a true appreciation of Indian literature. It is matched by an opposite tendency, smaller but more vocal, voiced by those who proclaim the glories of Indian literature in tones that are often more royalist than the king. Such enthusiasts have done something to counteract the Macaulay outlook; but they have also done a good deal of harm by strengthening the erroneous impression that Indian literature is something of an entirely different order from that of the West. The two opposed outlooks have more in common than at first sight appears. Both exaggerate what they believe to be the peculiarly Indian elements in the literature, with the difference that while the one finds these elements strange, incomprehensible, and repulsive, the other finds them exotic, mysterious, and attractive. Both have kept alive ideas of 'the mysterious East'—ideas that 'East is East and West is West and never the twain shall meet'—and such ideas have now been so widely held, and for so long, that the very words Eastern, Oriental, Indian, and so on now carry something of these connotations with them. An unduly heightened consciousness of the difference between East and West is traditional with us now. Had it not been so, it would have been realized long ago that many 'peculiarly Indian' features of Indian literature are in fact not peculiarly Indian at all, and that still less are they mysterious once their background is understood.

This is certainly true of the eighteenth-century Urdu literature with which this book deals. Its atmosphere is markedly different from that of eighteenth-century English literature, and this is indeed partly due to the fact that the one is English and the other Indian. But a much greater part of the difference arises not from the national but from the social and historical setting. Eighteenth-century English literature is already unmistakably modern; eighteenth-century Urdu literature is still essentially medieval, and it differs from contemporary English literature only about as much as medieval European literature does. Realization of this fact does not, by a long way, remove all the difficulties of understanding it, for a medieval literature also presents problems to modern readers, but it does at least change their conception of the nature of these difficulties, and they can at any rate safely banish the idea that in approaching Urdu literature, they will be dealing with another race of men who were the product of a national tradition entirely alien to them, and whose ways, despite every effort on their part, are therefore likely to remain inscrutable. Our own experience of teaching Urdu literature to English and European students shows that once the historical setting has been explained, the main obstacles to an appreciation of the literature are overcome. That is why we have devoted the first chapter of this book to a description of that setting.

It may be helpful here to say something of the plan of the chapters which follow. We have tried wherever possible to let the literature speak for itself, with only the minimum of comment, and this aim has largely determined the arrangement of the chapters. Although on the title page the poets are named in the order that comes naturally to anyone acquainted with Urdu poetry, we begin, in Chapter 2, with the satirist Sauda, for it is to his work that a knowledge of the historical setting is most directly relevant. Next comes Mir Hasan, whose long romantic poem offers very little difficulty to the English reader, and prepares the way for the more directly realistic love poetry of Mir. And Mir is taken last.[5]

This part of the book was the most difficult to write. Since Mir is the greatest poet of three, and in our view one of the great love poets of world literature,

---

[5] Throughout the book we have used their names without diacritical marks. The *i* of Mir corresponds roughly to the *ee* sound in *meet;* the *au* of Sauda approximates to the *ou* of *loud;* and the *a*'s in Hasan to the unstressed *a* in *above.*

we have done our best to enable the reader to appreciate him. But the task was not an easy one. Most of Mir's best poems are in a form known as the *ghazal*, and the ghazal was the product of a long tradition which had evolved set conventions affecting both its form and its content. These needed to be fully explained, and even when that had been done, there remained the task of presenting the ghazal itself. Ideally, this meant translation, but the extreme conciseness imposed by the ghazal form, and the wealth of suggestion and allusion packed into each of its lines, confront its translator with difficulties so great that we had originally felt them to be insuperable. However, friends who read our first draft (and to all of whom our sincerest thanks are due) nearly all insisted that the attempt should be made, and we have now made it—with what success we must leave it to the reader to decide.

In general, direct translation of continuous passages has been only one of our means of presentation. We have used it more in Chapter 2 than elsewhere, for Sauda's poems go very well into the sort of verse which Nevill Coghill has done so well in his translation of Chaucer's *Canterbury Tales*. While we have not aimed at a close and literal adherence to the Urdu, we would claim that our English version taken as a whole does reproduce faithfully the spirit and substance of the original. Elsewhere we have given abridged prose versions of the original poems—a method suggested partly by Rex Warner's admirable presentation of Greek stories in his *Men and Gods* and *Greeks and Trojans*. We would stress that in such poems we have taken care not to introduce any matter of our own. For example, in the abridged prose version of Mir Hasan's narrative poem which takes up the greater part of Chapter 3, we have not departed from the original in any way, and there is no detail of incident or description and no line of dialogue which does not occur in the original work. The same point holds good of the other poems thus handled.

We must hope for readers of fairly catholic tastes, readers who, to elaborate the point by familiar examples, enjoy literature as diverse as Rabelais, the Arabian Nights, and the English metaphysical poets. If the coarseness of Rabelais puts them off, so will the coarseness of Sauda; if the Arabian Nights' naive delight in fantasy and disregard of the complexities of characterization offends their sophisticated taste, they will not find much to admire in Mir Hasan; and if the ingenious conceits of the metaphysical poets seriously impair their appeal, so will similar features of Mir's poetry. But if they like all these things, we can hope that they will like these three poets of Mughal India too.

This book is not, in the deplorably narrow sense which the words have come to bear in academic circles, a 'scholarly work'. But we hope that it may interest the scholar as well as the general reader, and we have therefore added footnotes in which those who wish to do so may find the basis on which the book has been built and check for themselves the validity of what we have written. Further, it would perhaps be prudent to forewarn scholars who bring specialist knowledge to the reading of the book that since it is not primarily addressed to them, they will not necessarily find in it discussions of the questions which particularly interest them. Our theme demands some treatment of eighteenth-century Mughal history, some account of Islamic mysticism, and some discussion of the role of convention in literature; but none of these themes receives the full, balanced treatment which would have been its due had we been studying it in its own right. On the contrary, we have deliberately excluded everything relating to these themes which does not have a direct bearing on the understanding of eighteenth-century poetry. In other words, our treatment of them is partial and incomplete, but it is avowedly and deliberately so.

It has not seemed desirable in a work of this kind to give in the text full transliterations of the names and the Urdu words that occur. In general we have confined ourselves to marking the long vowels where these occur in the body of the word. (Final vowels may be assumed to be long.) Full pointing is, however, provided in the footnotes, bibliography, and glossary. Urdu words are italicized at their first occurrence, but not thereafter.

The map on p. 27 is reproduced by permission of Oxford University Press from *An Historical Atlas of the Indian Peninsula* by C. Collin Davies.

Readers may be interested to know how this book came to be written. The conception of the work, which was planned as the first of several on Urdu literature, was Khurshidul Islam's, and it was he who, after repeated readings of the collected verse of Mir and Sauda, selected the poems and verses we would aim to present. We then read them together, with Khurshidul Islam explaining all the nuances of the original that needed to be conveyed in translation. Ralph Russell then drafted the English translation. The translation was discussed and modified until we were both completely satisfied with it. In this way we produced a first version by 1958. Further discussion then led us to include some more verses in the chapter on Mir. Khurshidul Islam explained these verses to Ralph Russell as usual and at this stage circumstances made it impossible for this work to be done in the same close co-operation as before. In consequence Ralph Russell had to finalize these translations on his own. He alone, therefore, is responsible for any inadequacies in this chapter of the book.

Our special thanks are due to Miss Hilary Davey for her help in the final stages of preparing the book for the press.

It remains for us to acknowledge the work of others who contributed to the book. First, our thanks to Professor Annemarie Schimmel, of Harvard University. It was she who recommended the inclusion of the Urdu originals of the translated verses. (Khurshidul Islam selected Ibrahim Illahabadi to do the calligraphy of these verses and undertook the laborious task of checking it.) She also made additions to our own footnotes—her additions are followed by the initials A.S.—and supplemented our bibliography with entries of works in French, German and Italian. Finally she wrote a foreword to this, our first published work in English.

The present edition is essentially a reprint of the first, and for technical reasons it has been impossible to make many changes in the text. Readers should note that Mir's two masnavis, summarized on pp. 96-98, are, we are not satisfied, about two different women. It should also be remembered that the 'I' of such masnavis cannot be safely assumed to be in every respect Mir as he actually was.

England   Khurshidul Islam
1990   Ralph Russell

CHAPTER ONE

The Eighteenth-Century Background

MIR, SAUDA, AND MIR HASAN were the poets of a society very much like that of medieval Europe. The great majority of its members were peasants, and in the last resort it was on the wealth they produced that society lived. The social organisation was a hierarchy. At the summit stood the king, from whom all power and authority derived, and to whom all his subjects, high and low, owed allegiance. He had a corresponding obligation to protect them and to promote their welfare, and in order that he might have the means to do so, the peasants gave up to him a proportion of their crop. Next in order to the king came the great nobles; by the king's authority they received in various forms a part of the social wealth, and they were bound in return to perform the customary services which he could demand of them—in particular, to render him military aid whenever he called upon them. In Mughal India a noble's rank was expressed in terms of the number of cavalry which the king could call upon him to provide; he was a "commander of five thousand," or whatever the figure might be. The cavalryman found his own horse, arms, and equipment. In addition to providing for the welfare of the people, the king and the nobility were expected, through patronage, to make provision for the intellectual and cultural life of society.

In theory this social organisation was seen as one which enabled all members of society to work in harmony for the common happiness of all. God had given each man his capacities and set him in that station in life for which those capacities fitted him; He had defined the rights and the

responsibilities of every class of men, and so long as every man—be he
noble or peasant—conscientiously performed the duties of his station,
society would prosper. These duties involved, in medieval eyes, a good
deal more than what modern man regards as the civic virtues. In modern
societies the general view is that every man's life is his own, and that
society should interfere with it as little as possible; he accepts, not altogether gladly, that certain minimum positive demands must be made of
him—that he must pay his taxes, for example—and that society must
forbid by law activities which are seriously harmful to it. But provided he
performs his minimum social obligations and refrains from breaking the
law, he regards the rest of his life as his own affair, and society need not
and should not be concerned with it. Such a conception is quite foreign
to the medieval way of thinking. Medieval society demanded of its members what modern society may only hope from them: it required of every
man a much more positive conception of his social duties, and over and
above that, the observance of a whole way of life which it held to be as
much society's concern as the individual's. A king or a noble had to be
more than an efficient statesman, administrator, and commander in war.
He also had to have all the attributes which the word "noble" in all its
senses still implies. He was supposed to be a man of inborn dignity, a
natural leader of men, a soldier personally skilled in all the arts of war
and as distinguished for his personal bravery as for his high birth. He had
also to be a widely cultured man, abreast of the arts and sciences of his
time, a liberal patron of learning and culture, and one qualified both by
taste and by training to appreciate what he patronised. The man of
learning had to master his heritage and study to develop it further. The
poet had to be well versed in his craft, and have something of significance
to say. The soldier had to keep his horse, his arms, and his equipment in
good order, and fight with courage, skill, and devotion in the service of
his lord. The peasant had to till his land well and pay promptly and
honestly that share of his produce which was his contribution to the
ordered running of society.

Society was actively concerned with every important aspect of men's
lives. In this respect, the most striking contrast between modern and
medieval ways appears in the attitude toward love and marriage.
In medieval society love and marriage are two quite separate things, and
medieval love poetry, whether of Western Europe or of Mughal India, is

hardly intelligible unless this fact and its main implications are understood. In Mughal India, in respectable Muslim families, marriage was a matter with important social implications, and it was generally arranged between the parents of the young man and the young woman. The *parda* (purdah) system was strictly enforced, and bride and bridegroom normally saw each other for the first time during the celebration of the wedding. Love was seen as a danger to ordered social life, and was persecuted accordingly. It is important to realise that the unfortunate lovers themselves shared this view of love. The character of Urdu love poetry is determined by this background.

In general, the force of convention was extraordinarily powerful in medieval societies and pervaded almost every department of life. A medieval society was essentially a static one. Political changes may have been many and violent, but they took place within a system of society which could endure unchanged for centuries together. The medieval ideals were correspondingly static. They envisaged no change to disturb the eternal order of things: all that was required with the passage of time was to elaborate and make more precise principles which in their general application had been known for generations; and in this way conventions were formed which had all the force of an age-old tradition behind them.

The literature and the literary life of society were markedly affected by this atmosphere. In eighteenth-century India the aspiring poet would as a matter of course approach a poet of already established reputation and ask him to accept him as his *shāgird*. The word is used in various senses—of pupil, disciple, and servant—and though the first is in this context the most appropriate English equivalent, the other connotations are by no means wholly irrelevant. The relation of the shāgird to his *ustād*, or master, resembled that of a vassal to his overlord, and society expected him to behave accordingly, acting not simply as his pupil in the art of poetry but as one under general obligation to him, bound to submit to his authority and, so to speak, to uphold his cause. In consultation with his ustād he would choose a *takhallus*, or poetic name. This would consist of a single word, and might or might not coincide with some part of the poet's real name. Every poet had to have one, for some of the poetic forms in which he would have to write prescribed the introduction of the takhallus into the final verse. The poet would generally, though not always, be known by his takhallus. Mir was a takhallus, and so was Sauda.

Mir Hasan was the poet's real name; his takhallus was Hasan. The guidance which an ustād gave to his shāgird consisted in "correcting" all his verses, and the word bore an all-embracing sense. The ustād would correct not only defects in metre and language, but also alter verses in any other way or simply delete them, in order to bring his shāgird's work into conformity with his own taste and judgement. A shāgird might with due respect question a correction and defend his own version, but the attempt would generally be a hopeless one unless he could produce authority for what he had written—that is, quote some parallel from the work of a classical poet. This characteristically medieval emphasis on precedent and authority was very marked in the eighteenth-century Mughal literary world.

When the young poet was considered to have acquired the necessary skill, he could take part in mushāiras. These were gatherings at the house or court of some eminent scholar or poet or noble—many nobles were in any case also poets—to which poets would be invited to recite their own work. Such assemblies had their own traditional procedure. Often the invitation would include a line of verse, and all who participated would be required to come with a poem incorporating this line, written in the same metre and using a rhyme scheme in harmony with it. The guests would be seated on the carpet and a candle would be passed round from one to another. As the candle came before him, each would recite his verse. The audience responded in terms of the elaborately courteous etiquette which tradition required. Polite exclamations of praise would greet a good line, and the poet would bow and salaam in acknowledgement. Criticism could also be expressed or, more commonly, delicately implied. A courteous request to the poet to repeat a line often indicated that there was felt to be some defect in it, and a poet quick enough to detect the fault and versatile enough to correct it extempore might do so. A poet whose verse was greeted with general approval in these assemblies might regard his apprenticeship as being at an end, though convention would require him throughout his life to treat his old ustād with all the respect due from a former shāgird.

The taste for poetry was (and still is) very widespread, for Indians do not suffer from that "successfully cultivated distaste for poetry"[1] of which the English have, with some justification, been accused, and a good

---

[1] Thompson, *History of India*, pp. 32–33.

poet would rapidly win fame. People would eagerly seek access to gatherings where it was known he was going to recite, and in various other ways his reputation would spread beyond his own city. There was as yet no printing, but in Mughal India, as in every country where Islam has spread, the art of calligraphy was highly appreciated and widely practised, and a great man might commission a good calligrapher to prepare him a copy of a favourite poet's verse. Or the poet himself might have a copy made for presentation to a patron. In the India Office Library in London there is a manuscript copy of Sauda's collected verse which was presented by the author to Richard Johnson, the British Assistant Resident at the court of Oudh during the last years of Sauda's life.[2] Of Mir it is said that his verses were so highly esteemed that men travelling to other parts of the country would have a few of them copied on a sheet of paper and take this to present to their host when they reached their destination. Such were some of the ways in which a poet's fame would spread far afield. Mir often speaks with pride of the spread of his own fame:

My poetry grows green not only in the northern plains.
In all the Deccan too the praises of my verse resound.

(II.258.17)

The metaphor is aptly chosen, for the great north Indian plain is some of the most fertile land in the world, and the metaphor suggests how abundantly his fame flourished.

A famous poet would not generally find it difficult to win the patronage of a great noble, who would relieve him from the anxiety of finding a livelihood, and enable him to devote his time to poetry. There is a modern prejudice against patronage which almost takes it for granted that no poet dependent on it can possibly write anything worth-while. "I can conceive of no system," says Macaulay, "more fatal to the integrity and independence of literary men than one under which they should be taught

---

[2] See T. F. Blumhardt, *Catalogue of the Hindustani Manuscripts in the Library of the India Office*, No. 146 (London, 1926), pp. 76–78. The inscription reads, "Mr. Richard Johnson, the gift of ye author Mirza Soudah."

to look for their daily bread to the favour of ministers and nobles. I can conceive of no system more certain to turn those minds which are formed by nature to be the blessings and ornaments of our species into public scandals and pests."³ There is no doubt that one of the effects of patronage in all ages has been to encourage sycophancy, but there is equally no doubt that it alone made possible the greatest works of literature and art that we possess, works produced by men whose integrity and independence were apparently in no way impaired by it. Patronage was to medieval society the normal, accepted way of providing for the development of learning and culture, and the relationship between the poet and his patron was, like every other medieval relationship, prescribed by long usage. Nothing in it sanctioned anything in the nature of censorship. The poet might be expected to write odes on state occasions, just as the modern British poet laureate is, and the result, in both cases, cannot often be rated as great poetry. But for the rest the poet was free to write as he felt inspired, and rather than the poet being expected to write what his patron would approve, it was the patron who was expected to appreciate what the poet wrote.

Great nobles would often welcome the opportunity to become patrons of famous poets, for their social prestige would be enchanced accordingly. There is nothing in the writings of Mir, Sauda, and Mir Hasan to suggest that patronage restricted their freedom of expression, and much, both in their writings and in traditional stories about them, which shows on the contrary that they wrote as they pleased—and not only wrote as they pleased, but in matters where poetry was concerned, spoke very much as they pleased too. There is a story that the Mughal Emperor once asked Sauda how many poems a day he composed. "When I am in the mood, about three or four couplets," Sauda replied. "And I can compose four complete poems as I sit in the lavatory," said the Emperor proudly. "Yes," said Sauda, "and they smell like it." A Macaulay might well find Sauda's Rabelaisian directness offensive to his sense of propriety; but he could hardly argue from it that patronage had been "fatal to his integrity and independence." On another occasion the Emperor had it conveyed to Sauda that he was prepared to confer on him the title of poet laureate. Sauda's comment was, "What difference will His Majesty's title make?

³ From Macaulay's speech of 1841 on copyright, in *Selected Speeches*, p. 160.

If anything makes me poet laureate, it will be my own poetry."⁴ Many similar stories are told of Mir as well, and it is striking that such incidents never resulted in a breach between the patron and the poet unless the poet himself chose to make it the occasion for one. Any ending of the relationship between them generally had other causes: in the eighteenth century the most common was the abrupt changes of fortune which would often deprive a patron of the means to pay the poet's stipend.

The medieval stamp is evident not only on the literary life of society but also on the literature itself. Convention, authority, precedent— these things ruled in the domain of poetry as they did elsewhere. There was a limited number of forms, most of them strictly and minutely defined, within which all poetry had to be written, and relatively detailed prescription extended to content as well as to form. Before he could use these forms, a poet had to master a complex system of prosody, from which no departure was permitted, and know how to handle an enormously elaborate "science of rhetoric," as it was called, in which figures of speech, subdivided into "figures of thought" and "figures of words" are analysed in amazing (and to our way of thinking quite pointless) detail, and rules for their use are laid down.

The three most important poetic forms were the ghazal, the qasīda, and the masnavi, and of these the ghazal was the most highly developed.⁵ Urdu took all of them from Persian, as English took the sonnet from Italian. The ghazal is a short lyric, in which themes of love predominate. (The word is derived from a root which means approximately "conversation between lovers.") Its form is bound by strict rules. The authorities on poetics vary as to the number of couplets it may contain:

---

4. The anecdotes of Saudā and the Emperor are from Muḥammad Ḥusain Āzād, Āb i Ḥayāt (14th printing, Lahore, n.d.), p. 149. Many modern critics are inclined to dismiss Āzād's stories as mere gossip, and therefore of no account. In our opinion this is too sweeping an attitude. At the time when Āzād wrote (Āb i Ḥayāt was first published in 1879), he had access to written and oral sources which we no longer possess today, some deriving from the accounts of men who had personally known the poets of whom he wrote. Where his anecdotes do not conflict with more reliable evidence and are consistent with the picture which emerges from a study of the poet's own work, there is no reason to reject them absolutely, even though means of positive substantiation may be lacking and points of detaiˈl, on occasion, demonstrably false. At the very lowest assessment Āzād's anecdotes are of value in showing the sort of impression their personalities made on their contemporaries.

5. For detailed definitions of the ghazal, qasīda, and masnavi see, e.g., G. D. Pybus, Urdu Prosody and Rhetoric (Lahore, 1924), pp. 59–60, 61–62, 63; Mirzā Muḥammad 'Askari, Āīna i Balāghat (Lucknow, 1937), pp. 17, 19–21, 22; Najm ul Ghani, Bcḥr ul Faṣāḥat (Lucknow, 1926), pp. 69–80, 80–92, 104–112.

there seems to be general agreement on a prescribed minimum of five, but the maximum is variously stated as eleven, seventeen, or some other figure. As a general rule each couplet must express a complete and independent thought, though it is permissible within the ghazal to connect several of the couplets to form a single statement. The unity of the poem is one not of content but of form, and is achieved by a common metre for all the couplets and a strict rhyme scheme (AA, BA, CA, DA, etc.), which may not be varied. The rhyme is almost always a double one (though this is not obligatory), its two parts being known as *qāfia* and *radīf*, terms which English writers on the subject have translated respectively as rhyme and end rhyme.

Their meaning can be illustrated from Flecker's poem *Yasmin*, which he calls "A Ghazel," though it does not in fact conform to all the rules of the ghazal, at any rate as the form is defined in Urdu.[6] In the rhymes "head, Yasmin," "said Yasmin," "shed, Yasmin," and so on, "head," "said," and "shed" are qāfia (rhyme), and the recurring word "Yasmin" is radīf (end rhyme). Flecker's use of the name "Yasmin" is an easy, if effective, solution to the difficulty of finding a double rhyme. In Urdu, where rhymes are more plentiful than they are in English, such simple devices are rarely resorted to. End rhyme of three, four, five, or even more syllables are not uncommon. Thus Mir, the greatest eighteenth-century exponent of the ghazal form, writes to his mistress:

اے گُل نو دمیدہ کے مانند

ہے تو کس آفریدہ کے مانند

Perhaps the flower in spring compares with you—
Yet what created thing compares with you?   (I.63.19)

Skilfully used, this double rhyming can be most effective.

Finally, the last couplet of the ghazal must introduce the takhallus of the poet. While in the ghazal themes of love predominate, these may treat either of earthly love between human beings or of the mystic love of the worshipper for the Divine Beloved. Many lines are capable of

---

[6] See *The Collected Poems of James Elroy Flecker* (London, 1916), p. 158. It is also included in *The Century's Poetry* (1837–1937), ed. D. K. Roberts (Harmondsworth, 1938), II, 298.

either interpretation. But many ghazals include lines on themes which have no conceivable connection with love—a practice that the poet could perhaps justify within the terms of the definition of the ghazal by the argument that even lovers talk of other things besides love. In general, the only thing which gives unity to the poem is its form. There is generally not even a unity of mood between the independent couplets that compose it: the mood may vary in one and the same ghazal between tragedy and broad humour.

The qasīda, which may be roughly translated as "ode," is defined in similar detail and with similar divergencies between the different authorities. Sauda is the greatest master of this form in our period. Some authorities prescribe a minimum of 7 couplets, others of 15, and yet others of 21. No definite maximum is prescribed by most authorities, though some limit it to 170 couplets. At all events it is a fairly long poem. Its rhyme scheme is the same as that of the ghazal. Most qasīdas are odes in praise of the poet's patron or of some other potentate, and are divided into parts, each of which has its technical name. The manuals of rhetoric divide qasīdas into two main classes: those which have a "preamble" (*tamhīd* or *tashbīb*) and those which do not. The permissible themes of the preamble are laid down: the poet may extol his own greatness, or describe the beauties of spring, or write of love or of the transience of the things of this world, or lament his illfortune. The preamble is followed by a second part in which the poet turns towards his main theme. The third part is devoted to singing the praises of the person to whom the qasīda is addressed; the fourth states the poet's request to him; and the fifth and last calls down the blessings of heaven upon him. The qasīda is, of all the classical forms, the least appealing to modern taste even in India and Pakistan, and nowadays qasīdas are rarely read and still more rarely written. Even in former times the qasīda was judged mainly as a *tour de force*, a form in which it was the poet's object to demonstrate his complete command of language and of the full range of rhetorical device rather than to express any deeply felt experience.

The masnavi, for which the name of Mir Hasan is most famous, is the least strict of the classical forms, for all that is prescribed is its rhyme scheme. It is a fairly long poem, rhyming AA, BB, CC, DD, and so on, like Chaucer's *Prologue*. It may be on almost any theme, but in Urdu the largest single class of masnavis consists of love stories.

A number of other forms similarly prescribe little more than the rhyme schemes. For example, there is the *mukhammas*, a form that Sauda frequently used. This is a poem consisting of stanzas of five lines each, the first four of which must employ the same rhyme. Often the fifth lines of the stanzas also rhyme together (AAAAX, BBBBX, CCCCX, etc.).[7]

These were the major forms in which Mir, Sauda, and Mir Hasan wrote their poetry. To the modern reader it might seem that the conventions by which they were bound must seriously hamper the poet's expression, and it is perhaps true that except for the masnavi, they exercised a tyranny which only a real poet could break. The general pressure of cultural opinion against any departure from established standards made originality difficult, and the strict conventions tended to encourage a preoccupation with form at the expense of content, and a refinement and overelaboration of rhetorical devices to the point where verse becomes nothing more than a display of technical virtuosity. But the greatest poets made themselves the masters and not the servants of this complex machinery, and used it to good effect. Mir made the ghazal, in many ways the strictest of all the classical forms, his chosen medium of expression, and only rarely violated its canons, but the freshness and vitality of what he has to say are not impaired by it.

To this somewhat generalised description of medieval society and its literary life must be added some account of the particular medieval society to which Mir, Sauda, and Mir Hasan belonged—that is, of the Mughal Empire, an empire which had been, not long before their time, one of the most splendid known to world history.[8]

Nominally, the Mughal Empire had been founded in 1526, for it was in that year that Bābur, the ruler of a kingdom based on Kabul in Afghanistan, invaded India, and by defeating a greatly superior enemy force at Pānipat, some fifty-five miles north of Delhi, established a titular sovereignty over the greater part of the north Indian plain. But its real

---

[7] For the mukhammas see Pybus, p. 66 (which, however, gives a false impression); 'Askarī, p. 23; and Najm ul Ghanī, pp. 96–98. The poem of Saudā summarised below, pp. 64–68, is a mukhammas.

[8] For the account of the Mughal Empire we have used a number of books, ranging from short, popular accounts to full-length histories. See the bibliography below. We have, however, often given our own interpretation to the facts which they present. Extracts from Mīr's narrative are translated, with some abridgement, from his Persian work *Zikr i Mīr*, ed. 'Abdul Ḥaq (Aurangābād, 1928).

founder was Akbar, Bābur's grandson, the third and greatest of all the Mughal emperors. He came to the throne in 1556, and during his long reign of forty-nine years he not only established Mughal power in fact as well as in name, but brought the Empire to the zenith of its achievement. By the time of his death in 1605 it comprised Afghanistan, all of northern India, and territories extending south to a boundary which would roughly correspond with a line drawn across the country from modern Bombay, in the west, to Cuttack, in Orissa, in the east. Within this vast territory Akbar established over the years a peace and prosperity which made later generations, living in a period when the Empire was dissolving in anarchy, look back to his reign as to a golden age, in which all the medieval ideals had been largely realised. It has been well said that in such circumstances "what passes for a memory is in fact an aspiration,"[9] but in this case idealised memory was much closer to historical fact than it has usually been.

Akbar himself came close to being the ideal medieval king. He came to the throne when he was only thirteen years old, and quickly showed himself to be a brilliant statesman, a most able administrator, and a fine soldier. He was a generous patron of the arts and sciences, and a great builder. He possessed, too, the personal qualities which a medieval society looks for in its king. He was a man of great physical strength, of strong will and commanding personality, brave to the point of foolhardiness, an excellent horseman, and not only proficient in all the skills of war but also, to a wholly exceptional extent, well-versed in all the learning of his day. "All . . . authorities agree in stressing the wideness of his interests and his eagerness for concrete facts; nothing came amiss to him in art or sport, in mechanics or theology, in metallurgy or natural history; and when the facts were in doubt, he was quick to devise experiments for their ascertainment."[10]

If, however, Akbar's empire enjoyed peace and prosperity, it was not because all classes gladly fulfilled their social duties, working in harmony with one another, but because Akbar mastered the problems which in real life arise in every medieval society. The greatest of these was to ensure that the allegiance which the nobility owed to the crown should be

[9] H. W. C. Davis, *Medieval Europe* (London, 1911), p. 23.
[10] See W. H. Moreland and A. C. Chatterjee, *A Short History of India*, 3rd ed. (London, 1953), p. 213.

real and not merely formal. For the nobles effectively controlled great resources of wealth and manpower, and if opportunity arose, they could use them to throw off their allegiance and act in disregard of the king's authority. It had to be the king's constant effort to prevent such opportunities arising, and all the time to strengthen his position as against theirs by every means open to him. One of the foundations of Akbar's greatness was the substantial success he achieved in doing this. He began by playing off one palace faction against another to the detriment of both; then, having made himself master in his own house, he set out to reduce the nobility as a whole to real and permanent submission. He knew how to estimate his own strength realistically, and set himself at each stage only such aims as he had the strength to achieve. Some of his vassals were left to enjoy virtual independence in their own domains, as long as they acknowledged the Emperor's authority and refrained from active opposition to his interests. But where he felt strong enough to enforce a more absolute submission, he was quick to do so. One of his basic policies was to combine the maximum conciliation with the maximum threat of force. He demanded from his nobles a real and absolute submission, but he was prepared to reward it on a scale which made submission offer better prospects than rebellion did. In this way he ensured that only the most unyielding persisted in resistance to him, and that against these he was able to bring overwhelming force.

As a result, the nobility during Akbar's reign was more effectively under the control of the crown than at any other period in the Empire's history. His nobles were, in effect, employees of the crown, and even the greatest of them were appointed, transferred, and dismissed entirely at the Emperor's discretion. Their services were recompensed on a scale which enabled them to live a life of great magnificence; but the obligations were correspondingly great, and no effort was spared to prevent any evasion of them. Some of the nobles were not assigned to a particular territory. Their duty was to appear regularly in attendance on the Emperor, to maintain a prescribed force in readiness, and to be prepared to undertake any task the Emperor might assign them; and these tasks might be of the most varied kinds—military, judicial, or purely administrative. Those who were assigned to particular territories governed them on the Emperor's behalf, and not in virtue of any right of their own. They too were paid, wherever possible, direct from the imperial treasury, and

where this was the case they had no claim whatever on the land or on the
produce of the land or on the land revenue paid by the peasantry in the
areas to which they were assigned. In other words, they had no direct control either of the wealth or of the manpower of their territories.

It is true that Akbar could not apply this system as universally as he
would have wished, and the *jāgīr* system was also not uncommon. Under
it a noble would be paid not directly from the treasury but by an assignment on the revenue of a village or group of villages estimated as adequate
to defray the legitimate expenses of his position. The nobles preferred
this system, because it gave them a greater measure of independence. For
precisely the same reason the Emperor disliked it, and resorted to it only
with reluctance. The nobility was not hereditary. In practice the sons of
a great noble would be appointed during his lifetime to an appropriate
place in the imperial hierarchy, but in theory neither wealth nor office
could be inherited, and in this way, too, the Emperor's position was
strengthened. Actually, the noble's main obligation was to maintain a
cavalry force appropriate to his rank. Under Akbar the highest ordinary
rank was that of a "commander of five-thousand"; commands of larger
numbers were reserved for princes of the imperial family.

Akbar could not have maintained such firm control over his nobles had
he not taken steps to win the active support of the rest of his subjects, of
the merchants and the peasants in particular. The merchants benefited
directly by the abolition of inland transit dues and other similar levies, and
by the maintenance of a currency "very much superior to that of contemporary European sovereigns."[11] The peasants' interests were safe-
guarded by vigilance to prevent any unauthorised demands being made
upon them and by the most careful attention to just assessment and collection of the land revenue. "The essence of his system . . . was that each
unit of area sown was charged with a sum of money (varying with the
crop) calculated to represent the average value of one-third of the produce . . . and this sum was collected at harvest, with an allowance for any
area on which the crop had failed to mature."[12] Revenue officials were
required to pursue a policy of agricultural development; they could advance loans to the peasant to meet the expenses of new development and
could vary the rates of revenue charged so as to offer inducements for the

[11] See S. M. Edwardes and H. L. O. Garrett, *Mughal Rule in India* (London, 1930), p. 218.
[12] See Moreland and Chatterjee, *History of India*, p. 226.

ploughing up of waste land or increasing the area sown to particularly valuable crops. Actual performance no doubt fell short of the high standards which Akbar prescribed, but still the peasantry prospered, and it is known that their condition was very much better than that of the peasantry in the rest of India, south of the Mughal boundaries.[13]

Some of these measures of Akbar ran directly counter to the interests of the nobles. For example, it had been they who had benefited from the levies on both merchants and peasants which were now forbidden. But even where their interests were not directly attacked, the indirect effect was to weaken their position considerably. The people saw the Emperor as the author of their prosperity, and rebellious nobles were thus deprived beforehand of any popular support.

The prosperity of the countryside was matched by that of the towns. Contemporary European travellers were greatly impressed by their size: their accounts describe both Agra and Lahore as being bigger than London, and Delhi at a slightly later period is said to have been nearly as big as Paris. Not only was Akbar in his day one of the richest monarchs in the world, but the standard of living of his subjects in all probability compared favourably with that of contemporary England under Elizabeth.[14] It was Akbar's reign and those of his successors Jahāngīr (1605–1627) and Shāhjahān (1627–1658) that produced the great gardens and the impressive buildings in red sandstone and white marble which are today the most tangible memorials of Mughal times. The Shalimar gardens in Kashmir, the Taj Mahal at Agra, and the Red Fort and the great mosque (the Jama Masjid) at Delhi are among the most famous of these. The last two were built by Shāhjahān, in whose reign the outward magnificence of the Empire reached its height. The famous Peacock Throne, which was made by his command, is a fitting symbol of this magnificence. It "was made of pure gold, studded with gems . . . the inner roof was enamelled, the outer covered with rubies and other jewels; twelve pillars of emerald supported the roof, which was surmounted by the figures of two peacocks, ablaze with precious stones. Between the peacocks was a tree set with diamonds, rubies, emeralds and pearls;

13 Cf. ibid., pp. 244–245.
14 For the size of the towns see W. H. Moreland, India at the Death of Akbar (London, 1920), pp. 13–15; Edwardes and Garrett, p. 237. For Akbar, "the richest monarch in the world," see Edwardes and Garrett, p. 307. For standard of living, see T. G. P. Spear, India, Pakistan and the West, 2nd ed. (London, 1952), p. 110.

three jewelled steps led to the Emperor's seat, which was surrounded by eleven jewelled panels, of which the middlemost bore as its central gem a splendid ruby.'' 15

The great age of the Empire extends over a century and a half, from 1556 to 1707, and spans the reigns of four emperors—Akbar, Jahāngīr, Shāhjahān, and Aurangzeb. Under the first three its capital city was Agra, but Shāhjahān planned to move the capital to Delhi, where he built what was practically a new city, named Shāhjahānābād after him; and the move was made shortly after his death. In this period the fame of Delhi spread far beyond the borders of India. It became ''a great and imperial city . . . with anything between one and two million inhabitants . . . the largest and most renowned city, not only of India, but of all the East from Constantinople to Canton. Its Court was brilliant, its mosques and colleges numerous, and its literary and artistic fame as high as its political renown.'' 16 Such was Delhi at the height of its glory, and such to all outward appearance it remained until in 1739 catastrophe overwhelmed it. In that year the Persian king Nādir Shāh invaded India, crushingly defeated the Mughal armies, entered Delhi without resistance, and after a brief occupation returned to his kindom carrying with him ''the accumulated treasures of eight generations of emperors.'' 17

These events dealt the Empire a blow from which it never recovered; but 1739 does not mark the beginning of its decline. That had begun much earlier. Symptoms can already be discerned shortly after Akbar's death, and become plainly evident in the second half of Aurangzeb's reign. After Aurangzeb died, the Empire began to break up rapidly, and had Nādir Shāh's invasion come years earlier, the result would almost certainly have been the same. But 1739 showed in a few short weeks, and with unmistakable clarity, how rotten the state of the Empire had become, and what were the factors which had made it so. The story is worth telling in some detail, for it formed part of the early memories of all three18 of the great eighteenth-century poets, and though in later years the personalities change, the forces which produced the catastrophe

15 Edwardes and Garrett, pp. 339–340.
16 Percival Spear, *Twilight of the Mughuls* (London, 1951), p. 1.
17 William Irvine, *Later Mughals*, ed. Jadunath Sarkar (Calcutta, 1922), II, 375.
18 This is true only if we accept the year A.H. 1140 (A.D. 1727–1728) as the date of Mīr Hasan's birth. Some authorities give the date as A.H. 1151 (A.D. 1738–1739). The point is discussed more fully in the first note to Chapter 3 below.

continued to operate throughout the century. The events which led up to the invasion need not concern us here, but for many months before it took place, the imperial court was aware of the imminent danger and did virtually nothing to prepare against it. The frontier province of Afghanistan had for years been neglected; it was left to the care of incompetent governors, and as a result of the intrigues of factions at court hostile to the governor and his friends, was starved of the funds necessary to effective defence. Even the Panjāb, the province which lay between Afghanistan and Delhi itself, was similarly treated. It had a strong and capable governor, but he was prevented from preparing a defence in any way adequate against so formidable an enemy as Nādir Shāh.[19] This was because he did not belong to the party dominant at court and was therefore feared (probably quite justifiably) as a potential rival. The result was that Nādir Shāh overran both Afghanistan and the Panjāb with comparative ease, and by January 1739 he had occupied Lahore. As he advanced, complete lawlessness spread everywhere among the population, for people no longer felt any deep loyalty to the Empire, and as authority broke down or became preoccupied in preparing resistance, men seized the opportunity to make themselves their own masters.

Meanwhile the Delhi court, having procrastinated until it could do so no longer, prepared to face the invader. The governor of the Deccan provinces, Nizām ul Mulk, the most able soldier and statesman in the Empire, had been called to Delhi and nominally given full powers to meet the threat. But in reality he was far from being in supreme control. At the court itself it was not he but a faction led by another leading noble, Samsām ud Daula, which was dominant, and Sa'ādat Khān, governor of the province of Oudh, represented yet a third centre of power. The mutual quarrels of these three were soon to prove disastrous to the Empire as a whole.

The imperial forces were given orders to move out to meet the invader as early as December 2, 1738, but they remained encamped outside Delhi for over a month, and when at last they did move, spent nine days in covering the fifty-five miles to Pānipat. Here they halted another nine days for the coming of the Emperor, who had at last heeded the unanimous

[19] The account of Nādir Shāh's invasion is based upon Sarkar's concluding chapters to Irvine's *Later Mughals.*

advice of his generals that he should join the army in person. The army then moved on another twenty miles to Karnāl, and there waited again for the coming of Sa'ādat Khān of Oudh. It was at length decided to entrench there, to surround the camp with a mud wall, and so to await Nādir's attack.

The imperial camp was huge—twelve miles in perimeter, according to one authority—and contained a total population of perhaps a million men, of whom only 75,000 were combatants. As against this, Nādir's army numbered about 55,000, and the total population of his camp about 160,000. One-third of this figure were servants, "but these were all mounted and some of them completely armed, so that they could take part in plunder and the defence of their baggage."[20] Thus the Persian force was very much more mobile and effective. It was able to hem in the imperial army completely, and within a few days all its food supplies were exhausted and there was nothing to eat.

The Indian side continued to show its incompetence when battle was ultimately joined. Sa'ādat Khān came out to battle first, with utterly inadequate preparation and against the advice of both Nizām ul Mulk and Samsām ud Daula. Samsām ud Daula's contingent later moved out to his support. Both forces were drawn upon the Persian artillery and suffered appalling casualties. Samsām ud Daula was mortally wounded; Sa'ādat Khān surrendered and was taken captive to Nādir Shāh. The Indian camp followers saw that their troops were leaving the field of battle and at once plundered their own camp so thoroughly that when the dying Samsām ud Daula was brought back, his servants had to borrow a small tent to shelter him in. Meanwhile Nizām ul Mulk, the ablest general on the Indian side, had remained completely passive. A contemporary historian suggests that this was because he hoped Sa'ādat Khān and Samsām ud Daula might be killed and his own position in the Empire thereby strengthened. The Emperor's contingent too had made no move. Nādir refrained from attacking them, and allowed them to retire within their walled camp.

The same evening Nādir told his prisoner Sa'ādat Khān that his aim was now to extract an indemnity from the Emperor, make peace, and return home. Sa'ādat advised him to send for Nizām ul Mulk and settle peace

[20] *Ibid.*, II, 338.

terms with him, and he himself wrote to the Emperor to the same effect.
Nizām ul Mulk accordingly appeared in the Persian camp the next day
with full powers to negotiate. After a long discussion it was agreed that
Nādir should be paid 5 million rupees as the price of his withdrawal, of
which 2 million were to be paid at once and the rest by instalments, the
whole sum being paid over by the time the Persian army had been withdrawn as far as Kabul. But agreement on these terms was short-lived.
Soon after the battle Samsām ud Daula died of his wounds, and a quarrel
at once began over the question of who was to succeed him in the post of
Imperial Paymaster. Nizām ul Mulk at first secured the appointment of his
son, but this so inflamed a rival candidate that he at once left the Emperor's camp and announced his intention of going over to the enemy,
and in order to bring him back, it was necessary to reverse the decision
and, for the moment, to give the office to Nizām ul Mulk himself. Meanwhile the news reached Sa'ādat Khān, who was still in Nādir Shāh's camp;
Sa'ādat had himself hoped to get the post, and his reaction now was to go
to Nādir at the first opportunity and persuade him to repudiate the terms
of the proposed indemnity. He said that Nizām ul Mulk had tricked him,
and that if he would march on Delhi he could secure 200 million rupees
in cash and jewels alone—forty times the amount of the indemnity
agreed with Nizām ul Mulk.

To show that he was in earnest, Sa'ādat Khān volunteered to bring all
his troops and property into Nādir's camp, and this was done. Nādir made
no overt move for several days, but all this while his blockade of the imperial camp continued, on the ground that no indemnity had yet been
paid. When the camp was reduced to such extremity that for five days the
soldiers had had nothing to eat, Nādir again summoned Nizām ul Mulk
for discussions. He went, knowing nothing of what had happened since the
first agreement had been made, and was now confronted with the demand
for 200 million rupees and told that he would be held captive until he
agreed to this demand. Nizām ul Mulk protested that to raise so vast a
sum would be absolutely impossible and that even Shāhjahān, at the height
of the Empire's glory, had never amassed more than 160 million rupees
in the imperial treasury. But Nādir Shāh was adamant, and he completed
his strangle hold two days later when the Emperor visited him and was
similarly detained as a virtual captive. The next day all the important
nobles were instructed to come over to Nādir's camp, and the imperial

army, still hemmed in by the Persians, was left without leaders. But they were now told that they were free to go where they pleased, and the camp broke up. Few of them escaped to safety. Roving bands of Persian soldiers plundered them without restraint, and so did the peasants, who were now in open insurrection.

The news of the imperial defeat at Karnāl reached Delhi within two days. It had been totally unexpected, and the whole city waited apprehensively to see what would happen. Twelve days later Nādir's advance party, which included Sa'ādat Khān, reached the capital, and on March 9, a little less than a month after the battle, Nādir Shāh himself rode in. That same night Sa'ādat Khān got the reward of his treachery. Nādir sharply rebuked him for not having raised the large sum which he himself had said could be extorted from Delhi, and told him that if he did not raise the money quickly, he would be personally beaten. Knowing that he could not possibly raise the sum, and unable to face the humiliation which awaited him, he committed suicide.

Nādir Shāh had not been in Delhi two days when, late in the afternoon of March 10, the Delhi populace rose against the Persians. There are conflicting accounts of the immediate cause of the rising, but once it began, it spread rapidly and Persian soldiers were everywhere set upon and killed by the people. Only the poorer classes took part in it. It seems that they alone, when the odds were overwhelmingly against them, showed a readiness to resist the invader and despoiler of their country.

Attacks on the Persian soldiers continued in full force until three o'clock in the night, slackened a little, and then revived again at daybreak. A conservative estimate is that 3,000 Persians were killed in the course of them. Nādir Shāh had at first refused to believe reports of what was happening; but he now took ruthless measures to crush the rising. At dawn on the 11th he armed, and rode to the Golden Mosque in Chāndni Chauk (then, as now, one of the main streets of the city), where he enquired in what parts of the city the rising had occurred, and then unsheathed his sword as the signal for general massacre in those districts. The killing began at about 9 A.M. and lasted till 2 P.M., when the Emperor sent the highest nobles of the Empire to intercede, and Nādir was persuaded to give orders for the massacre to end. It is estimated that some 20,000 people had been killed. Houses had been looted and burned, men put to the sword regardless of age, and women made captive, Many had killed their wives and daughters to save them from dishonour, while others committed suicide by throwing themselves into the wells. For some days afterwards the corpses lay in the streets, for no one dared to touch them, and the stench became intolerable. Nādir then gave permission for them to be removed. But Delhi's sufferings were not yet at an end. On Nādir's orders all the granaries were sealed and guarded, and bodies of cavalry were posted to prevent anyone entering or leaving the city. Famine broke out, and even when after some days Nādir permitted people to go out of the city to buy food, they had to encounter bands of Persians who for thirty to forty miles around were plundering and looting on the highways and in the villages.

Meanwhile the systematic plunder of the capital was taking place. The Emperor had to give up all the crown jewels, the famous Koh-i-Nūr diamond, and the Peacock Throne. The nobles and their ladies were also compelled to surrender enormous wealth, and finally all the well-to-do citizens of Delhi were ordered to contribute half their property. Torture was used to compel them to do so. The total spoils thus accumulated were certainly not less than 150 million rupees, and may have been considerably more. In addition the booty included some hundreds of elephants and many thousands of horses and camels.

Finally, after two months in Delhi, Nādir Shāh was ready to depart. He now restored full power to the Emperor, and in exchange, all the Mughal territory west of the Indus was ceded to him and lost to the Empire for ever. In addition he could claim much territory east of the Indus by right of conquest, and though it continued to be governed by Mughal officers, Nādir's right to the revenue was not disputed. Then he set out on his return home. The peasantry rose in the rear of his returning army and plundered what they could from his baggage train.[21] Some idea of India's loss may be gained from the fact that on his return to Persia, Nādir remitted the revenue of the whole kingdom for three years.

By modern standards we do not know much of the lives of the eighteenth-century Urdu poets. But we do know that in 1739 Sauda was already a grown man, that Mir was sixteen or seventeen years old, and that

---

[21] *Ibid.*, II, 374.

Mir Hasan was a boy of eleven or twelve.[22] Sauda and Mir Hasan were both born in Delhi; so far as we know, they had always lived there, and presumably were still there in 1739. Mir was born in Agra, but we know that he had come to the capital a year or more before the invasion, and it is not impossible that he had stayed on there, though it is more likely that he had returned to Agra.[23] Thus it is probable that Sauda and Mir Hasan personally experienced the occupation of Delhi, and possible that Mir did also. At any rate Mir's personal fortunes were deeply involved. For about a year his main source of income had been a monthly allowance from Samsām ud Daula, and when he was killed at Karnāl, this abruptly stopped. We know too that all three men continued to live in Delhi after 1739, though in Mir Hasan's case it was not for long—perhaps for another three or four years. Sauda stayed till 1757, and Mir remained longest of all, for he lived there from about 1740 to 1760, and again, after a prolonged absence, from 1772 to 1782. Thus all three saw with their own eyes the contrast between the capital as they had known it in their boyhood and as it became after the invasion. On the two older men in particular this contrast made an unforgettable impression, as their writings show, and it was deepened by experience of the misfortunes which continued to befall Delhi almost without respite during the years they lived there. Moreover, to all three of them Delhi was not like any other city; the fall of Delhi was to them the fall of a whole civilisation, and one so catastrophic that they felt that the whole universe in which they lived was different. Thus Mir writes:

اس عہد کو نہ جانیئے اگلا ساعہد میر

وہ دو راب نہیں وہ زمیں آبراں نہیں

[22] One cannot be more precise, because the dates of their birth are known (or, in Mir Ḥasan's case, estimated) only in terms of the Muslim calendar. The Muslim year rarely falls wholly within the Christian year, and strict accuracy nearly always demands that the A.D. equivalent be given as, e.g., 1738–1739, as long as the exact birthday, or at least the month of birth, is not known. In this book we have given dates throughout in terms of the Christian calendar. Where our sources give the Muslim date alone, we have given the Christian equivalent in the way just described; but one occasionally finds important dates given both in Muslim and in Christian terms, and in such cases we have assumed (though one cannot vouch for this) that the precise Christian year was known to the writer, and have adopted his date. G. S. P. Freeman-Grenville, in *The Muslim and Christian Calendars* (London, 1963), gives the detailed correspondence of dates.

[23] Qāẓī 'Abdul Vadūd's article in *Ma'āṣir* (Jan. 1956), p. 170.

D

This age is not like that which went before it.
The times have changed, the earth and sky have changed.

(II.290.16)

Some of the forces which brought about the fall of the Mughal Empire
have already shown themselves clearly in the story of 1739. To begin
with, an Emperor who no longer possesses any real authority is alike unable to command that active good-will of the mass of his subjects which
Akbar had enjoyed, and to control the great nobles. Further, all effective
power is in the nobles' hands, and they act only in their own interest, so
blinded by mutual jealousies that even when all are threatened by a common danger, they cannot or will not combine against it.

This state of affairs had developed well before 1739, and it was to continue throughout the century until in 1803 the British occupation of
Delhi put an end to the anarchy and, in effect, to the Empire too. The
shift of the centre of power from the crown to the warring factions of the
nobility was not due solely to the individual weaknesses of successive
Emperors, important though this cause was. It was also an indirect consequence of the increased burdens laid upon the peasantry after Akbar's
death. The magnificence of Shāhjahān's reign was founded upon this increased exploitation, and it was continued under Aurangzeb in order to
pay for the ceaseless warfare which, from early in his reign, became an
almost permanent feature in the life of Mughal India. In this way the
crown alienated the support of the most numerous class of its subjects,
and this necessarily resulted in an increased relative strength of the
nobility. So long as the Emperors remained personally strong and capable,
this fundamental weakness in their position was to some extent concealed. But Aurangzeb's immediate successor was the last who possessed
any real ability, and from 1712 successive Emperors diminished in
political stature until they were in fact much less powerful than the great
nobles nominally subordinate to them.

One of the clearest signs of the Empire's decline was its disintegration
into virtually independent dominions. In some of the most important
provinces this happened without any overt conflict between the provincial
governors and the central power. While the emperors were strong, no
governor was allowed to govern his province for a term of more than four
years, but from 1707 onwards in many of the key provinces a different

picture emerged; the exceptionally long rule of a governor led to the founding of a dynasty, and the governorship was handed down from father to son. True, the governorship was not formally hereditary, but each succeeding governor did in fact arrange to be appointed as such by the emperor. These virtually independent dynasties date in Bengal from 1707, in the Panjāb from 1713, in Oudh from 1723, and in the Deccan provinces from 1724–1725.

As the provinces one by one fell away from the Empire in all but name, the territory under imperial administration progressively dwindled until it comprised little more than the area around Delhi. Within this shrinking area violent struggles developed between rival nobles for the spoils of high imperial office, leading more than once to armed clashes in the streets of the capital itself and to atrocities against emperors and other members of the imperial family who were the pawns in their struggles. Up to 1753 some of the rulers of the provinces were sometimes among the contestants. In 1748 Safdar Jang, the governor of Oudh, succeeded in becoming Vazīr,[24] or chief minister, of the Empire, and in holding the post until 1753; the Emperor then dismissed him, but it took a six-months' civil war to compel him to relinquish office.

However, the disruption of the Empire was not the work of the nobility alone. Plebeian movements of revolt also played an important part. As the crown increasingly lost the support of the people, and as the lawlessness and disorder produced by the fighting between rival powers in the land laid increasing burdens upon them, the peasants learned to look after their own interests and refused to give up their produce except when confronted with a force they could not oppose. Thus in 1758 the Vazīr, accompanied by the Emperor in person, had to mount a regular military campaign in the country west of Delhi in order to exact tribute from the villages. "In this region the sturdy villagers from behind their mud walls frequently offered stout resistance and fought the Vazīr; they could be subdued only by . . . artillery . . . On 19th September, when the Emperor and Vazīr were . . . following two different routes, the people of Bhiwani, matchlock in hand, shut their sovereign out of their village, while the local robber population carried off many . . . carts laden with baggage from both divisions of the imperial army."[25]

[24] The "Vizier" of the Arabian Nights.
[25] Jadunath Sarkar, *Fall of the Mughal Empire*, 2nd ed. (Calcutta, 1950), II, 120–121; cf. also II, 288–290.

The more adventurous peasant people went further than self-defence, and plebeian movements of which the peasantry formed the backbone arose in a number of areas to wage active warfare against their common enemies. Of these the most remarkable was that of the Sikhs in the Panjāb. The Sikhs had originated as a popular religious sect in the sixteenth century, and the community still has this character. But in the eighteenth century it was social discontent which rallied to their standard the Panjābi peasantry and the poorer classes of the town population,[26] and made them in the latter half of the century the strongest power in the Panjāb. Their movement was also an expression of the growth of national feeling, and many Sikhs to this day regard their community as the natural leadership of the Panjābi nationality. In no other movement is this blend of social, religious, and national elements as evident, but in all of the plebeian movements which combined with those of the aristocracy to disintegrate the Empire, these three elements were perhaps present in varying degrees.[27]

This internal disintegration was hastened by the external pressures to which the Empire was subjected—from the south, the northwest, and the east—and it was these which in the end decided the Empire's fate. The threat from the south was the first to develop, in the form of one of the part-national, part-religious, and part-social movements of which we have spoken. Akbar had begun the expansion of the Empire beyond the northern plains into the Deccan, and his successors contined the process. It began to meet determined resistance from the Marāthas, a predominantly Hindu people whose homeland, Mahārāshtra, corresponds to the modern Indian state of that name, and comprises, very approximately speaking, the western half of the Deccan. They were among the earliest of the modern Indian peoples to develop a strong national consciousness, and under their great leader Shivaji they began a determined struggle to free themselves from Mughal rule. The second half of Aurangzeb's reign was occupied with almost continuous war against them, but without lasting success. By about 1720 their power was paramount in the Deccan, ·

[26] *Ibid.*, I, 425.
[27] In our view the standard histories overstress the religious aspect of these movements, with a consequent underemphasis on the national and social aspects. Yet these same histories to some extent provide the data and the estimates to support our view. Thus, on the Sikhs, see Irvine, I, 72–84, and esp. 82–84. On the Marāthas see esp. Edwardes and Garrett's striking statement in *Mughal Rule*, p. 127.

and when in 1724–1725 the six Deccan provinces of the Empire virtually seceded, Mughal power outside northern India came to an end. But the Marāthas did not rest content with control of the Deccan. From 1720 they began to push northwards, and became a factor of ever increasing importance in the affairs of northern India. They demanded and received for themselves or their nominees the governorship of imperial territories, fought as mercenaries in the struggles between the north Indian powers, and raided and pillaged far and wide on their own account. Their power steadily increased until 1761, when they were crushingly defeated by the Afghan king Ahmad Shāh Abdāli, invading from the northwest. But they returned by 1771, and from that date until their defeat by the British in 1803, were the real rulers of what remained of the Empire.

From the northwest, in 1739, came the invasion of Nādir Shāh, which has already been described. On Nādir's death his mantle fell upon Ahmad Shāh Abdāli, who succeeded to Nādir Shāh's Afghan territories and to the Mughal provinces which had been ceded to him. He too was a constant menace to the Empire, invading in 1748, when he was repulsed; in 1757, when he occupied and plundered Delhi as thoroughly as Nādir Shāh had done; and in 1760. On this last occasion he stayed in India a full year, preparing for a full trial of strength with the Marāthas. In January 1761 he defeated them so overwhelmingly that for ten years they ceased to be a significant force in northern India; but he himself withdrew to Afghanistan shortly afterwards. After that, in repeated incursions, he never got farther than the Panjāb, where the Sikhs were in permanent revolt against his and every other authority, and in 1767 he had virtually to admit defeat at the hands of this "entire nation in arms,"[28] as they have been called, and retire permanently to his own kingdom.

In the East, in Bengal, the British established themselves by their victory at Plassey in 1757. But Bengal had already ceased in all but name to be a province of the Empire some fifty years earlier. Like the Marāthas and the *de facto* independent rulers of great provinces like Oudh and the Deccan, the British were still *de jure* subjects of the Mughal Emperor, and in this period they did not pursue a strongly aggressive policy against the Emperor. That was to come later.

Together, the working of these internal and external forces destroyed the Empire, and it was during the process of its destruction that Mir,

[28] Sarkar, II, 296.

Sauda, and Mir Hasan lived their lives. The picture of the Empire which they saw before them towards the middle of the century, when they were young men, is somewhat as follows: To the west, all the territory beyond the River Indus had been lost since 1739. The Panjāb had for years been either virtually independent or subject in varying degrees to Nādir Shāh or to his Afghan successor, Ahmad Shāh Abdāli, though the Sikhs were increasingly making themselves the real power in the land. South of that, Rājputāna was in the hands of its various chiefs, many of whom were in turn subordinate to the Marāthas. South of that again, Gujarat was under Marātha control. Moving eastwards from there, the Marāthas were supreme practically all the way across the peninsula up to the southern limit of the north Indian plain. In the plain itself, beginning in the east, Bengal and Bihar had long been virtually independent of the Empire and were soon to pass under British control. West of them lay Oudh, also virtually independent, and west again, between Oudh and the River Ganges, territories settled in the sixteenth century by immigrants from Afghanistan, and now constituting the kingdoms of Rohilkhand and Farrukhābād. Beyond them, but to the south of Delhi, was the Jāt kingdom, built up by peasant chieftains who began as little more than highwaymen on the Delhi-Agra road. The territory under the direct control of Delhi had shrunk to a comparatively small dominion around the capital itself.

It might be concluded that, thus left to itself, Delhi must have enjoyed comparative peace. But this was not so. On the contrary, no other city had to endure so much as Delhi did. The reason was that Delhi was the imperial capital and normally the seat of the emperor; and although lacking in all real power, the emperor was nonetheless constitutionally the supreme authority, and no power was legitimate unless formally derived from him. And so it was not only the invasions of Ahmad Shāh Abdāli that Delhi had to fear. Within India itself every aspirant for power sought the control of Delhi and of the emperor's person. The city was repeatedly occupied by the armies of contending powers, and occupation almost always meant looting, burning, and extortion upon its citizens. Even in the short-lived intervals of peace, there prevailed misery, uncertainty, and lawlessness.

The history of the years 1753–1757—years in which both Mir and Sauda were in the city—well illustrates what it meant to live in Delhi in

INDIA
IN THE LATE
EIGHTEENTH CENTURY

Approximate Boundaries ·—·—·—·—
British · · · · · · · · · · · · ·
Under Hindu Rulers · · · ||||||||||||
Under Muslim Rulers · · ☐

that age. In March 1753 Safdar Jang, who held simultaneously the governorship of Oudh and the office of Vazīr of the Empire, was dismissed
from office by the Emperor and "given leave" (that is, commanded) to
return to his province. This was the result of the intrigues of a hostile
faction, and he refused to comply with the Emperor's orders. The result
was civil war, which lasted from March until November. Both Safdar
Jang and his rivals, led by the sixteen-year-old Imād ul Mulk, called in
outside help. Safdar Jang's main allies were the Jāts, and in the course of
the fighting he instigated them to plunder old Delhi, where, in contrast
to the new city built by the Emperor Shāhjahān, only the poorer sections
of the population lived. The Jāts did their work so thoroughly that they
added a phrase, *Jāt gardi*—"Jāt affliction" or "Jāt invasion"—to the
vocabulary of Urdu, and in later days their excesses ranked in Delhi
people's memory with those of Abdāli's invasions. Imād ul Mulk relied
upon the Marāthas, who were ready to sell their armed support to anyone
who could pay a high enough price; and it was thanks mainly to them that
Safdar Jang was defeated and Imād, at the age of seventeen, made Vazīr in
his place. Before being invested by the Emperor with the robe of office,
Imād had sworn on the Holy Quran never to betray him. That same
morning he deposed him and enthroned one of the princes in his place.
The deposed Emperor was thrown into prison, together with his mother,
and was later blinded by having a red-hot needle drawn across his eyes.[29]
    In Mir's first collection of ghazals there is a verse which seems to be a
direct reference to this event:

I lived to see the needle drawn across the eyes of kings
The dust beneath whose feet was like collyrium ground with pearls.

(I. 103.4)

The verse contains a characteristic play on words. Collyrium, made
usually of ground antimony, was used by men and women alike to tinge

---

[29] Sarkar does not mention the blinding, but Shaikh Cānd, in *Saudā* (see the first note to
Chapter 2 below) writes of it on p. 8.

the eyes with, both because this was considered to make them more attractive and because it was believed to have medicinal properties, enhanced if the collyrium were mixed with ground pearls. Collyrium was applied with a large, blunt needle, and it was this same needle that could be heated red-hot and used to blind a man. So that the first line of the couplet could refer equally to the applying of collyrium and to the blinding—the sort of conceit which, like the English Elizabethans, Mir's contemporaries loved.

The new Vazīr was desperate for money. Much of his inherited personal fortune had been spent in the civil war against Safdar Jang, and the support of the Marāthas had been gained by the promise of a huge subsidy which he had no means of paying. He was not capable of establishing good order in the areas nearest to Delhi and so ensuring a flow of revenue from which he could meet his needs; he therefore resorted to levying forced contributions from all except those who had the armed strength to resist. The imperial family was the first to suffer, from confiscation of estates and of treasure and jewellery. Attempts were made to extract money from the nobles and the rich, and when this plan failed for lack of the necessary power to enforce it, from the traders, artisans, and common people in the markets. This too produced little result: the bazaars were closed in protest, and thousands of people assembled under the palace windows protesting to the Emperor. He, to his credit, supported them, threatening to fast to the death if Imād persisted in his measures, and Imād had for the moment to drop the idea. But he made a further attempt only two months later, seizing and beating the citizens in order to compel them to pay. This continued for six weeks, until public outcry compelled the abandonment of this attempt as well.

Meanwhile the Marātha armies stayed close to the capital, and it was clear that they would not withdraw until their promised subsidy was paid. For eight months, from June 1754 to February 1755, they moved about in the villages round Delhi, living off the country, looting the villagers, and robbing travellers, pilgrims, and even high imperial officials. Much of the normal grain supply of the city was cut off, and scarcity and high prices added to the misfortunes of the people. Only after Imād had alienated to them sufficient land (including crown land and some of the privy purse estates) to provide for the payment of his debt to them, did they at last withdraw.

This was not all. In the territory around Delhi lay estates whose revenue was earmarked for the maintenance of the Emperor and his family, and for payment of the palace servants, the imperial artillery, and the palace guards. But this revenue was now appropriated by the Vazīr, and the imperial family itself had to suffer extreme hardship in consequence. Contemporary historians speak of occasions when imperial princesses went three days together without food, and of the Emperor having to go about on foot because no conveyance could be provided for him. The palace servants and guards went unpaid for years at a time—in 1754 their pay was already three years in arrears—and had to live as best they could. It was not surprising in such circumstances that they paid little attention to the Emperor's needs and no longer regarded themselves as bound to perform duties for which they were not paid. The soldiers in particular resorted to the most desperate measures in order to live. They rioted continually in the capital and even in the imperial fort itself. They attacked and plundered the houses of the wealthy; chased, stoned, and manhandled the high officials responsible for paying them; and on one occasion forced their way into the Vazīr's house and carried off the meal which had been prepared for him. When an Imperial Paymaster died in 1756, they refused to allow him to be buried until they had received some satisfaction. In the same year they blockaded the fort and prevented even food and water going in until they had gained their demands. This general lawlessness was sometimes encouraged by the imperial officials. Thus the Vazīr himself, unable to raise the money to pay the soldiers, is accused by contemporary historians of encouraging them to plunder the property of the well-to-do. In 1757 the chief of the Delhi police was widely believed to be in league with gangs of armed burglars, shielding them in return for a share of their spoils.

When in 1757 Abdālī again invaded India, Imād could not offer even the slightest resistance, and all Delhi trembled at the news of his approach. Those who had the means to do so evacuated their families to Jāt territory, and then followed themselves. A force of the Marāthas barred their way, and acting on orders from Imād, turned them back, but not before extorting money from them. The Jāts also took full advantage of those who sought refuge with them, knowing that the refugees were in no position to resist their demands.

On January 28, 1757, Abdālī rode into the capital. As he did so, his escort dispersed to loot the markets and houses, but Abdāli was concerned to see that whatever spoils Delhi could be forced to give up should come to him, and severe punishments soon put an end to the individual enterprise of his soldiers. Attention was first concentrated upon the nobility. Their servants, and where necessary they themselves, were, without distinction of sex, subjected to torture to compel them to disclose their buried hoards of treasure, and the houses of those who had fled from the city were broken into and looted. Next, the entire population was systematically despoiled: the city was divided into sections, and a regular staff appointed to levy contributions house by house. Many died under torture, which was everywhere used to extract the very maximum that could be extorted. This process lasted for sixteen days. A few more days were taken up in commandeering the necessary transport to carry away the spoils to Afghanistan.

It was at this time that Sauda left Delhi, and though there is nothing to indicate that he intended at this stage to leave the city permanently, in point of fact he never returned. Mir, however, stayed on for another four years. The most summary account of these years shows that Delhi's sufferings were far from over. It was given a short respite for a month while Abdāli's armies campaigned in the country south of Delhi, looting, raping, killing, and burning, until water contaminated by the corpses of their victims caused an outbreak of cholera in their camp. They now made all possible haste to return to Afghanistan. During the last days, when Abdāli was halted near the capital, arranging the final details of the withdrawal, Delhi was again plundered by hordes of his soldiers. But at last, early in April, the march back to Afghanistan began. The Afghans carried away with them an enormous booty. For Abdāli's goods alone 28,000 transport animals were needed, and his cavalry marched on foot, loading their booty on their horses.

When Abdāli departed, he left as his plenipotentiary in Delhi Najīb Khān, an Indian Afghan who had actively assisted him in his invasion. In June, Imād, again aided by the Marāthas, returned to drive him out. He succeeded, but Delhi had to endure siege and famine for a month before Najīb would surrender. The following year the Marāthas threatened to put Delhi to plunder if tributes which Imād owed them were not paid, and did in fact plunder the northern suburbs before Imād, for the moment, bought them off.

By early 1760 the Marāthas were at the height of their power, and had even ventured to attack Abdāli's Indian domains. But this provoked Abdāli to invade once more, and in January 1760 he and his Indian ally Najīb defeated the Marātha army ten miles north of Delhi. This time Abdāli did not enter the city, but made his camp some miles to the south. According to Mir,'this did not save it from looting and atrocity.[30] It was quite near enough to Abdāli's encampment for his soldiers and those of Najīb to make their way there in considerable numbers, and Mir describes what they did:

In the evening Rāja Nāgar Mal [Mir's patron at the time] left the city, and in due course safely reached the forts of Sūraj Mal [ruler of the Jāt kingdom]. I stayed behind to look after my family. After evening, proclamation was made that Shāh Abdāli had granted security to all, and that none of the citizens should be in any fear. But night had scarcely fallen when the outrages began. Fires were started in the city and houses were burnt down and looted. The following morning all was uproar and confusion. The Afghans and Rohillas [Najīb's soldiers] started their work of slaughter and plunder, breaking down the doors, tying up those they found inside, and in many cases burning them alive or cutting off their heads. Everywhere was bloodshed and destruction, and for three days and three nights this savagery continued. The Afghans would leave no article of food or clothing untouched. They broke down the walls and roofs of the houses, and ill-treated and tormented the inhabitants. The city was swarming with them. Men who had been pillars of the state were brought to nothing, men of noble rank left destitute, family men bereft of all their loved ones. Most of them roved the streets amid insult and humiliation. Men's wives and children were made captive, and the killing and looting went on unchecked. The Afghans humiliated and abused their victims and practised all kinds of atrocities upon them. Nothing which could be looted was spared, and some would strip their victims even of their underclothing. The new city [Shāhjahānābād] was ransacked.

---

[30] Contemporary histories, it seems, do not speak of the looting of Delhi on this occasion, and Sarkar's account (II, 161) naturally follows theirs. However, from the fact that Delhi was spared the occupation and systematic plunder which had taken place under Abdāli's own direction three years earlier, it does not necessarily follow that it was left unmolested, and we see no reason to doubt that Mir's account is, in essentials, reliable.

On the third day some sort of law and order was introduced, but the officer in charge himself completed the work of despoliation; and when at last the looters were driven out of the new city, they simply turned their attention to the old, where they put countless people to the sword. For seven or eight days the tumult raged. Nobody was left with clothes to wear or with enough food even for a single meal. Many died of the wounds they had received, while others suffered greatly from the cold. The looters would carry off men's stores of grain and then sell it at an extortionate price to those who needed it. The cry of the oppressed rose to heaven, but the king [Abdāli], who considered himself a pillar of true religion, was quite unmoved. Large numbers of people left the city and fled into the open country, where many of them died. Others were carried off by force to the invader's camp. I, who was already poor, became poorer . . . My house, which stood on the main road, was levelled with the ground.[31]

A year of suspense and uncertainty followed, as Abdāli and his Indian Afghan allies on one side and the Marāthas on the other mustered their full strength for a clash which all could see would be more fateful in its consequences than any event since 1739. The result was anything but a foregone conclusion. The Marātha force which Abdāli had defeated was only a fraction of their total strength, and as the year went by and they moved up from their main bases in the Deccan, it sometimes looked as though they, and not Abdāli, were likely to win the coming battle.

Mir was in particular agitation and distress during this year. In July the Marāthas occupied Delhi. Mir left the city about the same time. "I have suffered many hardships in this city," he told his patron. "Perhaps I may find peace and comfort elsewhere."[32] He continues: "I set out, taking my family and dependants with me. I did not know where I was going, but set out, trusting in God to lead me. After walking all day and undergoing great hardship, we had covered ten to twelve miles. We spent the night under a tree in the courtyard of an inn. In the morning Rāja Jugal Kishor's[33] wife passed that way, and seeing our plight, took us along with her to Rasāna, and did all she could to make us comfortable." After some

---

[31] *Zikr i Mīr*, pp. 85–88.
[32] *Zikr i Mīr*, p. 90.
[33] A highly placed noble and a former patron of Mir.

time he settled in Kumbher, in the Jāt kingdom; but there was nobody there who could make any permanent provision for him. He relates an experience of this period at some length: [34]

One day when I was sitting wondering where my next meal was coming from, I had the idea of going to visit Āzam Khān, the son of Āzam Khān the elder, who had once been a great noble and was a good and generous man. At any rate, I thought, it will pass a pleasant hour or two. Accordingly I went and sought him out in Sūraj Mal's stables, where those who had been ruined in Delhi were now living. God bless him! he enquired tenderly after me. I told him all that had happened to me, and all who were present listened in shocked distress. Then when the hookah was set before me I recited [a verse of Urfi [35]] and one or two others appropriate to the occasion, until I was myself moved to tears. After a while I noticed that Āzam Khān seemed worried. I asked him what was the matter. "It is nothing," he replied. "No, tell me," I said, "What is it?" He said, "I was thinking how when you used to visit me in Delhi I would have all kinds of sweets brought in and we would sit and eat them together. And now I haven't even crude sugar to make you a drink of sherbet." "All those things," I replied, "were for happier days. For my part, as you well know, I am not a slave to my belly. And times change. That was a time for sweet things, and this is a time for bitterness." As we were conversing a woman came in at the door bearing a tray on her head. She came to Āzam Khān and said, "Sa'īd ud Dīn Khān's sister sends you these sweets with her blessing." As he turned back the tray cover, Āzam Khān's face lit up; turning to me he said, "I have long grown used to fasting: there have been days when I have not had so much as a piece of bread or a mouthful of water, let alone such luxuries as sweets. You are my guest. These are for you. Give me a little and send the rest home." "There is too much here," I said, "I shall not know what to do with it all." "Your son Mir Faiz Ali will know how to use it," he replied. In the end, at his insistence, I allowed him to send a large dish of the sweets to my house, and it was on them that we lived for the next two days.

[34] Ẕikr i Mīr, pp. 91–93.
[35] A Persian poet, born in 1555–1556 in Shirāz, court poet of the Mughal Emperor Akbar, who became famous through his high-styled qasīdas. 'Urfī died in 1590–1591. (A.S.)

Not long after this he resumed his connection with his old patron, Rāja Nāgar Mal, and both remained in the Jāt country. Mir explains why: "Delhi in those days was little better than a wilderness, which every six months was laid desolate afresh. Besides, a man cannot wander from place to place forever. In the Jāt country there was peace, under a prosperous ruler, and we settled down there under the shadow of his protection." [36] His words do not exaggerate. He had himself experienced the plunder by the Afghans in January. In July came the Marātha occupation, and in January 1761, after their crushing defeat of the Marāthas at Pānipat, the Afghans again moved in to loot whatever was left to be looted. Mir saw the effects when he visited the city a little later:

> The scene of desolation filled my eyes with tears and my mind with the most solemn thoughts. At every step my distress and agitation increased. I could not recognise the houses and often lost my bearings. Of the former inhabitants there was no trace, and no matter whom I enquired about, I was told that he was not there and nobody knew where he might be found. The houses were in ruins. Walls had collapsed. Cloisters and wineshops alike were deserted . . . Whole bazaars had vanished. The children playing in the streets, the comely young men, the austere elders—all had gone. Whole quarters were in ruins, their lanes desolate. Everywhere was a terrible emptiness . . . All at once I found myself in the quarter where I had once lived. I recalled the life I used to live, foregathering with my friends in the evenings, reciting poetry, and living the life of a lover—weeping at nights for the love of beautiful women, writing verse to them, and passing my days in the company of those whose long tresses held me their captive, and knowing no peace when I could not be with them . . . In those days I had really lived. And what was there now? Not a soul whom I even recognised and with whom I could hope to pass a pleasant few minutes in conversation. I came away from the lane and stood on the deserted road, gazing in stunned silence at the scene of desolation, and filled with abhorrence at what I saw. And there and then I made a vow that as long as I lived, I would never come this way again. [37]

---

[36] *Zikr i Mīr*, p. 95.
[37] *Zikr i Mīr*, pp. 99–100.

Mir left Delhi soon afterwards, and it was ten years before he returned. But wherever he went, he saw the decay of the civilisation he loved. In this same year of 1761 he revisited his native city of Agra after an absence of more than twenty years, and stayed there for four months. Agra had not suffered as much material destruction as Delhi had, but the city seemed empty to him. "On two or three occasions," he writes,[38]

> I went right through the city, meeting scholars and holy men and poets, but none could give peace to my restless heart. I said to myself "Great God! This is that city where in every other street were fine houses and gardens, inns, cloisters, mosques, schools and seminaries, and where scholars and doctors of law, divines and learned men, saints and mystics, physicians and teachers and poets and writers were seen on every hand. But now I see no place where I could rest in peaceful enjoyment, and no man in whose company I could rejoice." I saw a scene of dreadful desolation, and grieved deeply.

No sensitive man could live in such an age and not be deeply influenced by all he saw happening around him; and the writings of Mir, Sauda, and Mir Hasan show how each in his own characteristic way reacted. All feel a deep regret at the passing of Mughal glory, and a life-long attachment to Delhi, which even in its decline symbolised for them all that was most precious in the values of Mughal India. It was these values which they sought to uphold, inspired by the idealised memory of their own child-hoods and what the Empire had been in their fathers' and grandfathers' day. Their methods differ. Sauda uses his power as a satirist to pillory those who contribute to the general decline in civilised standards, whether in personal or social life. Mir Hasan condemns by silence, with-drawing from the decadent world around him and holding up before men's eyes a picture of one moulded nearer to his heart's desire. In Mir the keynotes are a deep, personal sorrow and an unshakable determina-tion to uphold in his poetry the principles in which he believed with all his heart and which guided his own life. But at this point we can turn direct to the poets' works and leave it to the reader to make his own appraisal.

[38] *Zikr i Mīr*, p. 104.

The Satires of Sauda

AN AGE LIKE THAT OF eighteenth-century Mughal India calls aloud for a satirist, and in Sauda it found one.[1] He was not a satirist alone. His collected verse is a bulky volume, including poems in all the main classical forms, and all have played their part in making him one of the great names in Urdu literature. Traditionally he is assessed not only as a great satirist but also as one of the only two Urdu poets to achieve real distinction in the difficult form of the qasīda. But it is his satires which today arouse the greatest interest, and these alone will be discussed here.

Sauda was of noble descent on both sides of his family, and was born and brought up in Delhi. His father died when he was still quite a young man, and he inherited a considerable fortune. But he was generous, and liking the good things of life, his money was soon spent. Even so, he never seems to have experienced any great hardship. He made his name as a poet quite early in life, so impressing his ustād that he used to tell people that Sauda could have said of him what the Persian poet Sāib (1601–1676) said of his ustād:

[1] Sources for this chapter are Shaikh Cānd, Saudā (Aurangābād, 1936), which is still the only substantial study of the poet; and Saudā's Kulliyāt (collected verse). No satisfactory edition of the Kulliyāt exists. The most recent is that of 'Abdul Bāri Āsī, 2 vols. (Lucknow, 1932). Unfortunately, despite the better arrangement of the poems and the very much greater clarity of the text, Āsī's edition is inferior in many respects to some of its predecessors, notably in that he has taken it upon himself to expurgate Saudā's verse of what he regards as obscene and objectionable matter, following an earlier edition "from which," to quote his complacent words, "these thorns had been cleared" (p. 18 of his Introduction). We have therefore preferred an earlier edition—that prepared by Momin's pupil, Mīr 'Abdur Raḥmān Āhī, and printed at Delhi in A.H. 1272 (A.D. 1856). Kulliyāt in the notes below means this edition. The edition is not easily accessible, and all but a few of the verses we quote are included in Khurshidul Islam's selection Kalām i Saudā (Aligarh, 1965). We have therefore added the references to this selection, abbreviated in the notes below as Kalām.

> Respect commands my silence, but the truth is
> My master is not fit to be my pupil.

Both his noble birth and his fame as a poet gave Sauda access to the courts of the nobility and ensured him a life of material comfort. We do not know who his first patrons were, but when he left Delhi in 1757, he had for some time been attached to the court of Imād ul Mulk, the Vazīr of the Empire whose political crimes have already been described. Imād seems, however, to have known and fulfilled his obligations as a patron, and there is nothing to suggest that Sauda found any cause for dissatisfaction with him in this respect. Subsequent patrons provided equally well for him. From 1757 to about 1770[2] he lived at Farrukhābād, under the patronage of the chief minister of the kingdom, and from then to his death in 1781 at the court of the Governors of Oudh, who were then the most generous patrons of Urdu literature in Mughal India. Richard Johnson, the British Assistant Resident at the court of Oudh, who is said to have known Urdu well and to have appreciated Urdu poetry, was among those whose acquaintance he made there.

His attitude to his patrons was, as we have seen, a healthy one. He was a great poet, and his obligation to society, which he fully accepted, was to practise and perfect his art. Society's obligation to him was, through the institution of patronage, to assure him the means of doing so. What he received from his patrons was his due; he owed them appreciation and respect, but nothing more than that. He maintained this attitude all his life, as a story of his last years shows.[3]

Sauda was living under the patronage of Āsaf ud Daula, the Governor of Oudh. Āsaf ud Daula was once out on a hunting expedition and the news came that he had killed a lion. Sauda at once celebrated the occasion with a couplet:

> See, Ibn i Muljam comes to earth again
> And so the Lion of God once more is slain.

---

[2] To be more precise, some time between A.H. 1183 (A.D. 1769–1770) and A.H. 1185 (A.D. 1771–1772). Cf. Shaikh Cānd, pp. 55–56.

[3] See Āzād, Āb i Ḥayāt, p. 169.

The point of the verse is in the play on the words "the Lion of God."
Lion of God is one of the titles of Ali, the cousin and son-in-law of the
Prophet, and Ibn i Muljam was the name of the man who assassinated him.
Āsaf ud Daula was a Shia, a sect of Muslims which holds Ali and his
family in special veneration, and to be compared, even in jest, with Ali's
assassin, was something he was not likely to appreciate. Āsaf ud Daula
heard of the verse, and on his return said to Sauda, "Mirza,[4] I hear you
have compared me to the murderer of the Lion of God." Sauda was quite
unabashed. He laughed and replied, "Well, it was a fair comparison. The
lion *was* God's, not yours or mine."

This independent spirit is one of his many attractive qualities. There
is nothing complicated about his character. He enjoyed life without any
inhibitions, and he liked others to enjoy it too. He thought he was a good
poet, and took a pride in being so. But he was not an arrogant man, and
made no pretensions to qualities which he knew he did not possess. "I am
not the fairest flower in the garden, nor am I a thorn in any man's path,"
he wrote of himself. "I am neither famous for virtue nor notorious for
vice . . . I seek nobody's favours, and want nobody to seek mine. People
may think well or ill of me as they please : I act as my nature prompts me."[5]

Acting as his nature prompted him meant, among other things, giving
free rein to a quick wit and an exuberant, often Rabelaisian, sense of
humour, as many stories of him show. On one occasion a friend of his
brought a young poet to see him. The poet had long been anxious to meet
Sauda, and had hopes of persuading him to be his ustād. After Sauda had
listened to a few of his verses, he asked him what takhallus he had chosen.
"Umedvār," he replied, meaning one who hopes for, or experts, or
aspires to something. Sauda smiled and said,

ہے فیض سے کسی کے شجر ان کا باردار

اس داسطے کیا ہے تخلّص امیدوار

Someone has made him fruitful : need he tell us
Why he has made Umedvār his takhallus?

4 "Mirzā" was the proper courteous form of address for a gentleman of Mughal (as opposed
to Persian) descent.
5 *Kulliyāt*, p. 363, lower margin, lines 18–20; p. 364, centre, line 1; and p. 355, centre,
line 14. *Kalām*, p. 207, lines 1–2, and p. 211, lines 4–5.

Umedvār, like the English "expectant," also means pregnant. The young man was covered in confusion, and decided both to change his takhallus and to look for another ustād.

On another occasion he was visited by a poet named Hidāyat. After the usual formalities Sauda asked him what he was doing these days. Hidāyat replied pompously, "The management of my affairs leaves me but little leisure, but my temperament constrains me from time to time to write some trifling verses, and occasionally I compose a ghazal." "Why waste time on ghazals?" Sauda replied. "You should write satires." Hidāyat was taken aback. "But whom should I satirise?" he asked. "That's no problem," said Sauda. "You satirise me and I'll satirise you." Having shown Hidāyat that he was not impressed by his pompousness, Sauda seems to have been content to leave it at that.[6] Otherwise Hidāyat would have found to his cost that to be the target of Sauda's satire was a painful experience.

One of such targets was Mir Zāhik, the father of the Mir Hasan of this book, and a man whom Sauda regarded as a sponger and detested accordingly. One day Sauda and another poet named Sikandar were at the house of Mirza Sulaimān Shikoh, a son of the Emperor Shāh Ālam, and their host was conversing with them when Mir Zāhik came in. Sulaimān Shikoh, who was well aware of Sauda's dislike for the man, greeted Zāhik politely, asked him to be seated, and had the hookah set before him. He then turned to Sauda and said, smiling, "Won't you recite something for us?" Sauda replied that he had not written anything recently, and then, with a gesture towards Sikandar added, "But he has just written a poem; I'll recite you the first verse":

یارب تو مری سن لے یہ کہتا ہے سکندر

ضاحک کے اُڑا دیوے کسی بن میں قلندر

گھر اس کے تولّد ہوا گر بچّہ بندر

گلیوں میں نچا تا پھرے وہ بنگلے کے اندر

روٹی تو کما کھاوے کسی طور مجھ ندر

---

[6] The anecdotes about Umedvār and Hidāyat are from Āzād, *Āb i Ḥayāt*, pp. 170, 171, respectively.

Sikandar craves this boon of the Almighty:
Rouse Zāhik up to lift his spouse's nightie.
And then when she brings forth his monkey-lad
He'll dance it through the streets of Faizābād
And earn his living by an honest trade.

Without waiting to hear any more, Mir Zāhik rose to his feet and threw himself upon the astonished Sikandar, while others rushed in to part them. Meanwhile Sauda stood on one side smiling; the verse was not Sikandar's, but his own.[7]

The incident illustrates both Sauda's character and his satirical style. Within five lines it is suggested that Zāhik is incapable of performing a husband's duties without divine intervention, that he is so apelike that most people would mistake his son for a monkey, that he lives by sponging on others, and that even going the rounds with a performing monkey would be a more honourable way of getting a living. Amidst this shower of insults only the last but one is at all seriously intended. There is a single motive for attack, but the attack is made with any and every weapon that comes to hand.

This method can be disconcerting to one whose ideas of literary polemic are based on the modern conventions that an opponent must be treated fairly and courteously, that personalities should be avoided, and that anything not strictly relevant to the point at issue should be excluded from the argument. But these are quite irrelevant to the satire of Sauda's day—and indeed to that of most countries and most ages up to quite modern times.[8] Sauda enjoyed all and more of the license that is

---

[7] Shaikh Cānd, pp. 82–83.

[8] The comedies of Aristophanes in ancient Athens, the polemics of Luther against the Pope, and the attacks of Milton on Salmasius illustrate in different countries and different ages that this was so. Thus E. H. Gombrich and E. Kris, in *Caricature* (Harmondsworth, 1940), p. 8, write, "Some of the woodcuts against the Pope which he [Luther] ordered Cranach to make are today hardly reproducible . . . they are illustrated libels, debasing the opponent as crudely as possible." Milton in his polemics addresses Salmasius as "busy puppy," "you slug you," and "you silly loggerhead." Another work against an anonymous opponent has such passages as: "'Salmasius will make the trumpet blow a deadly blast.' You announce a new kind of harmony; for to the terrors of that loud-sounding instrument no symphony bears so close a resemblance as that which is produced by accumulated flatulency." And: "Take away, O ass! those panniers of airy nothingness; and speak, if you can, three words that have an affinity to common sense; if it be possible for the tumid pumpkin of your skull to discover for a moment anything like the reality of intellect." Milton, *The Prose Works*, ed. J. A. St. John (London, 1848), I, 15, 17, 232, 242, respectively.

still granted to the modern political cartoonist, who may ridicule the personal appearance and habits of his target, though these have nothing to do with the point of his cartoon. The atmosphere of his satires is the atmosphere of the open-air political meeting, where speaker and heckler are all the time trying to score off each other, and the audience thoroughly enjoys every hit that goes home, no matter how irrelevant it may be to the subject under discussion. In the last resort they are not deeply malicious, though that is not to say that they didn't hurt. They did, and they were meant to. Not all of them are personal attacks. Some are sheer clowning, like modern slapstick comedy. One is a ferocious attack on the intolerable heat of the Indian summer.[9] But most of them are, like the verse on Mir Zāhik, directed against people who are specifically named. And if modern taste has grown unaccustomed to this sort of thing, it had at any rate one great advantage, and Sauda did not have to complain, as Swift did, that "satire is a sort of glass wherein beholders do generally discover everybody's face but their own."[10]

One in which the victim is not named lampoons a rich man for his meanness.[11] Sauda introduces his subject:

ہے خدا کا یہ ایک ثمرۂ نور

جس سے روشن ہے آسماں کا تنور

کس زباں سے ہو اس کا شکر ادا

نعمتیں کیا کیا ان نے کیں پیدا

میوے ہیں باغ میں زمانے کے

واسطے کھانے اور کھلانے کے

---

9 *Kulliyāt*, pp. 138–140. *Kalām*, pp. 103–104.

10 Swift, *A Tale of a Tub* and *The Battle of the Books* (London, 1948), p. 172.

11 *Kulliyāt*, pp. 141–144. *Kalām*, pp. 145–151. Passages translated are *Kulliyāt*, p. 141, upper margin, line 20, to lower margin, line 1, and lower margin, lines 6–13; p. 142, centre, lines 7–8; and p. 144, upper margin, lines 1–4 and 19–20. *Kalām*, p. 145, lines 1–6; p. 146, lines 4–5; p. 149, line 15, to p. 150, line 11; p. 150, lines 16–17; and p. 151, lines 6–7.

فضل سے اس کے کچھ نہیں ہے کمی

ایک وہ کیا کرے جو ہم ہوں دنی

سنیو یا روکردوں ہوں میں اک نقل

جس کو باور کرے نہ ہرگز عقل

God filled the world with numberless good things,
That every man might eat and have to spare;
Men live in a vast orchard, fit for kings,
Laden with fruits enough for all to share.
The ordinary man like you and me
Gives thanks that He provides for us so well.
But what is He to do with such as he
Who figures in this tale I'm going to tell?

He goes on to relate how an acquaintance of his once went to visit a rich nobleman. Hardly had he been admitted when the sky clouded over and it began to look like rain. His host at once became extremely agitated, and forgetting even the normal courtesies with which a visitor is welcomed, began to ask anxiously whether he had brought a cloak or shawl which would give him some protection if it should happen to rain on his way home. He replied that he had not, for he had not expected rain when he left home. Shortly afterwards the rain began. The host went and fetched a waterproof and laid it before his visitor, exclaiming against his evil fortune and lamenting that one who had not visited him for so long should be put to all the inconvenience of going home in the pouring rain. The other, who knew that a man of his host's wealth and position could put him up for the night without the slightest inconvenience, was genuinely puzzled at his words and replied:

بولے یہ سادگی سے کیا ہے ضرور

بھیگتا جاؤں گا میں اتنی دور

رکھے خالق سلامت آپ کی ذات

نہ کھلے گا تو میں رہوں گا رات

Why all this agitation, my good lord?
What need to fancy me in such a plight?
I need not hasten home; be reassured.
If it keeps on like this I'll stay the night.

At these words his host turned pale, as though his guest had dealt him
a mortal blow, and in even greater agitation he spoke constantly about
the rain, sending his servants out repeatedly to look at the sky and see if
there were any sign of it clearing up. But when the steady downpour continued, he realised that other measures would be needed. For a while he
conversed with his visitor, dwelling at length, for his benefit, on a tradition of the Holy Prophet, which tells how he reproved one of his ac-
quaintances for visiting him too frequently; and when it was time for
dinner, he excused himself, saying that he had to go to the lavatory, but
telling his guest to send for the steward and order anything he wished.
The visitor accordingly did so. The steward came only after being repeatedly summoned, and having at length appeared, said that no food was
ready, that there were no provisions in the house, and that the tradesmen
had found it so difficult to extract payment for what they supplied that
they had all long since refused to deal with the house any longer. Then,
warming to his subject, he launched into a long and contemptuous account of his master's unspeakable meanness—this speech forms the bulk of
the satire—ending with an incident which was meant to convince his hearer
that he could not expect to receive the slightest hospitality at this house:

سارے گھر کا ہے اس کے چشم و چراغ   ایک فرزند یہ رکھے ہے الاغ

آشنا اپنے کی ضیافت کی   اُن نے اک روز یہ حاقت کی

اک رکابی طعام و دیگر بس   نہ ضیافت کہ جس میں ہو رنگ رس

یاد آیا اُسے چھٹی کا دودھ   تس پہ یوں پیش آیا یہ مردود

چاہتا تھا کرے یہ اس کو عاق
اورماں کو بھی اس کی دیوے طلاق

بارے لوگوں نے آکے سمجھایا
تب یہ جورڈ کے حق میں فرمایا

پتھر اس کے عوض تو کیوں نہ جنی
کاش پھنس مرتا واں یہ ناشدنی

یارو مجھ سے تو لا ولد بہتر
میرا بیٹا اور اس قدر ابتر

اس کا دادا بھی گرچہ تھا عیاش
اس سلیقے سے پر کرتے تھا معاش

جو کوئی اس کے گھر میں نوکر تھا
رات کو اس پہ یہ مقرر تھا

پھرتا دہ ٹکڑے مانگتا گھر گھر
لاتا آفتا کے آگے جھولی بھر

اچھے چن چن کے آپ کھاتے تھے
برے تنخواہ میں لگاتے تھے

پیدا کر گئے تھے اس طرح اجداد
سو یہ بدبخت نے ہے یوں برباد

میں تو آپ ہی کو جانتا تھا فضول
پر یہ مجھ سے بھی نکلا نامعقول

گرے پیسے یہ سب اڑا دے گا
اینٹوں تک بچ بچ کھا دے گا

تھی بزرگوں کی اپنے تو یہ چال
کرتی ہیں یاں ضیافتیں پامال

خوب۔ جو کچھ اٹھا خزینے سے
لواتا لیق کے مہینے سے

This fellow has a son, a stupid boy,
But none the less his father's pride and joy.
Do you know what he did, the silly fellow?
One day, feeling particularly mellow,
He asked a friend to lunch—'twas nothing much—
A plate of greens and lentils, or some such.

You should have seen his father's agitation.
You'd think his son had feasted half the nation.
He swore he'd cut him off without a shilling;
Divorce his mother too: *he'd* not be willing
To call her wife who'd borne a son so monstrous!
Then, less infuriated and more pompous,
He called her and proceeded to hold forth:
"O would that you had never given birth!
Or else brought forth a stone! Or else miscarried!
Better by far if I had never married.
Better by far die childless than have one
So utterly unworthy for a son!
His grandsire was a great voluptuary.
But still, he was no spendthrift—no, not he!
He planned his operations like a soldier
And sent his servants, haversack on shoulder,
To beg from door to door for scraps of food,
And bring them back to him; anything good
He'd pick out for himself. Then he would say
"The rest is yours"—and dock it from their pay.
That's how our family fortunes were amassed,
And was it all for this, that he at last
Should leave us naked 'gainst the winter's blast?
I thought *myself* extravagant, but he
In reckless spending outdoes even me.
He'll rapidly exhaust our buried hoards,
Pull down the house, and sell the bricks and boards.
And all for senseless prodigality!
Well, since the thing is done, I'll have to see
Where lies the true responsibility.
His tutor should have taught the boy more sense,
So he shall pay the bill . . ."

The steward concluded by saying that the visitor would get nothing here,
but that his own humble dwelling was not far away and he would be very
welcome to dine there if he wished. The visitor thanked him and returned

home, and the next day came and related the whole story to Sauda, who concludes:

On such a perfect nobleman, I say,
May God send down His curses night and day.

Another satire is on the gluttony of Mir Zāhik.[12] It depicts a number of separate scenes rather than telling a connected story.

He only has to hear a saucepan rattle,
And like a soldier digging in for battle,
He'll take up his position by the door.
Nothing can shift him then: that god of war,
Rustam himself, might rise up from the tomb
And try his strength against him. He'd stand firm.
He'd fight to the last breath and never yield
Until his corpse was carried from the field.

It is enough to catch a whiff of food cooking for him to fly to the place and sit there beating his head with both hands in an agony of impatience and looking like a great fly which sits on the food washing its face with its front legs. When food is set before him, he rushes at it as a soldier

---

[12] *Kulliyāt*, pp. 144–147. *Kalām*, pp. 156–161. Passages translated are *Kulliyāt*, p. 144, centre, lines 4–5, and p. 145, upper margin, lines 11–18. *Kalām*, p. 157, lines 2–3; p. 158, lines 2–4; other verses not included in *Kalām*.

rushes to loot a house, feverishly gathering everything up in case anyone
should come and disturb him before he can finish, and his hands flash back
and forth between the plate and his mouth as nimbly as those of a fencer
hard pressed by a determined opponent. So obsessed is he by the thought
of food that it dominates his mind even when he is alone with his wife.
He

جو رُوا اپنی پہ جب کرے ہے نظر

اس سے کہتا ہے تب یہ گیدی خر

کچھ ترے پاس اے حمیدہ ہے

تیری انگیا میں گاؤ دیدہ ہے

یا چھپائے ہیں تو نے قُرصِ پنیر

سچ ہی کہہ در نہ ہوں گا میں دلگیر

کجے خوشتک پہ ہاتھ پھیراؤ جان

کس طرح کی یہ پنجہ کش ہے نان

Fixes his lady's bodice with a stare,
"Tell me," he asks, "What have you got in there?
Are they two loaves? Or two delicious cheeses?"
Or, if his hand should stray into her breeches,
"What's this I feel," he cries, "So soft and warm?
Newly-baked bread?[13] If so 'twould do no harm
To let me eat it. Why do you hide it from me?"

Another satire is directed against an ignorant *hakīm*,[14] or one who
practises the traditional Greek system of medicine as developed by the
Arabs—a system still widely prevalent in all countries which have a large

---

[13] Saudā uses the word *panjakash*. This was a kind of bread bearing the marks of five fingers.
[14] *Kulliyāt*, pp. 151–153. *Kalām*, pp. 137–141. Passages translated are *Kulliyāt*, p. 151,
lower margin, lines 3–6 and 16–20; p. 152, centre, lines 5–9; and p. 153, upper margin,
lines 7–8. *Kalām*, p. 137, lines 1–2, 5–7, and 10–15; p. 141, lines 3–4.

Muslim population. In this case Sauda launches his attack without any general preamble:

صدر کے بازار میں ہے اک دبنگ

عارِ اطبّاؤ طبابت کا ننگ

شکل ہے شیطان کی اور غوث نام

جگ میں ہلاکو کا ہے قائم مقام

قاتلِ ہندو و مسلماں ہے وہ

نسخہ نہ لکھتا کبھو وہ بد سرشت

بھرتے نہ انساں سے دوزخ بہشت

جب سے مریضوں کو دے ہے دوا

کام میں ہے مرگ معطّل شفا

There's a hakīm, the mention of whose name
Makes every good physician blush with shame.
Down in the main bazaar you'll find his house;
He looks like Satan, yet his name is Ghaus.[15]
Since he took up his practice people say
Death works while Healing takes a holiday.
None whom he treated ever yet got well;
His patients populate both Heaven and Hell.
Worthy successor to Halāku Khān,[16]
He massacres Hindu and Musalman.

[15] Ghauṣ is a title of a Muslim saint.
[16] Halākū Khān was the grandson of Chingīz, or Jenghiz, Khān, and commander of the Mongol hordes which overran the Muslim 'Abbāsid Empire. When he took Baghdad, he ordered a general massacre of the population of the city and of the surrounding country.

ہو کے کسل مند جو دہ بے حیا
اپنے تئیں آپ کرے ہے دوا
مردہ شو، مولودی و تابوت گر
گھیرتے ہیں آن کے سب اُس کا گھر
دیں ہیں دُہائی وہ بصد قیل و قال
ان میں سے ہر ایک کرے ہے سوال
اپنی دوا آپ تو ظالم نہ کر
میرے کس و کو، کی طرف کر نظر
خوب جو کرتا ہے تو آپ ہی دوا
اور کوئی آپ سا مجھ کو بتا
روزی سے خاطر ہو مری تاکہ جمع
بھیجوں تری گور پہ گل اور شمع

This idiot once felt slightly indisposed;
He dosed himself with his own preparations.
Corpse-washers, mourners, coffin-makers, all
Thronged round his door with earnest supplications:
"You'll kill yourself! How can you be so cruel?
Have pity on our wives and families!
How shall we earn our bread when you are gone?
We need you more than you can realise—
Well, if you must then, tell us someone who
Makes out the same prescriptions as you do,
And we will promise (given what we crave)
Always to keep fresh flowers on your grave."

The poem goes on to describe how a man went to consult him and was given a prescription to take to the druggist to be made up. The druggist took one look at it, and asked the man to describe the hakīm who had given him it. From the description he at once recognised that it must be Ghaus, whereupon he launched into a long diatribe against him (which takes up the rest of the poem), cursing him heartily and quoting numerous instances of his complete incompetence. Sauda concludes:

تھاغرض اس نقل ــــ سے یہ مّدعا

تاکہ تو ایسے کی نہ کھاوے دوا

The moral is, make this a golden rule:
Don't go for treatment to this bloody fool.[17]

Ignorant, self-important frauds like hakīm Ghaus are the target of a great number of satires. One of Sauda's favourite butts was a "learned" Kashmiri named Nudrat. This man did his best to acquire a reputation for virtue, learning, and poetry alike; but he seems in fact—if Sauda is to be believed—to have been a close spiritual kinsman of

. . . the peerless paper lord, Lord Peter,
Who broke the laws of God, and man, and metre.

There is perhaps no other figure whom Sauda attacks so often and so mercilessly in his satires, sometimes in terms which shock even one accustomed to his coarseness. But the best of them is less crude, and concentrates on exposing Nudrat's pretensions to be a great scholar and poet:

فاضلوں کی تو بزم میں ہوتے ہو جاکے شعر خواں

شاعروں پاس آپ کہتے ہو نحو و صرف داں

دولوں ہوں جمع جس جگہ پھر پھر تھیں واں جگہ کہاں

بولو جو داں کچھ آن کرسب کہیں تم کو مہرباں

گھوڑے کو دو دو نہ دو لگام منہ کو تنگ لگام دو

---

[17] The whole tone of this satire reminds one of Robert Burns' *Death and Doctor Hornbrook*.

Where scholars are assembled, you're a poet;
Where poets gather, a grammarian.
Both claims are false, but how are they to know it?
They can't catch Nudrat! He's too spry for them!
But what when both are met? If you speak there,
These are the words you'll very quickly hear:
  Give your old nag full rein, but curb your tongue! [18]

About satires like these Sauda might well have given his readers the same advice as Rabelais gave his: "You . . . may not too easily conclude that they treat of nothing but mockery, fooling, and pleasant fiction . . . You must open this book and carefully weigh up its contents. You will discover then that the drug within is far more valuable than the box promised." [19] What in essence his satires all assert is that it is not too difficult to fulfil your elementary obligations to your fellowmen and to society at large, and that if you fail in them, he has the right to tell you so plainly and to make you smart for it. This down-to-earth approach engages one's sympathies much more than a high moral tone would do. But in any case Sauda did not like the high moral tone. He knew that it was all too often the mark of people who could see failings only in other people, and never in themselves; and he left no one in any doubt about what he thought of such people: [20]

Pious severely censures me, I hear,
On evidence Abstemious supplied him.
Sauda will not resent that, never fear,
But I would just respectfully remind him:
  That which Abstemious saw fit to do
  For me, he very well may do for you.

I never understood what prompts a man
To ferret out the vices of his neighbours.

---

[18] *Kulliyāt*, p. 357, upper margin, lines 12–16. *Kalām*, p. 196, line 13, p. 197, line 2. The last line is a refrain that follows each of the 15 verses.
[19] *Gargantua and Pantagruel*, trans. J. M. Cohen (Harmondsworth, 1955), pp. 37–38.
[20] *Kulliyāt*, p. 355. *Kalām*, pp. 211–212. The translation represents a considerable abridgement of the original, but draws upon most of the stanzas.

Surely a decent human being can
Find a much better object for his labours.
    The rosary was meant for other things
    Than counting up a fellow-creature's sins.

Suppose my every sin a deadly one—
Does that stop *you* living a life of piety?
I sin in my own way, involving none:
Does that in any way corrupt society?
    Does it require the strictures of the pious?
    Ask any normal person free from bias.

I wish this tribe would learn another trade;
But meanwhile let them heed this friendly warning:
I cannot spy; that's not the way I'm made:
I go to bed at night and sleep till morning.
    And yet I also know a thing or two;
    You'd best leave me alone: be off with you!

In another short poem he tells how he was approached by an acquaintance who warned him not to make any man his friend, because there are no friends who prove true once they are put to the test. Sauda records his words and then writes:

یہ سن کے اس سے کہا مسکرا کے ہم نے دانے
شکایت اتنی کسو کی کوئی بیاں نہ کرے
بھلے برے کے تجھے امتحان سے کیا کام
یہ شکر کر جو کوئی تجھ کو امتحاں نہ کرے

I heard him out; then, smiling, said to him:
"It is not good to speak so ill of men.
Who made *you* judge of others? You had best
Thank God that no one puts *you* to the test."[21]

---

[21] *Kulliyāt*, p. 315, centre. *Kalām*, p. 68. The lines translated are *Kulliyāt*, p. 315, centre, lines 13–14. *Kalām*, p. 68, lines 8–9.

F

The attitude these poems express helps to explain why Sauda was so popular in his day, when people saw and condemned the degeneracy all round them, and wanted to see their feelings expressed, but were too conscious of their own human failings to sympathise with the conventional moralists. The poems also help to correct a false picture of Sauda to which Urdu critics of the Victorian age gave currency and which is still quite commonly presented. This picture represents him as a proud, irascible man, very conscious of his powers as a satirist and always ready to use them at once against anyone who did anything to upset him. This idea of him arises from a failure to understand the conventions of eighteenth-century satire. What has already been said on this point is not special pleading for Sauda. The few satirical poems of Mir and Mir Hasan are in the same convention as his—a fact these critics seem to have overlooked, for none of them draws similar conclusions about their character. The truth is that no such conclusions can legimately be drawn, either about them or about Sauda. Mir Hasan, for example, has always been thought of as a man of gentle and courteous disposition; his contemporaries go out of their way to praise these qualities in him, and no subsequent writer has seen any reason to question their testimony. Yet manuscripts of his verse include a satire written in reply to Sauda's attack on his father, Mir Zāhik, and couched in terms so scurrilous that modern editors do not venture to print it as it stands.[22] The outrageous charges made in verse of this kind have nothing to do with the writer's serious estimate of his adversary. One of Mir Hasan's works is a short account of the Urdu poets,[23] and in it he gives high praise to Sauda, adding in passing that he was a frequent visitor at Sauda's house, and was always treated with kindness and affection.

In Mir's case the evidence is even more substantial. The high regard in which Mir and Sauda held each other is well known. Yet they satirised each other in terms which, if taken at their face value, would lead to quite the opposite conclusion. For example, Sauda was very fond of dogs, and Mir wrote a satire attacking him for this.[24] He used many sticks to beat him with, including the argument that Islam regards the dog as an

---

[22] An expurgated extract is quoted in Maḥmūd Fārūqī, *Mīr Ḥasan aur Khāndān ke dūsre shu'arā* (Lahore, 1956), pp. 42–43.
[23] Mīr Ḥasan, *Taẕkira i Shu'arā i Urdū*, quoted in Shaikh Cānd, *Saudā*, p. 84.
[24] *Kulliyāt i Mīr*, ed. 'Abdul Bārī Āsī (Lucknow, 1941), p. 823.

unclean animal, and the suggestion that Sauda's ostentatious love of dogs is nothing but self-advertisement, necessary because he had no other qualities that would attract anyone's attention. Whether Mir really attached any weight to the views of orthodox Islam on the dog is questionable, for he himself had once kept one.[25] And it is quite certain that Mir did not really think that Sauda had any need to advertise himself, for we know that Mir fully shared the current opinion of him as one of the greatest poets of his day. The whole piece is in lighthearted vein, and probably means only that Mir—in common, no doubt, with many others —thought the attention which Sauda devoted to his dogs extravagant, a little ostentatious, and rather ridiculous.

Sauda replied to Mir's attack in a short piece of about the same length.[26] He takes the argument about the attitude of Islam at its face value and replies that he fully accepts that dogs are unclean animals; but after being in contact with them, one only has to bathe to be clean again. He argues that there is therefore no harm in keeping dogs, and goes on to say that there is one dog, however, which a man should on no account cherish, and that is the dog of his own baser impulses. Love for this dog so contaminates a man that no amount of bathing will make him clean. Let those who want to teach others the way they should live preach against all attachment to this dog; and above all let them see to it first that they themselves are free from such attachment—a plain suggestion to Mir that if he is so concerned with godly living, he should first concentrate on correcting his own faults. The whole thing amounts to a mild rebuke to Mir—not perhaps wholly undeserved—for being too ready to tell others what they ought and ought not to do.

Mir is the target of another short satire[27] in which Sauda says that one of the best calligraphers of his day came to him complaining bitterly that Mir was ruining his reputation for him. "How so?" asked Sauda. The man replied that Mir brought him verses of the classical poets to write out, but insisted on "improving" them. When other people saw them, not knowing that Mir was responsible for the changes, they blamed them on the carelessness of the calligrapher. Here again, the serious intention

---

[25] He preferred cats, however, and this too is made the occasion for a hit at Saudā: "Now if he had kept cats, then I would own / That he had shown himself a man of sense."
[26] *Kulliyāt*, p. 363, lower margin to p. 364. *Kalām*, pp. 207–208.
[27] *Kulliyāt*, p. 316. *Kalām*, p. 170.

is simply to take a hit at Mir for the readiness with which he passes literary judgements, both on the poetry of his own day and on that of the past.

In short, in such exchanges there is on both sides a point of criticism quite seriously intended, but it is accompanied by a good deal more which is not. Serious judgements were another matter. Mir wrote of Sauda as "Pre-eminent among the poets of India . . . and worthy to be called the poet laureate of Urdu."[28] One of the most famous anecdotes about him tells how, when he was asked to name the great poets of his day, he replied without hesitation, "First Sauda; secondly, myself" (adding after a pause that a third poet, Mir Dard, was "half a poet").[29] The names of the two poets—"Mir and Mirza," as their contemporaries called them— were regularly linked together, and they themselves must have approved of the judgement this implies, for they use the phrase in their own writings.[30] There is an anecdote which shows that Sauda did not consider anyone and everyone entitled to attack Mir.[31] He was present on one occasion at a gathering where he was approached by a self-styled poet named Khāksār,[32] who asked him to compose an extempore satire on Mir. To his delight, Sauda agreed to his request. A couplet ostensibly ridiculing Mir's personal appearance was greeted with roars of laughter in which Khāksār joined until, when the laughter showed no sign of dying down, it dawned upon him that the verse described not Mir but himself.

All this shows that one poet might lampoon another in the most extravagant terms without this necessarily implying any real feeling of enmity between them. It does not, of course, mean that such enmity never existed between the satirist and his victim. Probably Sauda cordially detested most of those whom he attacked by name. But even then it is important, before forming conclusions, to distinguish the essential theme of the satire from the rest and to assess its underlying tone.

That Sauda was not at all the arrogant, touchy, waspish person that some have made him out to be is well illustrated by an incident which

---

[28] Mīr, Nikāt ush Shu'arā, ed. Ḥabīb ur Raḥmān Khān Shīrvānī (Aurangābād, n.d.), pp. 32–33.
[29] Āzād, Āb i Ḥayāt, p. 216.
[30] Cf., for example, Mīr, Kulliyāt, p. 826, line 11; and Sauda, Kulliyāt, p. 155, lower margin, lines 12–13.
[31] Shaikh Cānd, Saudā, pp. 78–79.
[32] Khāksār means humble, but the name was hardly an apt one; he thought himself a far better poet than Mīr, and had conferred upon himself the title of King of Poets.

occurred during the last period of his life in Lucknow.[33] There was a man named Ashraf Ali Khān who had spent fifteen years in compiling a selection of Persian verse taken from the works of the great poets. When he had completed it, he took it to Fākhir Makīn, who enjoyed the reputation of being the best Persian poet of the day, and asked if he would consent to look over it. Fākhir Makīn made all sorts of difficulties, but in the end took the selection and began to look through it. Ashraf Ali Khān later heard to his consternation that he was crossing out the verses of even the greatest poets, on the ground that they were meaningless, and was making drastic alterations in others. He at once went to him, and having after much persuasion got the selection returned, went with it to Sauda. He told him of all that had happened, and of how distressed he felt at what Fākhir Makīn had done, and in the end asked Sauda to undertake the revision of the selection. Sauda replied that his knowledge of Persian was not adequate to the task; he felt sure, he said, that a scholar like Fākhir Makīn·must have good reason for what he had done; if Ashraf Ali Khān could not bring himself to accept Fākhir Makīn's corrections, he should approach other eminent Persian scholars, and named five whom he considered competent to undertake the task. Ashraf Ali Khān pointed out in reply that Fākhir Makīn held the very poorest opinion of those whom Sauda had named, and again asked Sauda himself to revise his selection. At length Sauda reluctantly agreed. When he began to examine the selection, he was astonished to find what Fākhir Makīn had done. The verses of great classical poets had been mutilated beyond recognition. Sauda then wrote a pamphlet which he entitled "Ibrat ul Ghāfilīn,'' or A Warning to the Heedless. In it he dealt with all the mistakes that Fākhir Makīn had committed in making his so-called corrections, and then went on to a detailed examination of all the mistakes in Fākhir Makīn's own Persian verse.

Fākhir Makīn heard of this with alarm, and at once took steps to prevent the thing becoming public knowledge. He first sent one of his best pupils, a man with some reputation as a Persian scholar in his own right, to dispute some of the points Sauda had made, but Sauda completely refuted all his arguments. He then took more desperate steps. He sent a gang of young bloods to compel Sauda under threat of violence to accompany them to Fākhir Makīn's house and settle the whole matter with him

33 Āzād, *Āb i Ḥayāt*, pp. 165–168.

there and then. Sauda had no alternative but to submit. On the way there they tried to humiliate him in public by provoking a clash with him, and the dispute was at its height when, fortunately for Sauda, the retinue of Āsaf ud Daula's brother Sa'ādat Ali Khān passed that way. Having ascertained what was happening, he compelled the men to release Sauda, and seating him beside him on his own elephant, went directly to Āsaf ud Daula. He was taking his meal at the time, but Sa'ādat Ali Khān went straight in to him and related the whole incident, expressing his regret that the ruler of Oudh apparently could not prevent such a thing happening even in the streets of his own capital. Āsaf ud Daula was very concerned. He at once came out, and having heard a more detailed account of what had happened, ordered that the rowdies should be expelled from the city and the quarter where they lived razed to the ground, while Fākhir Makīn was to be commanded to appear at once at court, just as he was. It was Sauda who interceded for his adversary, saying that the help already given him was sufficient protection, and that what was after all in origin a literary dispute should be settled by literary means. Āsaf ud Daula deferred to his wishes and Sauda was allowed to go home, escorted as a precaution by some of the Navvāb's own soldiers.

The next day Āsaf ud Daula rebuked Fākhir Makīn sharply before the whole court, and told him in conclusion: "If you possess the poetic talent you claim, compose a verse against Sauda here and now in his presence." Fākhir Makīn replied, "That is more than I can do." "Yes," said the Navvāb, "but you could set these devils on Sauda and let them drag him from his house into the street and humiliate him. *That* was not more than you could do." He then turned to Sauda and indicated that he should speak. Sauda, never at a loss, at once recited a *rubāi* in Persian, which may be freely translated:

The learned class in every land reveres thy name;
O crown of poetry, who has not heard thy fame?
Three errors in two lines! Pray you correct them, friend;
For "class" read "ass"; for "crown" read "clown"; for "fame"
read "shame."

The story is interesting not only because it shows Sauda to have been a modest man, capable of exercising restraint and tolerance even under great provocation, but because it also shows the great honour and respect in which a good patron was expected to hold a great poet.

Most of Sauda's satires are personal, in the sense that they attack particular people, often by name. But in some of them personal merges with social satire, because it is public figures who are under attack. And in addition to these there are others which directly satirise social institutions. In his social, as in his personal, satire Sauda spoke from a standpoint very close to that of the ordinary man. He stood by the medieval ideals of social life, and was not prepared to abandon them, no matter how generally they had ceased to be observed in his own day. He attributed the decay of the Empire to the selfish neglect by men of all classes of the duties to society appropriate to their station; and he therefore saw the remedy in himself doing his duty to society according to his lights, and in persuading or shaming others into doing theirs. As a satirist, he played his part by attacking any departure from the social ideals in which he believed. Like most men of his age, he looked for inspiration to the past, or more accurately, to an unconsciously idealised part, which in fact represented his aspirations for the future. Many passages show how this idealised memory sustained him, so that while the contemporary scene often aroused his anger and sorrow, he did not succumb to pessimism.

In demanding, so to speak, that his social ideals be realised, he did not feel that he was demanding the impossible, for he believed that they had already been realised once before—and only a generation or two before his time. Thus one of his satires contrasts the Delhi of former times with that of his own day.[34] There was a time, he says, when the administration was firm, vigorous, and incorruptible, and the people of the city lived a good life in peace and prosperity, assured that their lives and property were secure. But today the city swarms with thieves and robbers, who go unpunished because the police are in league with them; the danger of assault is always present, so that men go out in the evening to a mushāira fully armed, as though they were going out to battle. Elsewhere he describes the age as one in which

سنتا ہمیں ہے درد رعیت کا بادشاہ

The king no longer heeds his subjects' cry.[35]

---

[34] *Kulliyāt*, pp. 136–138. *Kalām*, pp. 130–133.
[35] *Kulliyāt*, p. 338, centre, line 14. (Not included in *Kalām*.)

And in another place he exclaims:

See the perverted justice of this age!
The wolves roam free: the shepherds are in chains.[36]

Sauda raised his voice against all these social ills, and the more effectively because his own conscience was clear. The standards he set for
himself were no less exacting than those he set for others who had a
different part to play in society, and his writings show how seriously he
took the responsibilities of his calling. They also show his confidence that
he was fulfilling them adequately, and reflect the pride and pleasure
which this gave him. He knew that in his age none could surpass him, and
only one—Mir—could equal him, and then only because Mir's superiority
in his own particular field matched his own pre-eminence in his. He
never rested content with what he had achieved, but always tried to perfect still further his mastery of his craft, and to keep himself always ready
to learn. He wrote towards the end of his life[37] that in the forty or more
years since he had made his name as a poet, he had tried all the time to
learn from the great poets of the past as a pupil does from his master, had
never withheld the praise that is the due of good poetry, even though it
was the work of his enemies, and that he still does not regard his own
poetry as incapable of improvement, and will continue as always to
listen attentively to criticism and to accept it where he feels it to be just,
even should the critic be the rawest and most unpractised of poets.

This receptiveness served him well. The mastery of his craft revealed
by his poetry is remarkable, particularly when one considers that Urdu
poetry in northern India was in its infancy when he and Mir entered the
field. He handles with ease the complex metres and figures of rhetoric.
His range of vocabulary is wide, and he never seems to be at a loss for
words, while at the same time he uses his vocabulary with economy,
giving the fullest expression to what he wants to say without wasting any

---

[36] *Kulliyāt*, p. 308, centre, line 6. *Kalām*, p. 107, line 3.
[37] Shaikh Cānd, *Saudā*, p. 75.

words. He writes on the most varied themes, particularly in his satires, and uses with uniform ease the range of vocabulary appropriate to each. His satires also show a wide and varied experience of life, a keen power of observation, and an impressive familiarity with the arts and sciences of his day, so that when he lampoons an ignorant hakīm or a self-styled scholar, he can carry the attack into his opponent's own territory. For all these reasons he speaks with the vigorous assurance of one who knows that his own position is unchallengeable. If he enjoyed a life of comfort and even luxury, he regarded this as no more than what was due to him as one of the two greatest poets of the age, each of whom, moreover, had in his own field raised Urdu poetry to a level never before attained. He was satisfied with his own part in the life of his age; he did not feel tempted, as a weaker man might have done, to blind himself to the reality of what he saw around him in case he should be compelled to face also the reality about himself; and he knew he had no need to protect himself from the possibility of counterattack by holding back in his denunciation of the vices and shortcomings of others.

Sauda was never overawed by anyone. Men with a countrywide reputation were attacked by name in his satires. The great religious leader Shāh Vali Ullāh is the subject of one of them.[38] Zābita Khān, the Rohilla chieftain, son of a distinguished father, Najīb ud Daula, who from Delhi had ruled what was left of the Empire with great ability for seven years after the momentous events of 1761, is satirised for his cowardice.[39] One full-length satire is a devastating exposure of Shīdi Faulād Khān, kotvāl of Delhi.[40] The duties of the kotvāl of a city correspond very roughly to those of a modern chief of police, though his powers and responsibilities were in many respects much wider. Faulād Khān, however, instead of protecting the property of the citizens of Delhi, was in league with the thieves and shared with them the proceeds of their activities.

In other satires he speaks out against evils too widespread to be attacked through satire against individuals. One pictures the chaos and inefficiency of the imperial army,[41] in which every man tries to evade his obligations and in which the skill, equipment, and courage without which no army

[38] Cf. ibid., p. 86. The poem is given in Kulliyāt, p. 108, where, however, no name is mentioned. Some manuscripts describe this as a satire on Shāh Vali Ullāh.

[39] Kulliyāt, p. 315.

[40] Kulliyāt, pp. 136–138. Kalām, pp. 130–133.

[41] Kulliyāt, pp. 113–115. Kalām, pp. 121–125.

can give a good account of itself in war are all wanting. Finally there are
two satires which give so comprehensive a view of the society of his day
that they are worth summarising at some length. The first[42] tells how a
man approached Sauda and asked him whether he could tell him of any
way to earn his living in Hindustan today. Sauda replied:

Better to keep silent than try to answer such a question, for even the
tongues of angels cannot do justice to the answer. There are many professions which you could adopt, but let us see what difficulties will beset
you in each of them these days. You could buy a horse and offer yourself for service in some noble's army. But never in this world will you
see your pay, and you will rarely have both sword and shield by you, for
you must pawn one or the other to buy fodder for your horse; and
unless the moneylender is kind to you, you or your wife must go
hungry, for you will not get enough to feed you both. You could
minister to the needs of the faithful in a mosque, but you would find
asses tethered there and men young and old sitting there idle and unwilling to be disturbed. Let the muezzin give the call to prayer and
they will stop his mouth, for no one cares for Islam these days . . . You
could become the courtier of some great man, but your life would not
be worth living. If he does not feel like sleeping at night, you too must
wake with him, though you are ready to drop, and until he feels inclined to dine, you may not, though you are faint with hunger and your
belly is rumbling. Or you could become his physician; but if you did,
your life would be passed in constant apprehension, for should the
Navvāb sneeze, he will glare at you as though you ought to have given
him a sword and buckler to keep off the cold wind. You will live
through torture as you watch him feed. He will stuff himself with
sweet melon and cream and then fish, and then cow's tongue, and,
with it all, fancy breads of all kinds; and if at any stage he feels the
slightest pain in his stomach, then you, you ignorant fool, are to blame,
though you were Bū Ali Sīna himself.[43] Why not become a merchant
then? But if you do, you must reckon with the possibility that the
wares you buy in Ispahan will not find a market in Hindustan,[44] and you

---

[42] *Kulliyāt*, pp. 111–113. *Kalām*, pp. 108–113.
[43] One of the greatest medieval authorities on medicine, known in Europe as Avicenna (d. 1037).
[44] The term here means northern India only.

will have to take them as far afield as the Deccan. You never know in the morning whether you will ever reach your destination for the day,[45] and your evenings will be passed in anxious reckonings of gain and loss. When you take your wares to some great man, you will be astonished at the way he speaks to you, and an observer, noting the price you are compelled to accept, would conclude that you are suspected of selling stolen property. Moreover, you will not get your money right away, but must go to the great man's agent for it, and though you show him authorisation to pay, he will tell you that he has not got the money to do so. So back you must go to his master, only to be told, "Take your goods back; my steward says they are too dear." But when you go for them, they are not to be found. So you lose both the goods and their price, and you must stand outside the great man's fortress hoping to waylay him as he comes out in his palanquin and lay your petition for redress before him. And do not think you can make a living from the land, for only if the rains are good can you survive, and you pass your days in dread of drought or floods . . . But perhaps you have thought of becoming a poet, for are not poets said to enjoy freedom from all care ? You will find it is not so. No one is such a prey to worry as he. He cannot even concentrate on his Id prayer,[46] for he is trying all the time to compose an ode to his patron. No sooner is it rumoured that the noble lord has fertilised his lady's womb than he must rack his brains for a chronogram,[47] ready for the birth of the child, and if she should miscarry, he must write such an elegy on the abortion that no one ever after will want to read those on Imām Husain.[48] If you think of becoming a teacher, bear this in mind, that men able to teach the greatest works of Persian literature today get

[45] An allusion to the robber-infested roads.

[46] 'Id is the day which marks the end of the month-long fast of Ramẓān. It is a day of great rejoicing. Congregational prayers are said on a big open space, since the mosques cannot contain the huge crowds.

[47] In the Arabic alphabet, adopted by Urdū speakers—as by most other peoples who embraced Islām—for the writing of their own language, every letter stands for a particular number. The dates of important events were marked by chronograms, or verses in which would be included a word or phrase made up of letters whose numerical value when totalled would give the date required.

[48] The grandson of the Prophet, who, with a band of his companions, was martyred at Karbala, in Iraq. The *marsiya*, or elegy, is one of the major forms of Urdū verse, and early became associated with the theme of Husain's martyrdom; it developed to its highest point after the close of our period.

paid no more than what will give them a cup of cheap lentils and two rounds of coarse bread to dine on. Calligraphers could once command great honours. But nobody appreciates their art these days, and even the greatest masters of the art must sit in the open street, soliciting work and selling their talents for a song. . . . Perhaps, then, in the end you will forsake all wordly professions and, taking no thought for the morrow, repose your trust in God. But do you know what will happen then? Your wife will think you a lazy good-for-nothing; your son will despise you; your daughter will think you have gone mad. And when your children begin to die of hunger, you must run after every great man's carriage and ask for the charity that your holiness deserves. And perhaps you may get a few coppers and a little chit saying, "This man merits your charity; he is a truly religious man and is learned in religious lore." In short, you will not find in Hindustan any means of earning a decent living. Peace and plenty have become empty words in this world. Some say that we shall know them in the next, but who can persuade himself that it is so? For my part, I think it only wishful thinking. Here, there is nothing but the struggle to live; there, nothing but the tumult of Judgement Day. Peace and plenty is an empty recollection: you will not find it either on earth or in heaven.

The second satire[49] tells how Sauda was approached by a person who asked him, "Why do you spend your days roaming aimlessly about? Why don't you buy a horse and ask for employment in some noble's army?" "Employment?" Sauda replied.

And can you tell me how it is sold these days? By the bushel or by the pound? Don't you know that only the wealthy and great can offer—or rather, *could* offer—employment? But how can they do so today? They can no longer realise the revenue from their estates. For years now the land has been a prey to lawless and rebellious men. Even the person supposed to be lord and master of twenty-two provinces no longer controls even the district of Aligarh.[50] All the real power belongs to lawless men. The great lords are helpless and impoverished. Their

---

[49] *Kulliyāt*, pp. 361–363. *Kalām*, pp. 114–120.
[50] A direct reference to the Emperor Shāh 'Ālam. The statement was literally true. Aligarh is only 80 miles south of Delhi.

peasants raise two crops a year, but their lords see nothing of either, and their agents on the spot are virtual prisoners in the peasants' hands, like a peasant kept in his creditor's house until he can pay his debt. So complete is the collapse of all order and administration that though the peasant reaps a harvest of gold, his lord does not see so much as a wisp of straw. How then can the lord keep the armed force he should? How can he pay the soldiers who should go before him when he goes out, or the horsemen who should ride behind him? They have fallen so low now that but for the beating of the drums to announce their coming, no one would know them for nobles. All their thought is of how to reduce their expenses, and if they do so much further, then even the drummers will be dismissed, and the palanquin-bearers who carry him —nay, the Navvāb himself sitting inside—will have to beat the drums themselves. But still they cling to their hollow greatness, though they have long forgotten how a noble should conduct himself, whether in peace or war. All their concern is to cling to their two peacock-feather fans and their robe of fur. Those who know the responsibilities of a noble and could discharge them have long since tested out the way things are run here and have withdrawn to their own dominions, leaving the Empire to its fate.[51] And now our all-wise nobles who are left have seen the conditions of the age and washed their hands of everything. They sit in their mansions surrounded by a little group of courtier-companions, with a man to fan them, and betel and spittoon before them, and if anyone should come to visit them, it all depends upon their mood whether they will see him or not. If the noble lord deigns to admit him and converse with him, let not his visitor be so rash as to speak of public affairs. "Brother!" he will be told, "for God's sake speak of other things!"

The ministers of the Empire have been summoned for consultation. See how they consult for the welfare of the state. The Imperial Paymaster is thinking up some scheme to stay at home doing nothing and still draw his pay, while the Chief Minister has his eyes on the silver knobs on the poles of the royal tent, and is calculating how much they will fetch in the market. They are all of them strangers to any sense of

---

[51] A reference to such men as the governors of the Deccan and of Oudh, who established their provinces as virtually independent states. Saudā blames the hopeless incompetence of the Emperor and of those who rule by his favour for this state of affairs.

shame. They spend their time in gambling and only come when summoned. A lifetime of their counsel has resulted only in this, that men who once lived in well-built houses now inhabit mud huts. Yet each of them is in his own estimation a veritable paragon. If war comes they creep out of their fortresses just long enough to draw up an army which, you may depend on it, will turn and run from every battle, soldiers who quake with fear even when they see the barber take out his razor to shave them, horsemen who fall out of their beds at night even at the dream of a horse rearing under them.

The royal treasury is empty: nothing comes in from the crown lands; the state of the Office of Salaries defies description. Soldiers, clerks, all alike are without employment. Documents authorising payment to the bearer are so much waste paper: the pharmacist tears them up to wrap his medicines in. Men who once held jāgīrs or posts paid from the royal treasury are looking for jobs as village watchmen. Their sword and shield have long since gone to the pavnshop, and when they next come out, it will be with a beggar's staff and bowl. Words cannot describe how some of these once great ones live. Their wardrobe has ended up at the rag merchant's. If the cow's tongue which comes out of their oven could speak, it would say, "Before my master could buy me, he had to do without three meals and sell his sable robe for next to nothing." Ask the steward who has charge of his beasts and cattle; he will tell you that there is neither grain nor fodder for them to eat and their condition is pitiable. The noble lord boasts of his elephants, but go to look at them and you will find an old blind she and a one-eyed bull, both without any hope of being fed and resigned to the prospect of death. The servants' hunger has made them bold and insolent. The doorkeeper, who should protect his master's privacy, cares nothing for his duties, and all and sundry get access to him. The cooks are told to prepare pulāo, but send up broth instead.[52] If the servant is told to straighten out the carpet on which his master is sitting, he will not wait for his master to rise, but will give a tug at the carpet there and then. But the truth is that servants and courtiers alike are weak from hunger and are not fit to perform even the lightest duties.

---

[52] The implication is that they use the ingredients of the ordered pulāo, or the money given them to buy these ingredients, to fill their own bellies. Pulāo is a rich dish prepared from rice, meat, and other ingredients.

The *salātīn*[53] are in such desperate straits that their clothes are all threadbare. They are ashamed to admit visitors to their homes and will slam the door in their faces rather than do so. Some are saying that if they are such a burden to maintain, it would be better to give them poison to take. In short, poverty has overtaken all, and a man may try his utmost for employment and still find none, unless he is prepared to emigrate as far afield as Ispahan or Istambul[54] . . .

How can I describe the desolation of Delhi? There is no house from where the jackal's cry cannot be heard. The mosques at evening are unlit and deserted, and only in one house in a hundred will you see a light burning. Its citizens do not possess even the essential cooking pots, and vermin crawl in the places where in former days men used to welcome the coming of spring with music and rejoicing. The lovely buildings which once made the famished man forget his hunger are in ruins now. In the once-beautiful gardens where the nightingale sang his love songs to the rose, the grass grows waist-high around the fallen pillars and ruined arches. In the villages round about, the young women no longer come to draw water at the wells and stand talking in the leafy shade of the trees. The villages are deserted, the trees themselves are gone, and the wells are full of corpses.[55] Jahānābād,[56] you never deserved this terrible fate, you who were once vibrant with life and love and hope, like the heart of a young lover, you for whom men afloat upon the ocean of the world once set their course as to the promised shore, you from whose dust men came to gather pearls. Not even a lamp of clay now burns where once the chandelier blazed with light. Those who once lived in great mansions now eke out their lives among the ruins. Thousands of hearts once full of hope are sunk in despair. Women of noble birth, veiled from head to foot, stand in the streets carrying in their arms their little children, lovely as fresh

[53] The *salātīn*, or princes, were the relatives and descendants of the imperial family, who, as may be imagined when the size of the imperial harems is borne in mind, were numerous. In 1836 there were no less than 795 receiving stipends of some sort. Cf. Spear, *Twilight of the Mughuls*, p. 39.

[54] Whereas formerly people flocked to India from the whole Islamic world and made their fortunes there.

[55] Of women who, in the days when armies were looting and raping, threw themselves into the wells to escape dishonour.

[56] Delhi.

flowers; they are ashamed to beg outright, and offer for sale rosaries made from the holy clay of Karbala.[57]

But Sauda, still your voice, for your strength fails you now. Every heart is aflame with grief, every eye brimming with tears. There is nothing to be said but this: We are living in a special kind of age. So say no more.

These two satires alone would be enough to show that the vehemence of Sauda's attack springs from a grievous awareness of all the evils of his day—in fact, that the mainspring of his satire, as of all good satire, is a deep compassion for humanity and a savage indignation against the conditions of an age in which humanity is degraded. And it is this that still gives his satires, two hundred years after they were written, a relevance and an interest for today.

[57] Cf. note 48 above.

CHAPTER THREE

Mir Hasan's "Enchanting Story"

MIR HASAN, the son of that Mir Zāhik to whom Sauda's verse brought so unenviable a fame, was born in Delhi probably in 1727 or 1728, and passed his early life there.[1] We do not know exactly when he left with his father to settle at Faizābād, in Oudh, but his own account tells us that it was "early in the days of my youth," and also that he did not want to go because it meant parting from a girl with whom he had fallen in love. From this we can infer that he probably witnessed the occupation, massacre, and looting of Delhi by Nādir Shāh in 1739. By comparison with

[1] The main source for the significant facts of Mīr Ḥasan's life is his own works. Two of these —the maṣnavī Gulzār i Iram and his taẓkira—contain brief autobiographical details. As indicated earlier, the date of his birth is disputed. Earlier authorities give it as A.H. 1140 (A.D. 1727–1728), but the most recent work on the subject, Maḥmūd Fārūqī's Mīr Ḥasan aur Khāndān ke dūsre shu'arā, states that the correct date is A.H. 1151 (A.D. 1738–1739). However, he gives no adequate evidence for preferring this later date. It is known, he says, that Mīr Zāhik left Delhi and reached Faizābād while Ṣafdar Jang was still ruler of Oudh—i.e., before 1754—and therefore favours a date around A.H. 1163–1164 (A.D. 1750–1751) for this event. Then, taking this as the basis of his calculations, and noting that Mīr Ḥasan says that it was "early in his youth" that he left Delhi, he rejects 1140 as the date of his birth on the grounds that an age of 23–24 cannot be described as "early youth." However, if 23–24 is too old, 12–13 is surely too young. Mīr Ḥasan says that he left Delhi with a heavy heart because he had fallen in love there—an important statement which the authorities, with their customary sense of decorum, pass over in discreet silence. Further, Mīr Ḥasan figures in Mīr's taẓkira, and this is know to have been written in A.H. 1165 (A.D. 1750–1751); and it is hardly likely that he would already have made his name as a poet at the age of 14. Lastly, the mere knowledge that it was during Ṣafdar Jang's governorship of Oudh that Mīr Ḥasan and his father left Delhi does not warrant fixing this event in A.D. 1750–1751, for Ṣafdar Jang had been governor since 1739. For these reasons we incline to think that A.D. 1727–1728, or soon after, is the likely date of his birth.

The text of the masnavī Sihr ul Bayān which we have used is that edited by 'Abdul Bārī Āsī (Lucknow, 1941).

G

Mir and Sauda, his subsequent life seems to have been uneventful, for the province of Oudh in which he lived enjoyed relative peace during this period. All the same, his life was not an easy one. His patrons, unlike Sauda's, seem to have been none too generous. Mir Hasan himself hints at this, writing that he "received enough to live on," while a contemporary writer says bluntly that he "lived in penury."[2]

Although several manuscripts are extant, his collected verse has never been published. It contains poems in all the classical forms, but like his great contemporaries, he excelled in one form in particular, and devoted his main attention to it. As Sauda is the master of the qasīda and of satirical verse, and as Mir is the master of the ghazal, so Mir Hasan is the master of the masnavi. He wrote eleven in all, and some of them are of considerable length. But his fame is based on one of them alone, so much so that it is regularly called "Mir Hasan's masnavi," as though it were the only one he had written. This is the masnavi Sihr ul Bayān (The Enchanting Story),[3] a long poem of over 2,000 couplets. Completed in 1785, only two years before his death, it won immediate acclaim, and its popularity remains undiminished to this day. If one can only deplore the neglect of his other works, it nevertheless underlines the extraordinary popularity of this one, which has been published and republished innumerable times. This is the story it tells:

In a splendid city there once ruled a great and powerful king. His dominion extended far and wide, and kings as far away as Central Asia and China acknowledged themselves his vassals. Words cannot describe the beauty and prosperity of the capital. The streets were all paved, the buildings all solidly constructed and of dazzling whiteness; tanks and wells, fountains and watercourses, abounded in the city, which was made beautiful with parks and gardens in every quarter; and over all towered the great fort where the king held his court. The extent of the city was vast, and such was the prosperity and good order which reigned there that men flocked to it from near and far, and those who arrived penniless, quickly became rich and prosperous. In its bazaars one might see the finest craftsmen of every land and clime, and the splendour of the main market was such that to enter it was to linger on,

---

[2] Both statements are quoted by Maḥmūd Fārūqī, p. 41.
[3] Sihr ul Bayān literally means "the enchantment of story."

unwilling to depart. In the fort all was luxury and enjoyment, and beautiful slave girls stood constantly ready to satisfy every need.

Yet amid all this prosperity and happiness the king was not happy. For though he was now advanced in years, he had no son to bring joy to his heart and to succeed to the throne when he was gone. One day he called his ministers to him and said, "It is time for me to leave the world. What use is all this wealth and magnificence when I have no son to succeed me? In my concern for the affairs of state I have neglected my duties towards God. It is better now that I should forsake my kingdom and give myself up to religious contemplation." His ministers replied, "Such a course is not good, your majesty. You are a king, and you cannot fulfil your religious duty by neglecting that which your position lays upon you. Devote yourself to the service of God, but do so by ruling as a great and good king should, so that on the Day of Judgement you can stand before your Judge with a clear conscience and a good heart. And do not commit the sin of despairing of God's mercy. Who knows but that you may yet have a son? Call the Brahmins, the astrologers and geomancers, and ask them what the future holds in store for you." The king accepted their advice, and on an appointed day the astrologers and others waited upon him to determine by their studies what would be the future course of events. Every method of divination was used, and all foretold that in due course a son would be born to the king. Finally the king called upon the Brahmins to speak. They replied, "Your Majesty will have a son as beautiful as the moon, and your grief is now destined to be turned into joy; if it is not so, then we are not Brahmins. But there is something else prescribed by fate. For twelve years your son is threatened by danger. He must never be allowed to go up onto the roof of the palace; nor during all those years must he venture outside the palace walls. His life is not in danger, but it seems that he is fated to dwell some time in the wilderness. Some jinn or fairy will fall in love with him, and he will fall in love with some lady." The king heard their words with mingled joy and grief, but resigned himself with a trusting heart to the will of God and spent much time in earnest prayer. And before the year was out, one of his queens was with child.

Eventually a beautiful boy was born, to whom the name of Benazīr was given. At the good news great crowds assembled outside the palace.

The king distributed his bounty generously as a mark of his rejoicing, and by his decree the occasion was celebrated with music and dancing, and with feasting and festivity which lasted for six whole days. Celebrations no less magnificent marked the boy's first birthday; when he learned to walk, slaves were set free in his name as a token of rejoicing; and his weaning, as he entered his fourth year, was again the occasion of public rejoicings.

The king now built for the boy a beautiful garden, and equipped it with buildings and furnishings of indescribable magnificence. There were canopies and curtains of cloth of gold, cords of gold and silver thread, screens adorned with fine paintings, carpets of velvet, lamps which as they burned spread fragrant perfume throughout the rooms, furniture studded with jewels, and mirrors on all sides to enhance the beauty still further. The garden was laid out with walks and watercourses of marble, lined with cypresses and other graceful trees and beautiful flowers. Sweetly singing birds lived in the garden, and lovely maids were always at hand to serve the prince and keep him company. In this atmosphere of beauty the prince began his education; from the beginning he showed great promise, and within a few years he had mastered all the traditional and scientific branches of learning. Rhetoric, logic, literature, medicine, astronomy, geometry, astrology, calligraphy, archery, cudgel fighting, music, painting, the use of firearms—he was well-versed in all; and, above all, he learned the human kindness and consideration which is the hallmark of a real man, loving the company of good and talented men and despising that of the mean and worthless.

So the years passed by, and Benazír reached his twelfth birthday. On this long-awaited day the king gave orders to prepare a state drive through the streets of the capital, and sent word that his son should be taken to the baths and then dressed in princely array ready to go out in procession. All that the king commanded was joyfully carried out. Lovely maidservants massaged his body and bathed him, joining happily in his involuntary laughter as the pumice stone tickled the soles of his feet; then they dressed him in clothes of the finest cloth and adorned him with jewels and pearls, and so made him ready.

Great was the enthusiasm of the people as the procession started out, amid a scene of breath-taking magnificence. As the prince came out, trays of pearls were scattered over his head and left where they fell on the ground for the bystanders to gather up. The city was a wonderful sight. The walls of all the buildings, the shops, and the houses were draped with decorations made of the finest silks and brocades, and big mirrors set up on all sides heightened the gaiety and colourfulness of the scene. There were horsemen riding two by two, lines of hundreds of elephants bearing their riders in gold and silver howdahs, palanquin-bearers dressed in resplendent livery hurrying here and there, and the flat roofs thronged with people dressed in their finest clothes, as the procession, to the sounds of drums and trumpets, and with standards and banners waving, made its way from the palace to the farthest bounds of the city. There the king and the prince refreshed themselves a while in a garden before returning as night fell to the palace. In the palace, revelry continued until late into the night.

It was the night of the full moon, and when the prince began to feel sleepy he thought how pleasant it would be to sleep, for the first time, on the palace roof. The maidservants conveyed his wish to the king, who gave his consent, stipulating only that watch should be kept over him as he slept.

But there had been a miscalculation. Unknown to the king and his servants, the twelve years of danger were not yet past, and one night still remained.

So the prince's bed was made on the palace roof, and he lay down to sleep in the quiet of the moonlit night and amid the scent of the flowers. Soon a cool breeze sprang up, and those who had been appointed to watch over him fell fast asleep. Only the full moon kept her watch above.

It so happened that a fairy,[4] travelling through the air on her flying throne, chanced to pass that way, and as she looked down, her glance fell upon the sleeping prince. Entranced by his great beauty, she brought her throne down onto the roof and advanced to where he was sleeping in a moonlight so brilliant that it seemed as though the whole earth and sky were radiant with it. She drew back the coverlet and

---

[4] "Fairy" is not really a satisfactory translation of the Urdu (and Persian) *parī*, for the English word suggests a tiny creature with gossamer wings, whereas a parī was a supernatural being in the form of a lovely woman. *Parī* has been naturalized in English as *peri*, but we have used the more familiar word despite its inadequacy.

pressed her cheek to his, and then carried him off, still sleeping in his bed, to the fairy kingdom.

When the maidservants awoke and found that the prince had vanished, they were overcome with grief. The bad news was quickly carried to the king and queen; the king himself came in tears to the spot from where the prince had vanished, but no trace of him could be found. As day broke, the news spread throughout the city, which was plunged into mourning. Even the trees and flowers, the birds and streams, seemed to join in the general sorrow, for though search was made far and wide and no expense was spared, there was no news of the prince to be brought back to the palace.

Meanwhile Benazīr was a prisoner in fairyland. The years passed by, and though he was treated with every consideration and surrounded with every luxury, he pined for the happy life he had led in his father's palace, surrounded by those who loved him. The fairy, who was named Māhrukh, tried all she could to dispel his grief, but without effect. One day she came to him and said, "Benazīr, you are my prisoner; but it makes me sad to see you pining like this. So listen to what I propose. Every evening I leave you here alone and go to visit my father, and in solitude you grow more and more dejected. So I will give you a magic horse, and for three hours every evening you may ride out on it and amuse yourself. It will carry you through the air wherever you want to go. But in return you must give me your written undertaking that if you give your heart to anyone else, then you will acknowledge your fault and accept my punishment." Benazīr accepted this condition, and Māhrukh gave him the magic horse[5] and showed him how to control it. After that he would go out every evening, but would always take care to return when the striking of the hour told him that his time was up.

He rode out one night at the beginning of the cold season. A cool breeze was blowing and the stars and the moon shone brightly in the sky, and as he rode on, he saw below him a lovely garden, and in it a building shining dazzling white in the moonlight. Attracted by the scene he came down onto the roof, and leaning over, tried to discover whether anyone were there. So charming was the scene that he made

---

[5] The words of the original make it clear that the "magic horse" was a kind of machine, and not a living creature.

up his mind to go down into the garden. He tiptoed down the stair and out of the door, and keeping in the shadows, made for a cluster of trees where he could see without being seen. As he looked around, he could see all the signs of people living there, and it was not long before he caught sight of a group of women sitting by a watercourse. In the centre sat a fifteen-year-old princess,[6] a girl of great beauty, reclining with her elbow on a cushion, and surrounded by her lovely hand-maidens as the shining moon is surrounded by stars. She was dressed in fine and delicate fabrics through which her fair body gleamed as the candle gleams in the chandelier, and was adorned with pearls and jewels of great price. Benazīr stood entranced in his hiding place, lost in admiration of her great beauty—the beauty of her form, and of her dress, and of her whole bearing—and as he stood there, one of the maidservants caught sight of him. Amid much excitement the word passed from one to another that someone was hiding behind the trees, until the princess herself heard it. In great agitation she called her maids to help her to rise and take her to the trees so that she might see for herself what was there. Though she summoned up all her courage, it was in fear and trembling that she went. In front of her walked some of her trusted maids repeating prayers for heavenly protection. When they reached the trees, they saw that a handsome young man was standing there motionless, either because there was no way of with-drawing from where he stood, or because love and amazement rooted him to the spot. He seemed to be about fifteen or sixteen years old, in the bloom of youth, finely dressed and adorned with jewellery. The girls were entranced at the sight of him, and quickly turning back, told their mistress, in the indirect way which delicacy demanded, of what they had seen, and assuring her that there was nothing to fear, urged her to come forward. Badr i Munīr (for that was the name of the princess) came forward, and as her eyes met those of Benazīr, both were smitten with love and fell down in a swoon.

With Badr i Munīr was her closest friend, the Vazīr's daughter Najm un Nisa, a girl of great beauty and full of the spirit of mischief. She now ran and fetched rose water, and by sprinkling it over her friend, succeeded in reviving her and helping her to rise. Benazīr too

---

[6] A year older than Shakespeare's Juliet.

had now come to his senses and was standing there lost in love and admiration. But Badr i Munīr averted her face from him and then turned and walked away, leaving him faint with love as he gazed at the nape of her neck and her shoulders and her slender waist and her long plait of black hair swinging across her hips. She knew very well the effect of her beauty upon him and was secretly glad. She wished to appear angry, but love was in her heart, and with her face hidden from him, she smiled as she said, "Who is this wretch who intrudes upon the privacy of my garden?" And so saying, she went quickly into the house, letting fall the curtain behind her.

Najm un Nisa came to her laughing and said, "Badr i Munīr, such deceitful airs are not good. Do not leave the young man to die of love for you. And you too should enjoy the pleasures of life and love while you are young: do as your heart tells you, and forget the heavy burdens which religion and society lay upon you. Your youth and beauty will pass away and never return, and missed opportunities do not come again. This handsome youth has come to you unbidden; so quickly make preparations to receive him and for the wine to flow." Badr i Munīr smiled and answered her, "Yes, Yes! I see! The young man has taken your fancy and I am to be the excuse for entertaining him." "I admit it," returned Najm un Nisa smiling. "It was I who fainted at the sight of him and you who revived me with rose water. Very well then, for my sake do as I tell you and send for him to come." With these words she quickly went and brought Benazīr and seated him in a room; and then taking Badr i Munīr by the hand, she brought her in and made her sit at Benazīr's side. Badr i Munīr came unwillingly, and took care as she seated herself that no part of her body should touch his. For a long time the two lovers sat side by side in embarrassed silence, each too shy to speak to the other, until Najm un Nisa lost patience and said to Badr i Munīr, "Why do you sit there without speaking a word? Here, take this cup and give it to your guest, and, if only for my sake, smile and talk a little." Badr i Munīr did not reply, but smiled and took up the cup, and then averting her face held out the cup to Benazīr and in indirect language invited him to take it. Benazīr laughed and drank first one cup and then another; then he in turn filled the cup and offered it to Badr i Munīr. With the wine their conversation began to flow more freely, and Benazīr told his whole story to the princess.

When he came to speak of the fairy, Badr i Munīr frowned and drew away from him and said, "You are welcome to your fairy and she is welcome to you. I am not one to share a lover with anyone else. You don't care for me, so why should I break my heart for you? Be off now, and do not come again." At these words Benazīr fell at her feet and cried, "Ah, Badr i Munīr! What am I to do if you turn me away? It makes no difference how much she loves me; what do I care for her? Body and soul I am yours and yours alone." "Take your head off my feet," she replied, "How am I to know what is in your heart?" But all the same she was pleased by his answer and no longer pressed him to go. And so as they sat talking together, the hour struck when Benazīr must leave. He started up and said, "Badr i Munīr, I must go. If I can escape again, I will come tomorrow at the same time. Do not think that there is any pleasure for me there, but what am I to do? I am completely within her power. God knows I do not want to leave you. I go leaving my heart here with you. Be kind to me and understand my plight." And so he went, leaving her as agitated as himself.

Somehow he passed the night with Māhrukh, and set himself to endure the heavy hours which must pass before evening came round again and he could fly to Badr i Munīr. She on her side awaited his coming with the same feelings in her heart. As she sat sadly alone, Najm un Nisa came to her, trying to drive away her sorrow and take her mind off her grief. "Tonight," she said, "I should like to see you dressed and adorned so that your beauty is seen in all its perfection"— and though Badr i Munīr scolded her, Najm un Nisa had only spoken what was already in her own mind. That day she bathed and performed her toilet with such care that she looked like a newly-wedded bride. Meanwhile, maidservants prepared the palace for the evening's meeting. They laid costly carpets on the floor, draped the rooms with hangings of silk and laid upon the bed coverlets worked with jewels. They made the rooms fragrant with flowers and with precious perfumes and brought in sweetly-smelling rare fruits. At the head of the bed they placed a richly bound volume of the selected verse of the great Persian poets Zuhūri and Nazīri, and another of the great Urdu poets, Sauda and Mir and Mir Hasan. Wine was made ready and detailed instructions given for the preparation of the food. In short, nothing was left undone, and when everything was ready Badr i Munīr went out to walk in the garden until evening.

Benazīr too prepared himself with special care for the meeting with his beloved, and when at last he was free to go, flew with all speed to the garden where she was walking.

She saw him coming and quickly hid herself behind some trees where she could stand unobserved and admire her lover's appearance. One of the maidservants came surreptitiously to her and asked her where they were to conduct the prince; and when they had seated him in the room which had been made ready for him, Badr i Munīr herself made her appearance in all her breath-taking beauty. Benazīr was fired with passion, and seizing her hand, led her resisting to sit by him. She struggled to free her hand, telling him scathingly to keep this warmth for the one he really loved; but he passionately rebuked her, telling her to torture him no more by such words but to sit at his side and give herself freely and unashamedly to his embrace. At length she was persuaded to sit down beside him, and as the wine cup passed from one to the other, they began to talk in a fashion which made the maidservants lower their eyes for shame and find pretexts one after another to withdraw from the room. Then Benazīr led Badr i Munīr to the bed, where they lay in one another's arms and drank the wine of union together, enjoying their love to the full. At length they came out from the bedchamber, the one radiant, the other pale, and sat silently together, still drunk with the wine of passion, until at the sounding of the hour, Benazīr rose with a start to take his leave. Badr i Munīr's face was the picture of distress: she neither looked at him nor spoke. "Darling, do not be angry with me; I shall come again," he said. "As you wish," she replied, and he left her, heavy at heart because she was displeased with him, and with the tears running down his cheeks.

But the following night he came again, and after that he would come every day; and in each other's company they would forget the grief which oppressed them during the hours of separation.

But fate never allows lasting happiness to anyone. One day a giant came to Māhrukh and told her that her captive had given his heart to someone else, and that as he flew over the garden, he had seen the two lovers standing hand in hand. Māhrukh was furious, and the moment

Benazīr returned, she poured out all her wrath upon him. "Did you not give me your written undertaking?" she cried. "Then prepare to honour your word, and take the punishment which I shall inflict upon you." At once she summoned a huge jinn and commanded him to drag Benazīr away to the desert and throw him down a dried-up well; there he was to be held imprisoned, and the mouth of the well closed by an enormous rock. The jinn was to feed him only once a day at evening, and no one was to pay any attention to his cries. So Benazīr was thrown into the dark well, from which there was no way of escape.

The next evening Badr i Munīr waited in vain for Benazīr to come, and the evening after that and the one after that. When several days had passed and she grew sick with love and sorrow and disappointment, she spoke to Najm un Nisa. "What can have happened to him?" she asked. Najm un Nisa, hoping to shock her out of her dejection, replied harshly, "Lady, are you mad? Do you think these handsome young men think twice about anyone? God alone knows where he is now or what he is doing. I have no patience with people who simply surrender themselves to love. Could you not control yourself? In love you must act as your lover acts. If he seems cool, you too be cool; if he inclines towards you, only then incline towards him." Badr i Munīr made no reply.

As the days passed she became immersed more and more in her sorrow, increasingly indifferent to all that went on around her. She would roam about the garden like someone distracted, lingering among the trees. She slept uneasily at night, and had bad dreams; and during the day she was always looking for some excuse to go to her bed, where she could be alone and weep. All appetite left her, and often when people spoke to her, she did not hear or could not bring her attention to bear on what they said, so that her answers had nothing to do with their questions. If others had not brought her food and drink, she would never have thought of it. Day and night Benazīr's image was before her eyes, and in her heart she talked to him alone. Sometimes she would sing poems of the sorrow of love, but generally even poetry had no charm for her. One day she rallied herself sufficiently to go into the garden and send for her dancing girl Aish Bāi to come and entertain her with song and dance. But though all the listeners were

held spellbound by the grace and beauty of her performance, to Badr i
Munīr the words and music only revived poignant memories, and
bursting into tears she left the garden and went to her bed to weep.

A whole month passed in this way, and still Benazīr did not come.
Badr i Munīr was on the verge of madness, unable to eat or sleep, completely heedless of her dress and appearance and even of the need to
preserve a decent discretion about her love. Najm un Nisa made one
more attempt to rally her. "Why do you grieve yourself so?" she said.
"You who could once have given wise advice to others are today yourself behaving like a fool. What madness is this, to give your heart to a
passing stranger? These travellers never stay in one place for long, and
wherever they go, there they declare their love. You should know
better, dear, than to give your love until your wooer has given unmistakable proof of his; and if he shows no concern for you, then you
too should banish him from your thoughts. He has his fairy and is content with her. Otherwise would he have stayed away so long?" Badr i
Munīr, gently but with deep emotion replied, "Listen to me, my dear.
It is not good to speak ill of people, for only God knows everything
about them. As for me, I know he is true at heart, and I am afraid only
for what may have happened to him, that for all these days he has not
come. Perhaps the fairy has heard of what happened here and has imprisoned him or given him over to some ogre to devour. I only know
that for him I have borne all the sorrow of separation, and I would give
my own life that he might live." Then bursting into tears she huddled
herself up in the corner of her bed and covered her head with the
coverlet.

When at last she fell asleep, she had a dream. She thought she saw,
in the middle of a vast desert, a well closed by an enormous stone from
which came the voice of Benazīr speaking of his love for her, and telling
her of his plight. She tried to call to him, but no sound would come,
and at this point she awoke. Though driven nearly to distraction, she
at first told no one of her dream. But at last she could contain herself
no longer, and calling her closest friends to her (and Najm un Nisa
amongst them), she revealed her dream to them. Najm un Nisa at
once made up her mind. "Do not weep any more," she said. "From
now on lay all your sorrows upon me. I am going to the desert to find
Benazīr and bring him back to you. If I live, I will return to throw

myself at your feet again. And if I die, why then, I die, and I will gladly die for your sake.'' Badr i Munīr implored her not to risk her life in so dangerous an undertaking, saying that her company was the one thing that gave her some consolation and that without her she would die. But Najm un Nisa replied, weeping, "I cannot bear to see you like this, for the grief it brings me is more than I can endure." And weeping all the time, she tore her fine clothes and threw them aside. Then, putting on the dress of a wandering Hindu ascetic, and taking a lute with her, she got ready to go. Badr i Munīr and her companions gathered around her weeping, telling her not to forget them and praying that God's protection might go with her and bring her safely back.

So Najm un Nisa set out to wander in the desert, in the hope that sooner or later she might find out where Benazīr was. Wherever she sat down for a while, she would play on the lute, and all living creatures would listen, enthralled by the music and by the great beauty of the player, which her simple disguise enhanced rather than concealed.

One bright moonlight night in the desert she sat down to play. It was the night of the full moon, which shone so brilliantly that it seemed as though a dazzling white sheet had been laid down over the earth. Every thorn and blade of grass shone bright and clear; the leaves of the trees glistened with light and beneath them light and shade mingled as though the moonlight had passed through a net. As she began to play, the birds and beasts forgot their sleep, the breeze began to dance in the treetops in ecstasy, and the very moonlight lay still as though entranced. And at this moment there happened to pass that way on his magic throne Fīroz Shāh, the son of the king of the jinns, a handsome youth of some twenty or twenty-one years. Hearing the sound of the lute, he brought his throne to earth and drew near to listen, and his eyes fell upon Najm un Nisa. One glance was enough to make him captive to her beauty, and sensing that her dress was some disguise he approached and spoke to her, asking what misfortune had impelled her to wander forth in her present style and where she had come from and where she wished to go. Najm un Nisa was quick to realise the effect of her beauty upon him, and smilingly rebuked him saying, "Turn your thoughts only to God or else return whence you came." Fīroz Shāh protested at her severity, promising to go if she wished, but asking first to be allowed to stay and listen to her playing. "Then sit there quietly," said Najm un Nisa, and she again began to play. Fīroz Shāh sat down on the sand in front of her and was soon lost in contemplation of her beauty and of the sweetness of the music. Najm un Nisa played on until dawn, and he sat there before her weeping unrestrainedly. She stopped, yawned, and placing the lute on her shoulder, rose to go, when Fīroz Shāh, quickly seizing her by the hand, brought her to his magic throne and carried her off protesting to his father's court. There he brought her before his father, praising her perfect mastery of the art of music, and urging him to persuade her to play for them. The king received her with great deference and placed a house at her disposal for as long as she wished to stay at his court. The whole day was passed in entertaining her, and when night fell Najm un Nisa was asked to sing and play on her lute before those assembled there. She expressed some displeasure at this request. "Ascetics are not concerned with singing and music, but only with God, and these repeated requests are not pleasing to me. But so long as I am in your house, I am under constraint to carry out your wishes." The king replied, "No, No! What are you saying? Your very presence here is a favour to us. If it is your own wish we will ask you to play, but God forbid that you should do so against your will." She replied, "You have spoken well; for not in commands but in submission will you attain your desires."

With this she began to play. The sweetness of the music moved every hearer to tears, but on none was its effect so profound as on Fīroz Shāh, who every moment fell more and more hopelessly in love with her. Gazing upon her, now from in front, now from other angles, sometimes watching her from behind one of the pillars of the great hall, sometimes in his imagination kissing her face, he moved restlessly among the audience, weeping all the time. She on her side stole occasional glances at him, noting with satisfaction the effect which she was having upon him, but quickly averting her gaze if ever their eyes met.

At length she stopped playing, though all those present felt as though they could have gone on gazing upon her and listening to her forever The king praised her performance highly and asked her to favour them every evening by playing to them and to stay as long as she wished, regarding the palace as her own and taking without ceremony whatever she wanted. Najm un Nisa replied disclaiming any interest in material things, but agreeing to his request. Secretly she was well pleased with the king's invitation, and saw already the possibility that through Fīroz Shāh she might yet achieve the purpose for which she had set out. After that she would go for a few hours every evening to the court, and when she had passed the time in pleasant conversation and in playing the lute, would return to her house.

Meanwhile the plight of the unhappy Fīroz Shāh grew ever more desperate, and Najm un Nisa took a delight in making it so. His simplicity was no match for her art. She showed herself now kind to him, now cold, until he was helplessly in her toils. One day in desperation he determined to speak out at the next opportunity, and finding her alone, threw himself at her feet. But before he could speak Najm un Nisa forestalled him. Smilingly she said, "What are you doing? Why are you so agitated? Has my long stay here become a burden to you? If so, I am ready to go, with my blessings upon you; there is no need to fall at my feet to implore me." Fīroz Shāh replied weeping, "Enough! I cannot bear to hear such words! Why do you still go on torturing me? Do you not know what has happened to me? I am devoted to you body and soul. But you are cold and unkind towards me: what is there that I can say to you?" Najm un Nisa replied, "Now tell me clearly what you mean and why you have fallen at my feet." Fīroz Shāh said, "My love, how can I conceal any longer the inmost desire of my heart? I cannot bear to go on living apart from you: marry me and make me your slave." At this Najm un Nisa laughed and said, "Then listen attentively to what I have to tell you; perhaps if you can do what I want, you too may be the gainer." "Tell me quickly," he replied. "I will do whatever is in my power." Najm un Nisa now told him her whole story, revealing who she was and why she had set out in her present disguise. She concluded, "You too are a fairy; if you search for him, you may find where Māhrukh has imprisoned Benazīr; then by your help we may be reunited and all our desires fulfilled; and perhaps you too may get what you want." "Give me your hand on it," he said, but Najm un Nisa scolded him, telling him not to presume. Fīroz Shāh then called his people together, and after explaining the situation to them, promised a rich reward to him who should discover where Benazīr lay confined. The fairies went out in search of him, and before many days had passed, one of them returned to claim his reward. Fīroz Shāh now sent a letter to Māhrukh rebuking her in the strongest terms and demanding that on pain of severe punishment she must give up Benazīr and swear never again to form any attachment to a human. Māhrukh was forced to agree, and she replied acknowledging her fault and asking only that the affair should not be made known to her father. And so at long last Benazīr, haggard and emaciated, was freed from his imprisonment and brought on Fīroz Shāh's magic throne to fairyland. When he arrived there, Fīroz Shāh left Benazīr at a little distance and went to Najm un Nisa. "Come," he said, "I have brought Benazīr." Najm un Nisa started up in agitation, and demanding to know where he was, would have gone straight to him had not Fīroz Shāh restrained her for fear that her uncontrolled joy might bring her to grief. Then taking her hand in his, he led her to where Benazīr was sitting. "Look at him well," he said. "Is he the one whom you are seeking or not?" "Yes! Yes!" she said. "It is! It is!" Then going near to the magic throne, she said, "Stand aside, fairy, and let me take his misfortunes upon me."[7] Fīroz Shāh replied smiling, "Very well, but mind you do the same for me afterwards." But she brushed him aside with an impatient gesture and started to walk round the prince, taking his misfortunes upon her. Then, falling on his neck, she wept without restraint. Benazīr, to his surprise, saw that it was Najm un Nisa, and asked in bewilderment how she came to be there and what had led to his release. Then as they embraced one another she told him the whole story; and from that day his grief left him and happiness was his once more.

One day soon after it was decided that all three of them—Fīroz Shāh, Najm un Nisa, and Benazīr—should fly on the magic throne to Badr i Munīr. They brought the throne down behind the clump of trees where Benazīr had concealed himself on his first visit to the garden, and Najm un Nisa told them to keep themselves hidden there while she went alone to Badr i Munīr to prepare her for the good news. When she came to where Badr i Munīr was, she fell at her feet, and for a moment Badr i Munīr did not recognise her. When she did, she

---

[7] A literal translation of the Urdū phrase. In former times a woman would signify her love and devotion to a person by drawing her hands over his head and then cracking her fingers over her own temples in token of taking all his impending misfortunes upon herself.

welcomed her with the utmost joy and affection, saying that she had never expected to live until her return. She tried her best to rise, but had become so weak that she fell to the ground in the attempt to do so, apologising for the weakness which made it impossible for her to stand. Najm un Nisa walked round her, taking her misfortunes upon her. She well remembered how pitiable had been Badr i Munīr's condition at the time when they had parted; but now the ravages of grief had reduced her to a still more pitiable plight, and the appearance of the house, the garden, and the maidservants all was such as could result only from prolonged neglect. The talk and happy laughter had long been stilled and the singers and musicians long silent; and as she surveyed the desolate scene, Najm un Nisa wept. Yet as the rumour of her coming spread, everything stirred to life; the maidservants thronged around her, expressing their joy at her return and wanting to know all about her adventures, until Najm un Nisa in desperation had to plead the fatigue of her long journeyings and ask them to leave her in peace, promising however that she would relate the whole story next day.

When they had dispersed Najm un Nisa looked around to see that no one was within hearing and then said to Badr i Munīr, "Princess, won't you take a stroll with me? There is something I have to tell you." Then when they were quite alone, she said to Badr i Munīr, "I have brought your Benazīr." At these words, Badr i Munīr fainted. When she had come to herself, she asked, "Is he really here? Or are you trying to tease me?" Najm un Nisa replied solemnly, "I swear to you by my life; if I am speaking falsely, may I die!" Then in answer to Badr i Munīr's questions, she told how she had found out where Benazīr was, and had brought about his release, and how, along with another, she had brought him here. "But see what misfortune this has involved me in; in order to bring your Benazīr, I have had to bring another captive too. Still, now let me bring Benazīr to you; the other I will find some means of sending away." At this the princess laughed aloud. "Why do you try to deceive me?" she said. "No more of such deceitful tricks! Go and bring them both quickly." "Will you appear unveiled before the jinn then," asked Najm un Nisa, "without first asking Benazīr?"[8] "Surely you do not think he will say no?" she

---

[8] A husband may allow (or command) his wife not to observe *parda* with his intimate friends.

replied. "But if you have any doubt, go first and I will wait. Go and ask him what his wishes are." Najm un Nisa went quickly, and calling out to them, summoned them to the house. Then she asked Benazīr if she should bring Badr i Munīr. He replied in astonishment, "What is the matter with you, beautiful one? Is there *parda* between brother and sister? Fīroz Shāh is a brother to me. Do I not owe my life to him? What then have I to keep from his eyes?" Badr i Munīr heard his words from behind the screen, and came out of her own accord. Going shyly to where he was sitting, she sat down by his side, and he felt as though for the first time he had begun to live again. Tears came into his eyes, and as they sat together, it was a scene to excite compassion. There they sat, their eyes red with weeping, a feverish flush on their pale cheeks, their whole form weakened and emaciated from the sorrow of their long separation, each weeping for the other's plight, until Najm un Nisa grew worried and spoke up. "Do you hear me, Badr i Munīr? Has not Benazīr wept enough tears already because of you, that you by your own weeping give him further cause for grief? Enough now! Where has he the strength to bear more sorrow? I brought him to you so that your love might make him whole. Talk to him now of happier things, and may God never give you cause to weep again." At this they all laughed, and the succeeding hours passed pleasantly in happy conversation. The night was already long spent when they had the food brought in, and after satisfying their hunger, the two couples each went to their beds to spend the rest of the night in loving converse and in sleep. Badr i Munīr and Benazīr long lay together, each recalling the misfortunes now so happily past. Benazīr told her of the hardships of his imprisonment, and of how only his love for her and the slender hope of reunion with her at last had kept him alive. She told him of the strange dream she had had, and of how this had led Najm un Nisa to go out in search of him. Meanwhile Fīroz Shāh and Najm un Nisa lay talking together, and for all four of them morning dawned all too soon. They rose, and turn by turn went to take their bath; and now Najm un Nisa showed that she had still not used the full extent of her power over Fīroz Shāh. When she returned from the bath, she was clothed from head to foot in garments of the finest red silk, edged with a border of gold thread. Her fair body gleamed through them as the flame gleams through glowing coals, and on her firm young bosom, brought into prominence by the tightness of her bodice, the dark nipples stood out in contrast to the fairness of her breasts. Fīroz Shāh was as though stunned as he gazed on her beauty, but shame and modesty would not let him speak.

And so the four lovers began to pass their days happily together. But at the back of their minds they were haunted by the fear that their happy life together might again be broken by enforced separation. They determined, therefore, to take steps so that they could be married and there would no longer be any need for concealment. While Badr i Munīr and Najm un Nisa visited their parents, professing their desire to be with them again for a while after being parted for so long, Benazīr and Fīroz Shāh retired to a city where they could make all the necessary preparations, and then got ready to act.

A letter in royal style was sent to Badr i Munīr's father, the king Masūd Shāh. "O kings of kings, pride of Jamshed,[9] peer of Farīdūn, scion of Sikandar's line, in whom are realised the hopes of the world: Rustam in valour, Hātim in generosity—I come as a poor guest to your dominions, brought hither by my fate, seeking your kindness with the request that you make me your slave.[10] Such has ever been the custom of mankind, for by such alliances the work of the world prospers. Men well know me and the line from which I am sprung. I am a prince, the son of king Malik Shāh, and young and old have heard my fame, for my name is prince Benazīr." He then went on to vaunt his noble ancestry, the formidable power of his army, and the vast extent of his wealth, and in the end, after every show of modesty and humility, wrote these words: "He who works against the Law of Islam is my mortal enemy; if you accept my proposal, it is well. If not, consider me already at your gates." Masūd Shāh read and reread the letter, and considered carefully what he should reply. He noted the strength of Benazīr's forces, and reflected that if it came to war, the struggle would be a

---

[9] Jamshed, the legendary Iranian king, is traditionally thought to be the inventor both of the wine and the cup; the "goblet of Jam" (*jām-e Jam*) is the marvellous glass which shows the whole world. Farīdūn is the Iranian king of yore who excelled by his justice; Sikandar is Alexander the Great, one of the leading heroes even in Muslim and Persian tradition; Rustam the great warrior of old Iran, is the hero of Iranian folklore and the central figure in Firdausi's epic *Shāhnāmeh*; Hātim was considered by the pre-Islamic Arabs as the model of generosity among the Bedouins, and his name has, for this reason, become proverbial in the Islamic East. (A.S.)

[10] I.e., give me your daughter in marriage.

heavy one and its outcome uncertain. Besides, what harm could there be in the proposed marriage? There was nothing unusual in the proposal: such marriages were made every day. There and then he sent the following reply: "After praise to God and his Prophet be it known that your letter has reached me. Were I not constrained by the Law of Islam, you should have seen what my answer would have been, and were I to demonstrate my power you should know that kings before whom you are nothing can lay no claim upon my consideration. Such vaunting as yours does not become a mere lad fresh from his mother's home and without the knowledge to discern what is good and what is bad. But what can I do? I am constrained by the ways of the world and by my regard for the Law of Islam, for he who departs from the road marked out by God and his Prophet shall assuredly not attain his ends. Let, then, a suitable date be decided. I have commanded you. Come!"

When the news of the betrothal became known, there was great rejoicing in the city, and in this atmosphere the preparations for the wedding were put in hand.

Eventually the longed for day arrived, and as the bridegroom's procession left the palace to make its way to the bride's house, people thronged to see it, some mounted on horses, some on elephants, some in carriages or palanquins, and some on foot. On all sides could be heard the clash of sword-hilt on shield as people moved about. Everywhere the drums were booming and the trumpets sounding. On platforms raised above the level of the streets, courtesans were dancing and singing as the wedding procession moved through the gorgeously decorated city. Thousands of lighted lamps lined the route and burned brightly on the top of the ceremonial arches. On all sides were raised platforms made beautiful with flowers and coloured lights and displays of fireworks. The bridegroom, his face veiled by the strings of pearls hanging from his brow, mounted on a fine, slow-stepping horse, fanned by fans of peacock feathers, surrounded by a transparent screen, and preceded by drums and music, came to the bride's house. There too festivities were in full swing as all the traditional wedding rites were duly performed.

After the marriage ceremony the bridegroom was led to the bride who was seated inside the palace, resplendent in her wedding dress, and there too the traditional rites were performed—the bridegroom was made to sit close to the bride facing her, she, however, remaining veiled. Then the Holy Quran was placed between them, and on it a small mirror into which the bridegroom looked, and as she removed her veil, he saw her face for the first time, reflected in the mirror. Then the bride was made to sit and sugar was sprinkled all over her, and the bridegroom ordered, with jesting and laughter, to take up the sugar with his mouth, now from her eyes, now from her lips, from her waist, from her feet. At length the time came for the bridal pair to leave for the prince's home, and the procession moved off amid scenes of undiminished merriment and rejoicing. Thus Benazīr and Badr i Munīr were united in marriage.

Only a few days later, at Benazīr's request, Najm un Nisa's father consented to give her in marriage to Fīroz Shāh, and with pomp and ceremony no less spectacular than that which had accompanied the wedding of the prince and princess, their wedding too was celebrated. And thus the heart's desire of all four lovers was accomplished.

Now came the time for them to part. Fīroz Shāh and his bride, promising often to visit their friends, departed on their magic throne to fairyland, while Benazīr prepared to bring his bride home to his parents' house. Returning with his army, he came to the outskirts of the city and pitched camp on the banks of a river. It quickly became known who he was, and the news spread like wildfire throughout the city that the vanished prince had returned. The news was carried to the king and queen too, but they could not believe that such good fortune could be theirs, and the king was only with difficulty persuaded to come and see for himself that it was none other than his son Benazīr. Benazīr saw him coming, and ran and fell at his feet crying, "Praise be to God that I am restored to your service once more!" The king, weeping copiously, raised him up and clasped him to his bosom and then fainted away from the excess of his joy.

The prince's return was greeted with universal rejoicing, and in token of their joy the people high and low brought gifts to the palace. Meanwhile Benazīr presented his bride to his parents. As they entered the palace, Benazīr's mother came forward to greet them, and embraced them both weeping tears of happiness. By the wish of his parents, Benazīr's wedding was again celebrated in his own city, and life and happiness soon returned in fu... measure to the capital and its people.

"And thus may you and I, "concludes Mir Hasan, "see our fortunes change. Thus may God reunite all dear ones who are parted; may we live, like them, in a thriving and prosperous city like theirs; may God rain his blessings upon my patron, the Navvāb Āsaf ud Daula, and may I, Mir Hasan, attain the happiness I seek."

In a prose summary a good deal is inevitably lost, for in the original a strongly rhythmical metre carries the story forward. Its basic unit is a foot of one short syllable followed by two longs, and the line consists of four feet, in the last of which the final long is dropped, so that the line runs ᴗ — — | ᴗ — — | ᴗ — — | ᴗ — .[11] English has the long-short-short of the dactyl and the short-short-long of the anapaest, but it cannot effectively match this metre, in which the regularity of the rhythm contributes a sense of continuous flow, while the preponderance of long syllables prevents the verse breaking into a gallop. Nor can an English summary easily convey the effectiveness of Mir Hasan's diction. He seems to write with effortless simplicity, yet he tells us at the end of the poem that the labour he had spent upon it had changed him into an old man, and we realise how much care lies behind the apparently spontaneous expression. All Urdu critics have been struck by the freshness and, so to speak, the timelessness of his language. One, writing a century after Mir Hasan's death, said, "His language is that which you and I speak today. Turn to the verse of his contemporaries, and you will find on every page words and constructions which today are obsolete . . . Turn to his, and, apart from a few words, what you find is as current now as it was then."[12] And after the lapse of another hundred years the words are still valid today.

The same apparent simplicity conceals the skill with which he uses the devices of rhetoric. Some of these—the vivid similes, for example—come across in English, but there are others that defy translation. Many depend upon verbal conceit of the kind one finds in the earlier plays of Shakespeare, and their use—in both poets—sometimes seems, to modern taste, to detract from the charm of the poetry rather than add to it. Aptly used, however, they do make an appeal—as where, early in the

---

[11] This metre is called *mutaqārib*, and was also used in the greatest epic poem of Persian literature, Firdausī's *Shāhnāmeh*. (A.S.)

[12] Āzād, *Āb i Ḥayāt*, p. 250.

poem, the king's earnest prayers for the gift of a son are described, and Mir Hasan continues: "Udhar lau lagāya to pāya cirāgh." The words *lau lagāya* and *cirāgh* bear both a literal and a metaphorical meaning. "Lau lagāna" means literally to light a flame and metaphorically to concentrate one's whole thought on something. "Cirāgh" means literally a lamp, but is also the regular metaphor for a son, who brings radiance to his parents' home. Here the metaphorical meaning is the primary one: the king concentrated all his thought on prayer, and obtained a son. But Mir Hasan has just told us that as part of his devotions the king set a lamp in the mosque and kept it constantly burning; so the literal meanings are also relevant and help to heighten the atmosphere.

The poem shows an equally firm grasp of the larger aspects of craftsmanship. It has the steady flow, the sense of proportion between the constituent parts, and the timely variation of theme which the art of narrative demands. The descriptive passages are, in general, long enough to add colour to the story, but not long enough to pall. There is an eye for vivid and significant details which evoke a whole atmosphere. Thus Mir Hasan, describing how Najm un Nisa ceases playing her lute as dawn breaks, says, "She stopped, yawned, and placing the lute on her shoulder, rose to go"—and the one word "yawned" conveys all the pretended indifference by which she aims to captivate Fīroz Shāh. In every part of the poem there are vivid touches like these—the young prince in the bath, laughing as the pumice stone tickles his feet; Badr i Munīr's long black plait swinging across her hips as she turns to go back to the palace; Benazīr at his marriage being compelled by the laughing womenfolk to take up with his mouth the sugar sprinkled over his bride; and many more.

The Enchanting Story belongs to what may be described as the Arabian Nights class of literature, and one does not therefore look for complex analysis of character in it; it is a tale, not a novel. But the portrayal of the characters is convincing, if not deep, and they are presented not through static descriptions but through their actions and their speech. When Najm un Nisa is first introduced, Mir Hasan's own comment on her is confined to just half a line, in which we are told that she is "a girl of great beauty and full of the spirit of mischief." After that her dialogue and her actions are allowed to speak for themselves. Once again, English can only partially convey the excellence of the dialogue. The whole tone—even the turns of phrase—of each speaker is in character. That of the Brahmin astrologers is proud and self-assured, and contains more Hindi[13] words than the other characters employ (except Najm un Nisa in her role of Hindu ascetic); Māhrukh's is shrill and coarse; Najm un Nisa's, mischievous, self-possessed, and full of humour; Badr i Munīr's, simple and sincere.

The appeal of the poem owes much to the skill with which Mir Hasan has blended romanticism with realism—literary methods that are too often regarded as mutually exclusive. All critics have agreed that the masnavi is a romantic poem; but generally all they have meant by this is that it is a love story with a happy ending, or that the supernatural plays a part in it. Both these things are true, but neither contributes much to the understanding and appreciation of the poem. The fact that the characters include supernatural beings is of quite minor importance; like the fact that the other characters are all royal personages or their close associates, it represents nothing more than Mir Hasan's use of a convention which had been established for this kind of romantic masnavi long before his day. The characters, both supernatural and human, are universal in their significance; their emotional experience is universal human experience; and it is with the treatment of this experience that Mir Hasan is concerned. *The Enchanting Story* is a romantic poem in a deeper sense. The poet does not place his story in a setting drawn from the real world which he sees around him, or from that of an earlier historical period; the world he portrays is largely an idealised world, in which the aspirations of the poet and of his audience are shown as being realised, and in which men live happily in a community where true love ultimately triumphs over all difficulties. Yet this world is depicted with all the power of the realistic method.

Mir Hasan's portrayal of love illustrates this method. The description of love and of the emotions to which the lovers' experiences give rise is absolutely real. But the setting is largely unreal. Neither in Mir Hasan's own day nor in the earlier period of the glory of the Mughal Empire, which he consciously recalls, did the course of true love run so smooth as it does in *The Enchanting Story*. As we shall see later, true love stories in the social conditions of Mughal India were nearly all tragedies. Of course,

---

[13] Hindi is the other literary form of the dialect on which Urdū is based. Its literature has a Hindu background in the same sense as Urdū literature has a Muslim background.

there are in the poem allusions to the need for secrecy and to the lovers' fears that discovery may dash all their hopes and doom them to enforced and permanent separation; but these things are touched on in the lightest possible way and are given no prominence. In real life the tragedy of separation is due to the conditions of social life; in *The Enchanting Story* it is due to the power of Māhrukh over Benazīr, a power achieved and maintained by supernatural means.

Much the same is true for Mir Hasan's picture of the society in which his story is set. He depicts a society in which the atmosphere is one of general happiness, a society abounding in wealth, where kings rule justly, where the leaders of society conform to the highest ideals that popular opinion prescribes for them, and where the subjects live in peace and prosperity. But here too the element of realistic description is strong. No city ever existed like that described in the opening pages of the narrative, but imperial Delhi had once resembled Mir Hasan's imaginary city in many ways, and it is the recollection of that Delhi which provides the basis of his picture. No prince ever existed so perfect in all accomplishments as the youthful Benazīr, but those familiar with the lives of such men as Bābur, the founder of the Mughal dynasty, and Akbar, its greatest representative, know that these men at an equally early age had accomplishments hardly less remarkable. The pomp and magnificence of the great royal processions are painted, so to speak, larger than life; but not so much larger that they do not bear a close resemblance to historical truth. Mir Hasan was still writing the masnavi when the British Governor-General visited Lucknow, and the fantastic magnificence of the welcome which Āsaf ud Daula gave him is well attested. Thus romance and reality are again fused into a single whole.

It may be because Mir Hasan wrote this, his greatest poem, so late in life, that his contemporaries did not rank him with Mir and Sauda. He himself ventured to differ from them. In the passage in the masnavi where he describes how in preparation for Benazīr's coming the maidservants placed "at the head of the bed . . . a richly bound volume of . . . the great Urdu poets, Sauda and Mir and Mir Hasan," he is, in a characteristically graceful way, asserting a claim to a place alongside them. One can only speculate as to the ways in which he felt he could compare with them. Perhaps he has in mind simply his mastery of the craft of poetry.

But the words could bear a deeper meaning: they could be a claim also that he upholds, with the same artistic power as they do, the values for which they both stand. And such a claim would be justified. His poetic method is distinct from theirs, but he does indeed share their essential outlook, and he fully deserves a place at their side.

CHAPTER FOUR

The Love Poetry of Mir

THE REPUTATION which Mir Hasan's *Enchanting Story* won him long over-shadowed that of other masnavi writers, and it was not until nearly a century later that the accomplishment of Mir in handling the same form began to be rediscovered.[1] His masnavis differ from Mir Hasan's in important respects, and we find for once that the textbook definition of masnavi suffers not from the usual fault of being overelaborate and over-precise but from the opposite defect. Masnavi means simply a poem in rhymed couplets. One has to add that, in Urdu at any rate, the largest single class of masnavis consists of love stories, and that these fall into two distinct classes. Some, like *The Enchanting Story*, are long romantic tales. Others are, in their essential story, directly realistic, and these are by convention much shorter poems. Mir's love masnavis are all of this second kind.

---

[1] The source for virtually the whole of this chapter is Mir's own verse, collected in *Kulliyāt i Mīr*. At the time when the chapter was written, the best edition was that of 'Abdul Bārī Āsī (Lucknow, 1941). The slightly more comprehensive edition by Dr. 'Ibādat Barelavī, published from Karachi in 1958, is marred by numerous copyist's mistakes, and as this edition is now, like Āsī's, out of print, we have not thought it worth while to undertake the laborious task of collating the references to Āsī's edition with the paging of Dr   Barelavī's and giving references in terms of the latter. There are six dīvāns of Mir's ghazals, and we have indicated in Roman numerals the dīvān from which each verse quoted has been taken. The references have been given as briefly as possible. Thus I.164.14 means that the verse comes from the first dīvān and will be found at line 14 on p. 164 of Āsī's edition of the *Kulliyāt*. Verses from poems not included in the dīvāns are referred to as (e.g.) *Kulliyāt*, p. 920, line 12

Perhaps the best of them is *Mu'āmlāt i Ishq* (The Stages of Love),[2] in which he tells the tragic story of his own love affair with a frankness that has caused most critics to pass over the poem in discreet silence. Mir was perhaps eighteen years old when he fell in love with a girl who was already married to someone else.[3] She seems to have been related to him, perhaps quite closely; for the poem suggests that she was not expected to observe parda towards him with the same strictness as would be demanded outside the family circle. The poem, which was written long after the events it describes, does not tell the whole story, but recalls and describes in a series of pictures those episodes which remained especially vivid in Mir's memory.

It all began, he says, when he heard others in the family talking about the girl, praising her appearance and bearing, her good qualities and her kind nature. He became curious to see her, and when he did, he at once fell in love with her, and she with him, though she at first hid this from him. What followed may be told largely in Mir's own words:

I would watch her whenever I was unobserved, but though my heart was full, I could not speak to her. Later we met discreetly when we could, and she was unfailingly kind and compassionate to me, though at times she would tease me too. For a long time things went no further than that, but in time we became more intimate, and she would let me hold her by the hand or touch her feet as I sat near her on the ground. I cannot describe her perfect beauty. She was as though cast in the mould of my desire, and her every limb was lovely. Her walk was incomparably graceful, and with all her beauty she was kind and loving too, and if she teased me, it was with such affection that it made me love her all the more. I would want to caress her, but she would only laugh, and would not let me. One day when she was eating betel leaf, I asked her to kiss me, and let me take the liquor of her mouth into my own; she laughed and refused at first, but later let me do as I wanted. Our love for each other increased, and I began to urge her to meet me where we should not have to fear any interruption. She too would speak of the same thing. But she kept delaying the day, and one day she said to me, ''No good can come of our love; how long

2 Literally, "Transactions of Love," but this sounds awkward in English, and "Stages" accurately conveys the structure of the poem. It occupies pp. 918–928 of the *Kulliyāt*.
3 *Kulliyāt*, p. 920, line 13.

can we go on pining for each other like this ?'' I was too consumed by love to see the truth of her words, but today I think of them and weep. How can I describe what I suffered in separation from her? At nights I imagined her with me, but the days were unbearable. For years we did not see each other again. I was indifferent to the world, and to my wife and my children and my family. I would think with longing of the days when, in spite of all difficulties and dangers, I would sometimes come to her and sit silently by her. For her sake all my relatives and friends had set their faces against me and called me mad, and the meanest and most contemptible people had taunted me to my face. At last the grief of separation became more than either of us could bear. We met, and this time satisfied all the yearning of our hearts. We were together for several days, but there came a day when we again had to part. It was not her fault. Our fate was against us. She said, ''It is best that we should part for some time. In love there comes a stage when such things have to be faced. Do not think I am forsaking you, and do not grieve too much. As long as I live, you will· be in my heart. I too grieve at this parting. But what can I do? My honour must be my first concern.'' I could not speak in reply. I sat stunned and silent before her, trying to keep back the tears and speaking only if she spoke. After night fell, we parted, and I went from her lane as one who leaves behind him everything that is precious in the world.

I bear my sorrow alone. There is no one to whom I can tell my secret. Sometimes a message comes from her and I live again, but mostly nobody comes. How can I live parted from her like this ? The memory of her is always with' me—her loveliness, her tender love for me, her gentle speech, her grief at my distress, her longing to see me happy—and every memory brings the tears to my eyes. I long to be with her again, and without her I shall die.

An affair of this kind involved the families of both sides in deep disgrace, for which they usually took their revenge on the lovers. In Mir's case they persecuted him so bitterly that they drove him mad, and this experience too he has described in another masnavi entitled *Khwāb o Khayāl i Mīr* (Mir's Vision).[4] He says he became afraid to look at the moon at night and yet felt an irresistible desire to look, and when he did

4 *Kulliyāt*, pp. 968–974.

he fancied he saw there the form of a lovely woman. Her image began to be before his eyes night and day, and he could neither eat nor sleep because of her. Sometimes she would be kind to him; at other times she would seem to be angry. His preoccupation with her became more and more complete, and his madness more and more pronounced. His relatives and friends were deeply concerned for him and tried to get him cured. After trying amulets, spells, and incantations without success, they resorted to more drastic measures, and had bitter medicines administered to him; and when he showed an inclination to run away, they shut him in a small room—"narrower than the grave," says Mir—and half starved him, giving him only an occasional crust of bread and drink of water. They were afraid to come near him, and for hours together he was left alone in this cell. At length they decided to try the effect of bleeding him. Mir gives a vivid picture of the bloodletting. He lost so much blood that he became unconscious, and remained in a swoon until the next day. Violent noises were made to arouse him from it, and his eyes opened upon the same scene of the leech standing there with the lancet in his hand. More blood was let, until his clothes were all dripping wet and he again fell into a swoon. For days together after that he only occasionally recovered consciousness, and his life was despaired of. But as the days passed, his strength returned to him, and his madness gradually left him.

Mir's love story is a tragedy, and the realistic love masnavi in Urdu always is. This is not because the poets select only the tragic stories for their themes, but because in the society in which they lived, love was a tragedy. In their day love and marriage were two quite separate things, and were generally regarded not only as separate but also as mutually opposed. When a young man reached marriageable age, his parents would look for a bride for him, and she would have to be a Muslim of social status comparable to his own. When a suitable candidate was found, negotiations with her parents would follow, and if these succeeded, the marriage would be arranged. The boy and girl did not see each other until they were already man and wife. The main danger to this ordered course of life was love, and society exerted every effort to forestall the danger or to deal with it drastically if it arose. Its main preventive measures were parda and early marriage. Parda meant the most complete segregation of the sexes: no Muslim boy was allowed to see the face of any Muslim girl who had reached the age of eleven or twelve, except where close kinship

precluded the possibility of their falling in love. In every house there
were separate women's apartments—the *zanāna*—and a woman who
went out of the house (which she rarely did) had to wear a *burqa*—a
flowing garment which enveloped her completely from head to foot; a
flap hanging down over the face, or a strip of material finer than the rest
across the eyes, enabled her to see out without others seeing in. Early
marriage was also a safeguard against love. Before marriage the boy was to
have no chance to fall in love; after marriage, society hoped, he would
have no occasion to.

In this way society did what it could to prevent love. When it could
not prevent it, it punished it, and punished it drastically. A boy and girl
who were unfortunate enough to fall in love brought great shame upon
their families, who generally retaliated with savage persecution and even
with murder, for the lovers were held to be violating laws upon which
the very foundations of ordered social life were based. It is most important that the modern reader should realise that the lovers themselves
did not quarrel with this view. They too believed that love was a force
which threatened to disrupt the foundations of society, and that society
was obliged to defend itself against it, even if they themselves were to be
the victims. Stories of love were common, and if the average man felt
sympathy for the lovers, he reacted also with the fervent hope that he
himself would never fall in love. The love poets themselves often express
this feeling. Thus Mir writes:

زنداں میں پھنسے طوق پڑے قید میں مر جائے

پر دامِ محبت میں گرفتار نہ ہووے

Live in the chains of slavery, and die in jail
But do not fall into the snare of love.   (I.165.16)

ان صحبتوں میں آخر جانیں ہی جاتیاں ہیں

نے عشق کو ہے صرفہ نے حسن کو محابا

To enter love's dominion is to throw your life away
For love makes no allowances, and beauty does not spare.

(I.24.24)

اگ تھے ابتدائے عشق میں ہم

اب جو ہیں خاک انتہا ہے یہ

I was all fire when first I fell in love:
Now at the last nothing but ash remains.   (I.136.10)

قیامت ہی یہاں چشم و دل سے رہی

چلے بس تو وہاں جا کے کرتے قیام

نہ دیکھے جہاں کوئی آنکھوں کی اور

نہ لیوے کوئی جس جگہ دل کا نام

Man's eyes and heart have plunged him in disaster—
If only he could go and make his home
Where no one ever looks into another's eyes,
And what is meant by "heart" is still unknown!

(I.90.13–14)

One verse pictures him on his deathbed, using his dying breath to impart
to a young friend the essence of his life's experience, and thinking how,
when he is dead, the boy will say:

وصیت میرے نے مجھ کو یہی کی

کہ سب کچھ ہونا تو عاشق نہ ہونا

Mir's last behest to me was only this:
"Do what you will, my son, but do not love!" (II.236.17)

In his masnavis the same ideas are reiterated. Love is a fire in which the
lovers burn to death, or a raging sea in which they drown.[5] One masnavi
concludes with the words:

---

5 *Kulliyāt*, p. 917, line 23; p. 901, line 10.

محبت نہ ہو کاش محلوق کو

نہ چھوڑے یہ عاشق نہ معشوق کو

Would that mankind were immune to love,
For it spares neither lover nor beloved.

(*Kulliyāt*, p. 899, lines 19–20)

A boy growing towards maturity would feel this fear of love more than
most, because he could not help feeling also the intensely strong desires
which come with adolescence. The parda system intensified these desires by denying him an outlet for them, and also by the very view of love
on which it was based; for its underlying assumption was that love is so
powerful a force that only the most stringent measures could hope to
combat it; and this very assumption helped to make it so. Thus the young
man desired love as strongly as he feared it, and the modern reader can
only with difficulty visualise something of the intense emotional stress to
which this subjected him. It is this all-pervading fear which in Urdu
poetry distinguishes the young lover from his counterpart in English
literature, where the young man "in love with love," the passionate
would-be lover who has no one to whom he can give his devotion, is a
slightly comic, though not unsympathetic, figure. In Urdu poetry the
comic aspect is overshadowed by the tragic.

Mir's masnavi *Darya i Ishq* (The River of Love)[6] shows what is likely to
happen to one in his position. The story begins with a description of the
boy and of his state of mind—"a handsome boy, tall and graceful as the
cypress, his heart within him softer than wax, and with love in every fibre
of his being"[7]—and goes on to tell how one day as he was passing down
the street he saw a girl looking at him from the window of one of the
houses. As soon as their eyes met, he fell in love with her, but she cared
nothing for him, and rising from her seat, she shook out the folds of her
dress and disappeared into the house. But he was in love with her, body
and soul, and from that day onwards he spent every moment he could near
her house, looking up again and again at the window at which he had first

[6] *Kulliyāt*, pp. 900–910.
[7] *Kulliyāt*, p. 901, lines 15ff.

I

seen her in the hope of catching sight of her again. People began to stare at him as they passed by, and some who thought he must have suffered some great mental shock showed sympathy for him. But it was not long before everyone realised what was wrong, and then he was blamed on all sides. His family and the girl's were near neighbours, and her parents soon came to suspect him. At first they planned to have him murdered, and so get rid of him once and for all, but then they reflected that responsibility might be traced to them and they would be disgraced. So they spread it about that the boy was mad, and egged people on to stone him and torment him. He was quite unaffected by all this, and the vehemence of his love continued as before.

At length the girl's family thought it best to send her away to stay with relatives who lived in another city on the other side of the river. She set out, seated in a closed palanquin and escorted by her old nurse. Her lover, who was at his usual place in the lane where she lived, guessed that it was she who was being taken away, and ran beside the palanquin, calling out to the girl inside to have pity on him and relent towards him. She did not answer, but the old nurse saw her opportunity and spoke to him encouragingly, holding out the hope that the girl would soon come to return his love and that one day they would be united. They reached the river, and went aboard the boat which was to ferry them across. When the boat was in mid-stream, the nurse took the girl's slipper and threw it into the water, and then challenged the boy, if he really loved her, to jump in and bring it back. He at once jumped in, but he could not swim and was drowned. The girl, who had until then been completely indifferent to him, was greatly moved by his devotion to her; but for the moment she said nothing.

Now that the young man was dead, there was no longer any reason why the girl should not be brought back home again, and escorted by her nurse as before, she set out on the return journey. As they made the return crossing, she told her nurse that she would like to see the river; for she had lived all her life in seclusion and had never seen a big river before. The nurse opened the palanquin so that she could see, and she asked a great many questions about all she saw, and in the end wanted to know where it was that the young man had jumped into the water and been drowned. When the boat reached the place, the nurse pointed it out, and the girl at once threw herself in and was drowned in the same spot. When the nurse reached home and told her parents what had happened, they ran lamenting to the riverside. The river was dragged, and the bodies of the two lovers, who in life had never been able to come together, were recovered clasped tightly in each other's arms.

Another masnavi tells the story of a young Afghan settled in Gujarat.[8] He was a strikingly handsome young man, and yet he enjoyed no less a reputation for the purity of his life, his modesty, and his devotion to his religion. So shy was he, says Mir, that if one of the houris of Paradise had advanced to meet him, he would have done his best to avoid her. Yet the day came when he too fell in love, with a young Hindu woman who he saw passing by in the street, and who looked at him as he glanced shyly at her. In the same moment she fell in love with him. But neither spoke to the other; they would see each other as she came up the road carrying water from the well, and that was all. In short, they behaved as true lovers should, and neither did anything which could bring the other into bad repute. A long time passed, and the woman's husband fell ill and died; and she, as the Hindu custom of *sati* (suttee) demanded, went to be burned on her husband's funeral pyre. When her lover heard of it, he ran to the place and threw himself into the flames, determined that if she must die, he too would burn to death with her; but bystanders rushed in and dragged him away, badly burnt, but still alive. They set out to take him home, where his injuries could be treated; but after they had gone some way, he asked them to lay him down for a while in the shade of a tree at the roadside, until he had recovered enough strength to continue the journey. He lay there the whole day until evening. For most of the time his eyes were closed, but whenever they did open, they turned to look back along the way they had come. As evening fell a woman was seen coming down the road, and as she drew near, she was recognised as the widow who had been burnt on the pyre that morning, looking now just as she had done in life. Everyone was too amazed to move as she went up to the boy and held out her hand to help him rise. Then hand in hand they walked away together down the road and were never seen again.

In *Sho'la i Shauq* (The Flame of Love) the story portrays a situation unusual in eighteenth-century life and literature alike, where the lovers are husband and wife. The central character is a young Hindu named

---

[8] *Kulliyāt*, pp. 911–917.

Parasrām.[9] He was a very good-looking boy, and was loved·and admired by many of his friends. Among these was one whose love Parasrām returned, and the two would spend much of their time in each other's company. But there came a day when Parasrām stopped visiting his friend, and for days together nothing was seen of him. When at length they did meet, his lover taxed Parasrām with his sudden indifference towards him and wanted to know the cause. Parasrām replied that he had recently married; he loved his wife dearly and could not bear to be parted from her a moment longer than was necessary; and she loved him with the same passionate devotion, so much so that he was convinced that she could not live without him. His lover replied: "I cannot believe it is so. This is only woman's deceit. Do not be taken in by it. What woman was ever constant in love? And what woman ever failed to survive her husband's death? Outwardly they are all fair, but within is deadly venom. God himself has spoken of their deceit:[10] no living being is more treacherous. The whole world knows of their treachery, and their deceit is on all men's tongues." He went on to say that if Parasrām doubted his words, he should put his wife to the test; then he would see that he spoke the truth. Parasrām agreed to do so, and a man was sent to his house to tell his wife that Parasrām had been drowned while bathing in the river. When she heard the news, she gave one despairing look towards the door through which Parasrām used to come, and then fell down in a faint and died.

When the messenger returned with the news of what had happened, Parasrām went nearly mad with grief, and his friend was overwhelmed with shame and regret. One day as he was wandering aimlessly about, Parasrām found himself at the riverside. A fisherman and his wife were talking together, and the wife was scolding her husband, because for the

9 *Kulliyāt*, pp. 890–899. An inevitable consequence of the parda system was the prevalence of homosexual love, and here as elsewhere Mīr portrays it without comment as one of the common manifestations of love. Some modern Urdū critics, especially those who pride themselves on having studied Western literature and assimilated its standards of taste, condemn classical Urdū poetry for the prevalence of this attitude, which, they claim, debars it from consideration as good literature. Such critics have either not noticed or have forgotten that, for. example, 126 of Shakespeare's sonnets out of a total of 154 are about his love for a beautiful young man. (Cf. G. B. Harrison's Introduction to the Penguin edition [1938], pp. 10–11.) One commonly finds with this school of critics that the application of their canons would condemn a great deal of the literature from the study of which these canons are allegedly derived.

10 The speaker means that God has spoken thus in the Qur'ān. (In fact, however, there is no verse in the Qur'ān declaring deceit to be an attribute of women in general.—A.S.)

past few days he had caught so little that his family had had to go hungry. He replied that just lately he had been afraid to fish at night, because every night a flame appeared on the river bank and a voice called out, "Parasrām! Where are you?" Parasrām that day seemed to become his old self again. He went to his friend and said that what was past, was past, and that there was nothing to be gained by grieving over it. Why should not they and a few friends go for an outing on the river that evening? His friend was delighted to see him so calm again, and readily agreed. When evening came they got into the boat, taking with them the fisherman whom Parasrām had heard speaking to his wife, for they needed someone who knew the river well and could make sure that they did not run into difficulties after darkness fell. Parasrām sat by him in the boat, and while the others were talking together, questioned him more closely about the flame he had seen and the exact spot where he had seen it. As they were talking, the flame appeared, and a voice was heard calling, "Parasrām, where are you?" Parasrām, in great agitation, got out of the boat unnoticed by the other passengers. The fisherman saw him standing as though in conversation with the flame, which seemed to stay still for a moment, then flare up and envelop him, after which it disappeared and was never seen again.

In spite of obvious differences, Mir's masnavis remind one of the English ballad. Both tell in a simple verse form a straightforward narrative, in which the situations and characters are of a kind thoroughly familiar to their audience, so that a few strokes are often enough to convey the whole picture and a few words of dialogue establish a full character. In both, the essential story is realistic, and though the supernatural element is also prominent, it blends in complete harmony with the rest and heightens the whole atmosphere. Above all, the atmosphere of both is at once tragic and heroic, for the themes of both are the stories of men and women who face with simple courage and dignity what they know to be an inevitable fate.

The similarities extend also to style. Indeed, the masnavi, the ballad, and the Homeric epic all have one striking feature in common: all use in a completely naive and undisguised way the conventions which are considered appropriate to the form, involving, for instance, a constant repetition of stock phrases, epithets, and similes, which nonetheless never seem to lose their freshness—perhaps because one finds alongside them an ability to rise to the very height of poetic power, where a bare statement in the simplest words makes an unforgettably vivid impact. Just as in Homer the sea is always "the wine-dark sea," the dawn "rosy-fingered," and the cattle "shambling," so in the ballads words like "fair," "red," "silver," or the numbers "three," "seven," "nine," and so on, are often employed with similar effect, an effect in which welcome familiarity blends with a seemingly inexhaustible freshness. With the masnavi it is the same, and one savours the descriptions of the "moon-faced" beauties, "tall and graceful as the cypress," whose hair is "long and black as the night of separation," whose eyebrows are "curved like the scimitar" and equally dangerous, and whose long eye-lashes are like sharp arrows that pierce their lovers to the heart. These are the comparisons which convention prescribes for Urdu love poetry and which the poet employs simply and naturally.

It seems also—as the textbooks recognise—that certain metres were also considered peculiarly appropriate to the masnavi. Of the five masnavis described above, three are in the same eleven-syllable metre as Mir Hasan's *Enchanting Story*: ◡ — —|◡ — —|◡ — —|◡ — (mutaqārib). The other two are in another metre, commonly used for the masnavi, and evidently a favourite with Mir. Its unit is basically a ten-syllable line, with a less regular, but still strongly marked, rhythm: — ◡ — —|◡ — ◡ —|— — (khafīf). More variations are permitted in this metre than in most, and once its rather complex pattern has been grasped, it makes a great appeal. Mir's own love story, *The Stages of Love*, is in this metre.

The masnavis cover only a relatively small part of Mir's love poetry. The rest is expressed in his ghazals, which make up not only the largest but also the best part of his poetry. They are much more difficult than the masnavis for the modern reader to understand and appreciate. In the first place, the ghazal form is completely strange to him. It has a closely knit, formal unity, and to our way of thinking, unity of form demands a cor-responding unity of theme, or at the very least, a unity of mood. And this the ghazal does not usually possess. Secondly, many of the experiences of love with which it deals are of a kind almost incomprehensible to one who has lived only in a modern society. Thirdly, the conciseness of the ghazal form, which requires the expression of an independent experience within a single couplet, has made it allusive in the extreme. The poet

assumes in his reader precisely what the modern reader does not possess—
a full knowledge of all the situations of love to which the social conditions of Mughal India gave rise. In the masnavi the poet can describe
these situations at some length; in the ghazal he has no room to do more
than hint at them, leaving it to the reader's imagination (as he safely
could) to supply the full picture. This same requirement of conciseness
produced also the characteristic diction of the ghazal; there was no room
to waste words, and every word was made to bear all the connotations of
which it was capable and which successive generations of ghazal writers
had given to it. Finally, there is an extravagance and exaggeration in the
emotional tone and language of the ghazal which the modern reader finds
it hard to accept.

A good many of these difficulties are resolved once their background is
understood. But it is as well to say at once that not all of them are. Some
of the unfamiliar features of the ghazal have simply to be accepted as
conventions to which the reader must accustom himself. Like most conventions in literary taste, they are not easy to accept when one first en-
counters them, but it is often easier and more profitable to accept them
than to attempt to reason about them. Nowadays the pun is regarded as
the lowest form of humour; yet Shakespeare and his audiences felt that
it heightened the expression of tragic emotion. They could probably not
have explained why it ought to be regarded in this way, but the modern
would not find it any easier to prove that his attitude is a more proper
one. Similarly, in approaching the Urdu ghazal he has to accept its lack of
all but formal unity, and to realise that whereas with us a unity of form
demands a unity of context, in eighteenth-century Mughal India it was
not so; the poet and his audience felt no dissatisfaction with a poem of
which every couplet, though linked by rhyme with every other, was a
separate entity.[11]

The intense, extravagant emotion of the ghazal is another matter.
This is not simply a convention of literature but also a true expression of
life, as the masnavi stories help to show. Brought up in isolation from
women, taught by society and by his own emotions to believe in the over-
mastering power of love, fearful of the drastic reprisals he must face if he

---

[11] The fact that Urdū poetry was, and still is, composed in the first place to be recited before
others, and not to be read in private, undoubtedly has a bearing on this feature of the ghazal
form. This point is elaborated in the Appendix, p. 273.

falls in love, himself believing that love is a danger to society, the lover is submitted to a strain which often proves literally unbearable and drives him mad. All such desperately intense emotions are expressed without restraint in the ghazal, and this unrestrained and frequently self-pitying expression is another stumbling block to the modern reader, who has been brought up to regard such things as unmanly. Dorothy Sayers, in explaining a similar feature of medieval French poetry, has put the point very well. "There are fashions in sensibility as in everything else," she writes. "The idea that a strong man should react to great personal and national calamities by a slight compression of the lips and by silently throwing his cigarette into the fireplace is of very recent origin." [12] One does not have to go outside English literature to see that this is true. Shakespeare's *Romeo and Juliet* is full of the same intense, extravagant emotion as the Urdu ghazal; and the fact that Romeo is a spirited, courageous, and resolute man does not prevent him from responding to the news of his banishment in a speech which equals in its passionate self-pity anything the Urdu ghazal can produce.

In short, to appreciate the ghazal one has to bear two things constantly in mind: first, the ghazal has its own conventions, and if some of these are strange to us, that does not necessarily make them absurd. Secondly, many features which may appear at first sight to be purely conventional are in fact a direct, natural expression of emotions that seem foreign to us only because we are no longer familiar with the situations that produce them.

One meets this sort of situation at the very starting point of Urdu love poetry. Love in the Urdu ghazal is always love at first sight. The modern tends to regard this as a romantic absurdity, quite remote from real life. From the real life which he knows perhaps it is remote, because he lives in a society where boys and girls mix freely, where a marriage is made by the mutual free choice of the two parties to it, and where love is seen as the prelude to marriage. He knows that the immediate strong attraction which even in his experience is sometimes felt between a boy and a girl is rarely an adequate basis for marriage, and because he knows this, and because there are plenty more fish in the sea, he plays down its importance. But his counterpart in Mughal India was in quite a different situation. He might go through life without ever experiencing passionate

---

[12] In the Introduction to her translation of *The Song of Roland* (Harmondsworth, 1957), p. 15.

love, without even seeing in his own community a beautiful girl whom he could love; and if some sudden accident of fate enabled him to do so, the impact upon him could be overwhelming. Considerations of a possible marriage did not affect his attitude towards her, for in any case he could only love her: he could never marry her. For him, therefore, love at first sight was not some rare, romantic absurdity, but the normal inception of love in the real-life conditions of his day.

Thus it is a real experience, and a common one, that Mir describes[13] when he writes to his mistress:

زلفیں کھولے تو تو تمک آیا نظر

عمر بھر یہاں کام دل بہم رہا

I caught a glimpse of you with hair dishevelled
And my distracted heart was yours for life. (I.40.25)

Or when he says:

ہوش و صبر و خرد و دین و حواس و دل و تاب

اس کے اک آنے میں کیا کیا نہ گیامت پوچھو

She came but once, but do not ask what left me as she went—
My strength, and faith, and fortitude, and will and heart and soul.

(I.133.19)

[13] We have throughout this chapter written on the assumption that the beloved of Mīr's ghazals is, like his mistress in *The Stages of Love*, the typical woman of parda society. *The Stages of Love* is itself substantial evidence for the view that for Mir's ghazals this assumption is probably justified. But in parda society, like every other in which there is drastic segregation of the sexes and a marked difference between the cultural level of men and that of women, love also found outlets in homosexual love and in resort to a class of cultured courtesans. Thus boys and courtesans, as well as respectable parda women, appear in the Urdū ghazal in the role of the beloved. In most verses the expression is too generalised for the class or sex of the beloved to be identifiable. In any case, in the philosophy of Urdu love poetry (which will be described in the next chapter), *all* beauty engenders love as its natural and proper human response, and there is no abhorrence either of pederasty or of love for courtesans. Nor is the concept of constancy a, so to speak, monogamous one. Constancy to one's beloved meant complete submission to her or his will: it did not necessarily imply that a man might not have more than one beloved. Mir, like most of the cultivated men of his day, must have mixed freely and intimately with courtesans. In the passage quoted on p. 35 above, the "beautiful women . . . whose long tresses held me their captive" can surely only have been courtesans.

Or in a line that expresses in a single image not only the compelling beauty of a woman but also the terrible danger which her lover must be prepared to face:

میرؔ تلوار چلتی ہے تو چلے
خوش خراموں کی چال ہے کچھ اور

> Mir, *let* the bright sword flash—in dreadful beauty
> A lovely woman's walk is something more. (I.71.15)

Or in a line like:

آنکھیں جنہوں کی زلف و رخِ یار سے لگیں
وے دیکھتے نہیں سحر و شام کی طرف

> Morning and night mean nothing any more
> To him whose eyes have seen her hair and face.
> (II.278.8)

The apparent simplicity of the line is deceptive, and it well exemplifies the extreme allusiveness of the ghazal technique. The first and obvious meaning is that one glimpse of her face and her hair is enough to captivate the young lover forever. But the words used suggest much more than this. In the ghazal the black night and the black hair of the beloved are regularly compared; so are the dazzling radiance of her face and the sun or the bright day. Thus one meaning of the couplet is that the beauty of the night and the beauty of the day recede into insignificance before the beauty of her hair and face. But the words also mean that for the lover the passage of time is unimportant: his love engrosses him wholly all his life through, and its intensity does not vary. Thirdly, the line may also suggest that true love continues unaltered not only by time but also by joy and sorrow alike. Where all love is clandestine, and where the lovers have to contend with a system organised for the very purpose of making impossible all contacts between boys and girls of marriageable age, such secret meetings as can be arranged frequently take place by day. The day symbolises therefore the joy of union, and the long nights (their length

affords another comparison with the beloved's hair), the grief of enforced separation. All these shades of meaning are relevant to the understanding of the line. And if the modern reader should object that this is to
read into the line more than is written in it, the ghazal poet and his
audience could reply in Olive Schreiner's words, "Certainly, the whole
of the story is not written here, but it is suggested. And the attribute of
all true art . . . is this, that it says more than it says, and takes you away
from itself. It is a little door that opens into an infinite hall where you may
find what you please." Olive Schreiner elaborates her point with another
comparison: "If we pick up the finger and nail of a real man, we can
decipher a whole story—could almost reconstruct the creature again,
from head to foot."[14] The image can be very aptly applied to the ghazal,
many of whose best lines are indeed in just this sense like "the finger and
nail of a real man."

Not all lines, of course, demand for their appreciation the degree of
background knowledge that this one does. There are many in which the
poet expresses his delight in the beauty of his mistress, and of beautiful
women generally, in tones that would be intelligible in any country and
any age:

جمع خوباں میں مرا محبوب اس مانند ہے

جوں ماہِ تابندہ آتا ہے کبھو تاروں کے بیچ

Where lovely women gather my beloved shines among them
As when the shining moon appears among the twinkling stars.

(VI.640.16)

سرگرم جلوہ اس کو دیکھے کوئی سو جانے

طرزِ خرام کیا ہے، حسن و جمال کیا ہے

Until you see her walk you will not know
What grace and poise and matchless beauty are.

(II.357.12)

---

[14] Ralph Iron (Olive Schreiner), *The Story of an African Farm* (London, 1896), pp. 171–172.

آنکلتا ہے کبھو ہنستا تو ہے باغ و بہار
اس کی آمدیں ہے ساری فصل گل آۓ کی طرح

Now and then she passes smiling, and for me the roses bloom
All the advent of the spring is in the grace of her approach.

(II.260.11)

ان گل رخوں کی قامت ہلکے ہے یوں ہوا میں
جس رنگ سے لچکتی پھولوں کی ڈالیاں ہیں

Their cheeks are fresh as roses, their swaying walk as lovely
As flower-laden branches moved by the morning breezes.

(III.412.24)

اتنی سڈول دیہی دیکھی نہ ہم سنی ہے
ترکیب اس کی گویا سانچے میں گئی ہو ڈھالی

A body beautiful as hers I never saw or knew of
As flawless is her form, as if cast in a perfect mould.

(VI.674.8)

ساتھ اس حسن کے دیتا تھا دکھائ وہ بدن
جیسے جھمکے ہے پڑا گوہر تر پانی میں

As the pure pearl shines through the limpid water
So does the beauty of her body shine.   (II.294.1)

گوندھ کے گویا پتی گل کی وہ ترکیب بنائ ہے
رنگ بدن کا تب دیکھو جب چولی بھیگے پسینے میں

In the hot season, when the sweat soaks through her bodice then I think
God gathered roses for His task and made her out of them entire.

(IV.503.24)

تنگیٔ جامہ ظلم ہے اے باعثِ حیات
پاتے ہیں لطفِ جان کا ہم تیرے تن کے بیچ

For you I live—whose tightly-clad, firm body
Teaches my soul what joy it is to live. (III.392.12)

لطفِ اس کے بدن کا کچھ نہ پوچھو
کیا جانیٔے جان ہے کہ تن ہے

Her body yields such joy, I know no longer
Whether it is her body or my soul. (II.360.12)

چشمِ مشتاق اس لب و رخ سے لحہ لحہ اٹھتی نہیں
کیا ہی لگے ہے اچھا اس کا کھڑا پیارا پیارا آج

Her lips and cheeks hold fast in thrall my yearning eyes,
How good her lovely face appears to me today! (V.553.5)

میرے اُن نیم باز آنکھوں میں
ساری مستی شراب کی سی ہے

Her wakening eyes, half-opened, seem to hold
All the intoxicating power of wine. (I.159.4)

نازکی اُس کے لب کی کیا کہیٔے
پنکھڑی اِک گلاب کی سی ہے

What words can tell the soft and tender beauty
Of the red rose's petal, or her lips? (I.158.21)

گلبرگ کا یہ رنگ ہے مرجاں کا ایسا ڈھنگ ہے
دیکھو نہ جھمکے ہے پر ادھ ہونٹھ لعلِ ناب سا

When did the petal of the rose, or the red coral match with theirs?
See how the colour of her lips glows with the purest ruby's fire.

(I.9.8)

یاقوت کوئی ان کو کہے ہے کوئی گل برگ
تمک ہونٹھ ہلا تو بھی کہ اک بات ٹھہر جائے

Some call them rubies, others rose petals
Just part your lips, and say the final word!   (I.181.20)

On the one hand Mir tries to convey his mistress' beauty by comparisons such as these. On the other, he feels that none of these things is
adequate to convey its overwhelming power. He tells her:

اے گل نو دمیدہ کے مانند
ہے تو کس آفریدہ کے مانند

Perhaps the flower in spring compares with you—
Yet what created thing compares with you?   (I.63.19)

جس گھر میں تیرے جلوہ سے ہو چاندنی کا فرش
وہاں چادرِ مہتاب ہے مکڑی کا سا جالا

In that house where the moonlight of your radiance lies spread
The moonlight seems as lustreless as does the spider's web.

(I.39.16)

And he tries to explain to others:

مشک و سنبل کہاں وہ زلف کہاں

شاعروں کے یہ شاخسانے ہیں

Let poets chatter on of musk and hyacinth:
When did such things match with *her* fragrant locks?

(II.297.7)

سرو و گل اچھے ہیں دونوں رونق ہیں گلزار کی ایک

چاہئے رُو اس کا سارُو ہو، قامت و لیا قامت ہو

The cypress and the rose are fine, and both adorn the garden—yet
Would that the rose had *her* cheek's beauty, would that the cypress had
her poise. (I.129.15)

Often, by a convention common in Urdu poetry, he represents things
which are proverbial for their beauty as overcome with shame when confronted with hers: the proud rose, the beloved of the nightingale; the
tall, slender, perfectly proportioned cypress, which, conscious of its
beauty, stands proudly aloof from the rest of the garden; the candle,
whose bright flame lures her lover, the moth, irresistibly to her, even at
the cost of his life:

قدِ یار کے آگے سرو چمن

کھڑا دُور جیسے گنہ گار تھا

Seeing her poise, the cypress in the garden
Stood afar off, as though it had done wrong. (II.247.13)

بلبل خموش ولالہ وگل دونوں سرخ و زرد

شمشاد محو بے کلی اک نسترن کے بیچ

کل ہم بھی سیرِ باغ میں تھے ساتھ یار کے

دیکھا تو اور رنگ ہے سارے چمن کے بیچ

The nightingale fell quiet, the tulip blushed, the rose turned pale
The cypress stood like one amazed, the eglantine distraught.
I too walked with my mistress in the garden yesterday
And all around I saw the changes that her beauty wrought.

(II.258.19–20)

آگے جب اس آتشیں رخسار کے آتی ہے شمع

پانی پانی شرمِ مفرط سے ہوئی جاتی ہے شمع

Her glowing, radiant face confronts the candle
And overwhelmed with shame, it melts away.   (III.401.17)

Alternatively, if nature possesses any charm which can be compared with
hers, that is because that charm is derived from her:

چشمک انجم میں اتنی دلکشی آگے نہ تھی

سیکھی لی تاروں نے اس کی آنکھ جھپکانے کی طرح

I never saw the stars so bright before:
It was her eyes that taught them how to shine.   (II.260.12)

کھلنا کم کم کلی نے سیکھا ہے

اُس کی آنکھوں کی نیم خوابی سے

It was her eyes, just wakening from sleep
That taught the rosebud its half-opened grace.   (I.207.23)

اب جونسیم معطر آئی شاید بال کھلےاس کے
شہرکی ساری گلیاں ہوگئیں گویا عنبربارا آج

Perhaps when it passed by that way my love was combing out her hair:
The scented breeze of morning brings a fragrance into every lane.

(V.553.7)

A boy who falls passionately in love for the first time in his life does not
find it easy to conceal the fact, and he had to prepare himself to pay the
penalties that society imposed, mounting progressively from the cold
hostility that the first suspicions produced to physical violence that might
even put his life in danger. But in many ways these were the least of the
possibilities he had to dread, for here he did know what was in store for
him. Much worse in his eyes was the uncertainty as to how the girl he
loved would behave towards him. Quite often, in the conditions of parda
society, she would not even have seen him, for she would not be without
her burqa except in circumstances where she thought no man could see
her, and she might continue quite unaware that she had been seen. But
even if she had seen him too, and sensed his love for her, she might well
feel indifferent or even hostile to him; for love at first sight is not
necessarily mutual. Whether indifferent to him or not, she reacted usually
with a new-found consciousness of and pride in her beauty, and realising
the power over her lover which this gave her, took a keen pleasure in
exercising it. All this is understandable; but it becomes doubly so when
one realises how rarely in Mughal society a woman could exercise such
power. She lived in a society in which man was her master in every
sphere and at every stage of her life. In childhood she was subject to her
father's authority, after marriage, to her husband's, and in old age, to her
son's; and this was not all. Under the joint-family system of Indian
society she would go immediately after marriage to live in the house of her
husband's parents, where she would be expected to subordinate herself
to a whole hierarchy of superiors—above all to her mother-in-law but
also to her husband's elder sisters and his elder brothers' wives. They,
whose life-experience was, like hers, one of subjection to male domi-
nance, often felt a compensating pleasure in dominating her, even in the

K

most trivial matters, and the young bride expected as a matter of course
that at least the early stages of her life in her new home would be a trying
experience. As late as the 1860s an Urdu novelist describes her situation:

> The freedom she had enjoyed in her parents' home was no longer hers.
> As soon as she arrived in her mother-in-law's house, everyone was
> intent on watching her and scrutinising her every action. One scans
> her features; another notes the length of her hair; another guesses her
> height; another examines her jewels; and another takes stock of her
> clothes. When she eats, they watch her all the time. How much did
> she put in her mouth? How wide did she open it? How many times did
> she chew it? And how much at a time did she swallow? If she gets up
> from her seat, they look to see how she robes herself in her mantle,
> how she holds up her skirts. And if she sleeps, they count the hours;
> what time did she go to bed? When did she get up? In short, every
> aspect of her conduct was under observation.[15]

The Muslim woman in Mughal India knew of no other kind of life and
did not question its rightness, though this is not to say that she did not
feel the hardness of her lot. But she in her turn would one day tyrannise
over her juniors, when seniority eventually gave her the right to do so,
and she might derive a similar pleasure from tyrannising over one—and
that too, a man—whom the accident of fate had put at her mercy. The
Urdu ghazal is full of the anguish which the lover felt when she did, an
anguish that mingles, however, with an involuntary admiration for her
proud self-possession and for the majesty with which she exercises her
tyranny over him. These very qualities, which are the source of so much
pain to him, make her even more attractive in his eyes. He looks at her
and thinks:

مر جاؤ کوئی پروا نہیں ہے

کتنا ہے مغرور اللہ اللہ

A man may die, and she will never care.
Oh God! Oh God! just see how proud she is!   (I.137.23)

15 Nazīr Aḥmad, *Mir'āt ul 'Arūs* (Delhi, 1898 ed.), p. 88. The translation is adapted from
that of G. E. Ward, *The Bride's Mirror* (London, 1903), p. 63.

جی گیا یہاں بے دماغی سے انھوں کی اور وہاں

سے جبیں سے چیں گئی ائے ابروؤں سے خم گئے

Her cruel pride has robbed me of my life—yet as she looks on me
Her eyebrows' curve, her furrowed brow tell of her high displeasure
   still.   (II.350.2)

فلک نے بہت کھینچے آزار لیک

نہ پہنچا ہم اس دل آزار سا

Fate has struck many blows, but none like that
   Which destined her to be my torturer.   (II.240.8)

And for all this, in the last resort, he blames himself. He should not
have let her see how he loves her, for it was her knowledge of his love
which made her for the first time conscious of her beauty and of the
power it put into her hands.

میرا اظہارِ محبت میں گیا جی تیرا

ہائے نادان بہت تونے چھپایا ہوتا

You told your love, and that was your undoing.
   Fool! You should have concealed it all you could.   (II.233.8)

Her complete absorption in her own new-found beauty is the theme of
many lines. Sometimes the tone is bitter:

وہ محوِ جمال اپنے ہے پروا نہیں اس کو

خواہاں رہو تم اب کہ طلب گار رہو تم

The study of her beauty occupies her. What are you?
Though you desire her and petition her day in, day out.
                                                      (III.407.7)

She is beautiful, and beautiful women are a law unto themselves:

They do as *they* think fit: no beauty yet
Took notice of what other people say.　　(II.296.25)

Sometimes, along with the involuntary admiration and the bitterness, there is a hint of sarcasm and mockery too:

Such pride in your fair symmetry, my love?
God marred you when He made you beautiful.　(III.396.20)

And sometimes the poet speaks in terms which, perhaps deliberately, leave one in some doubt as to how they should be interpreted:

My idol, my fair torturer stood before me:
Stricken with awe, God came into my mind. (II.228.15)

Several interpretations are possible. The verse *may* be a direct tribute to his mistress. So awe-inspiring is her presence that he turns to God to sustain him, as one does in moments of great stress. Or, so majestic is she that she brings to mind the majesty of God himself. Or, Mir may be saying sarcastically, "The airs she gives herself! Who does she think she is? God Almighty?" In addition to which, the contrast between the "idol" of the first line and the "God" of the second suggests other trains of thought. All of which is entirely characteristic of the ghazal idiom.

The experience of his mistress' calculated cruelty towards him was one which every lover had to undergo. But it might be motivated by things other than a real indifference. Even a girl who responded to him with a love as spontaneous and complete as his own was likely to treat him in the same way. For her both the penalties and the prizes of love were greater than they were for him. A man might have a love affair in his youth, and once the scandal had died down, still be able to take his place in the normal life of society. That was not possible for a woman, and if once her love was discovered, things commonly ended with her suicide. Yet the prospect of being truly loved by a man contrasted so markedly with the normal course of her life that it seemed infinitely attractive to her, despite the almost certain penalty she must some day pay. For one in her position the whole problem was to know whether her lover did love her truly, and whether he had the devotion and the courage to remain true to her in the face of every trial, and so sustain her in all she would have to undergo. And so, if she could, she would conceal her love from him and put him to the test, offering him every discouragement until she could feel that his steadfastness was proved. Which is not to say that she didn't at the same time exult in her beauty and take pleasure in her power to make him miserable.

Her lover understood all this very well. He accepted that it was for him to prove his devotion to her, and he would try all he could to do so, hoping that her indifference would prove to be only feigned, or that even if it were real, his constant devotion might one day change it into love. He did not conceal the emotional stress to which this subjected him. The modern Englishman is naturally reticent about such things, but the ghazal poet, equally naturally, pours out with all the extravagance that he feels, the violence of his love and pain, self-pity and humiliation, anger and bitterness. He tries to explain what he, and all true lovers, feel:

عشق ومحبّت کیا جانوں میں لیکن اتنا جانوں ہوں س

اندر ہی اندر سینے میں سینے دل کو کوئی کھاتا ہے

I do not know what love and passion are.
How can I tell? But this alone I know
Within the inmost chamber of my breast
Something is tearing at my heart always.   (V.609.22)

گھبرا کے یوں لگے ہر سینے میں دل تڑپنے
جیسے اسیرِ تازہ بیتاب ہو قفس میں

As the new-captured songbird beats his wings against the cage
So beats my agitated heart, imprisoned in my breast.   (III.420.10)

دل جلتے کچھ بن نہیں آتی حال بگڑتے جاتے ہیں
جیسے چراغِ آخری شب ہم لوگ نبڑتے جاتے ہیں

When once our hearts catch fire no power avails to save us from our fate
Like lamps that burn throughout the night we too are steadily consumed
(V.588.16)

Not only is the violence of his own feeling destroying him. He has also
to contend with the persecution from society which a lover had to face:

اس کی طرف جو لی ہم نے ہے اپنی طرف سے پھر اعالم
یعنی دوستی سے اس بت کی دشمن ساری خدائی ہوئی

I take my stand for her—the world turns and assails me:
I am her friend—and all creation is my enemy.   (V.602.8)

کہے ہے جس کو ملامت جہاں میں ہی ہوں
اجل رسیدہ، جفا دیدہ، اضطراب زدہ

Whom all the world reviles and persecutes, that man am I—
Struck down by fate, and by her cruelty, and my distress.
(I.138.14)

But worst of all is her callousness and cruelty:

کیا جانے ہوتے ہیں سخن لطف کے کیسے

پوچھا نہیں ان نے تو ہمیں پیار سو اب تک

How should I know the meaning of fair words?
She never yet asked kindly after me.   (I.82.21)

دوستی یاری الفت باہم عہد میں اس کے کرم نہیں

یہ جانیں ہیں مہر و وفا اک بات ہی گویا مدت کی

Friendship, devotion, mutual regard—
All are outmoded fashions in her eyes.
She thinks that love and loyalty are things
One reads about in tales of days gone by.   (III.437.14)

لطف و مہر و وفا وہ کیا جانے

ناز ہے خشم ہے عتاب ہے میاں

مہر و وفا و لطف و عنایت ایک سے واقف ان میں نہیں

اور تو سب کچھ طنز و کنایہ رمز و اشارا جلنے ہے

To taunt and sneer and wound and speak unkindly—
She has all these accomplishments, my friend;
Friendship and love and graciousness and kindness
Are things that she could never comprehend.

(V.607.5; III.417.12)

How complete is the contrast between her attitude and his:

میں جی سنبھالتا ہوں وہ ہنس کے ٹالتا ہے
یہاں مشکلیں ہیں ایسی وہاں یہ سہا ہلے ہیں

I nurse a wounded heart; she laughs and turns away.
Such is my heavy grief: so light she makes of it.   (II.305.5)

وہاں سے جز ناز و تحتر نہیں کچھ یہاں سے میرے
عجز ہے دوستی ہے عشق ہے غمخواری ہے

From her, pride and disdain and nothing else—from me
Honour, devotion, love, strength to sustain her.   (V.617.21)

And with all this it is he whom she and society alike hold guilty:

یہاں مہر تھی وفا تھی وہاں جور تھے ستم تھے
پھر نکلے بھی تو میرے یہ ہی گناہ نکلے

On my side, love and loyalty: on hers, vindictive cruelty.
And this they know; yet it is I must bear the brand of infamy.
(II.342.9)

In some lines he addresses her direct, reproaching her, appealing to her pity or to her sense of justice, suggesting even that if she rejects his love, it will be her loss as well as his.

بن کچھ کہے سنا ہے عالم سے میں نے کیا کیا
پر تو نے یہ نہ جانا اے بے وفا کہ کیا تھا

My lips returned no answer to all the world's revilings;
But what was that to you, love? You did not even notice.
(I.47.4)

کرتا ہے کون منع کہ سچ اپنی تو نہ دیکھ

لیکن کبھی تو میرے کے کر حال پر نظر

See your own beauty and rejoice: I never said "Do not do so."
But sometimes spare a glance for me, and see what it has brought me to.
(I.65.14)

دشمن ہیں اپنے جی کے تھارے لئے ہوئے

تم بھی حقوق دوستی کے کچھ ادا کر دو

For love of you I count my life as nothing.
Is nothing in return then due from you? (II.316.22)

پامال کرکے ہم کو پچھتاؤ گے بہت تم

کمیاب ہیں جہاں میں سر دینے والے ہم سے

Trample me in the dust then—and rue the day you did so;
You may not find another to lay his life down for you.
(I.155.10)

Sometimes he imagines her companions pleading his cause for him:

تم کبھو میر کو چاہو سو کہ چاہیں ہیں تمہیں

اور ہم لوگ تو سب اُن کا ادب کرتے ہیں

You should love Mir the way that he loves you.
The rest of us all hold him in regard. (III.423.11)

Along with verses in which all his intense emotions are expressed, one
finds others in which a certain wry humour is evident, an awareness that

there is something in his position, and in hers, and in the whole situation which some might feel to be a little ludicrous. This note appears in many instances. He sees how all his devotion seems to go for nothing; it cannot stimulate even her sympathy, let alone her love; and he thinks to himself:

کہتے ہیں آگے تھا اُبتوں میں رحم
ہے خدا جانے یہ کب کی بات

People have told me beauty once was kind—
That must have been God knows how long ago.   (I.59.10)

He imagines people telling his fair, cruel beloved:

حسن تو ہے ہی کر و لطفِ زباں بھی پیدا
میرے کو دیکھو کہ سب لوگ بھلا کہتے ہیں

Beauty you have—now find fair words to match it.
This is what makes men speak so well of Mir.   (II.290.8)

—not knowing that of all the examples they could hold up to her, none could be more inappropriate than his, for it is he above all others who provokes her cruelty.

Sometimes he jokes even at his mistress' expense. Like every true lover, he knows that she is sensitive in the extreme and quick to take offence at the slightest cause; and he accepts this as her rightful prerogative. But he is impudent enough to suggest that she is not the only one: he too may feel as she does, and she should bear this in mind. He tells her:

دل کی کچھ قدر کرکے تے رہیو تم
یہ ہمارا بھی ناز پرور تھا

Have *some* consideration for my feelings:
My heart was delicately-nurtured too.   (I.42.20)

And:

I am more sensitive, my love, than even you can be;
For you have but to knit your brow, and I am like to die.

(I.17.10)

This rather wry humour is especially characteristic of Mir. It derives in the last resort from a sureness of himself, a complete confidence that he has the strength to stand all the tests of love without breaking, and can therefore see them and love, and his mistress and himself, without illusion, and even laugh at what he sees. In some verses he speaks ruefully of his fame as a poet, and smiles at its pitiful irrelevance to his standing as a lover:

We have no common ground on which to meet.
If only *you* had been a poet too!   (IV.485.13)

Men come from south and east and west in hopes to get a glimpse of me
Sad, that it should be you alone care nothing for my company.

(III.437.12)

This calm, humorous acceptance of his position is well-expressed in a short ghazal devoted wholly to the theme. In this stage of love, Mir says, complete devotion on his side and complete indifference on hers are part of the natural order of things, and if people suggest anything to the contrary, they are lying:

هم اور تیری گلی سے سفر دروغ دروغ

کہاں دماغ ہیں اس قدر دروغ دروغ

تم اور ہم سے محبت تھیں خلاف خلاف

ہم اور الفتِ خوب دگر دروغ دروغ

غلط غلط کہ رہیں تم سے ہم تنک غافل

تم اور پوچھو ہماری خبر دروغ دروغ

کسو کے کہنے سے مت بدگماں ہو میرے سے تو

وہ اور اُس کو کسو پر نظر دروغ دروغ

I would be fancy-free? They lie! They lie!
Can such presumption be? They lie! They lie!
You are in love with *me*? Absurd! Absurd!
I love another she? They lie! They lie!
No! No! I *never* cease to think of you.
You asking anxiously? They lie! They lie!
They have their doubts of Mir? Pay them no heed.
He is not false, not he! They lie! They lie!

(I.80.4, 5, 6, 8, 9)

The humorous note persists when he puts to one side the distress which her cruelty is inflicting on him, and calmly avows his love for her, asserting that this is no crime and that she has no right to punish him:

کچھ تھیں ملنے سے بیزار ہو میرے درنہ

دوستی ننگ نہیں، عیب نہیں، عار نہیں

You do not want my love, but all the same
To love you is no slur, no fault, no shame. (III.415.20)

Or if it is a crime, then not he but she should be called to account; for if
he loves her, it is because her loveliness compels him to:

The guilt is mine alone, then—simply because I love you?
But why are you so lovely? *You* should be called to answer.

(V.615.7)

Despite all this, in loving her, he makes no demands of her; he may ask
for everything, but he demands nothing as of right. He comes not to demand her love, but to offer her his own, and he tells her that while she
is free to reject him, she should consider that in doing so, she may be
throwing away something that is precious. This point too is sometimes
made in quite a flippant tone. Speaking to all mistresses, and in the name of
all lovers, he says,

دلبراں دل جنس ہے گنجائشی
اس میں کچھ نقصان نہیں سرکار کا

Fair mistresses, accept the hearts we bring you.
You can't lose—and perhaps you'll even gain. (VI.631.22)

He means what he says, and what is here put almost jokingly is elsewhere
expressed in real earnest:

آئینے کو بھی دیکھو پر ٹک ادھر بھی دیکھو
حیران چشم عاشق دیکھے ہے جیسے ہیرا

Yes, gaze into your mirror too; but for a moment glance this way:
Intent on you, your lover's eyes shine brilliant as diamonds.

(II.229.21)

All the allusive power of the ghazal form is here brought into play, so that it "says more than it says, and takes you away from itself." It says, like the verse quoted earlier, that the lover thinks his mistress' preoccupation with her own beauty fully justified, and asks only that she should spare an occasional glance for him. But the second line carries the clear implication that if only she will look his way, she will see something more arresting and more valuable to her than what she sees in the mirror; and this implication is reinforced by the use of words which carry a wide range of allusion. "Mirror" itself is one such word. "Mirror" is regularly used as a symbol of beauty; it is often used metaphorically of the beauty of the universe, for the universe itself is conceived of by the poets as a great mirror created by God in order that His divine beauty might be reflected. And on a more mundane level, as we have seen in *The Enchanting Story*, mirrors were set up as part of the preparations for great occasions of public rejoicing. Thus the mirror itself is a thing of great beauty for the beloved to gaze upon, in addition to which it shows her her own perfect beauty reflected in it. Yet even so, she is asked to look into her lover's eyes, and the very first word suggests that they can compare with the mirror. The root meaning of the word *hairān*, here translated as "intent," means at a loss—at a loss because overwhelmed by some emotion—in this case, by the emotional impact of the beauty that it sees; and it is a regular epithet of the mirror, which is pictured as staring intently, as though hypnotised, at the face reflected in it. Once the comparison with the mirror is established, the poet goes further and compares the lover's eye with a shining diamond, which is at once more bright, more beautiful, and more valuable than a mirror is. It is so not only because it holds the promise of all that her lover's complete devotion can give to her, but also because it can even fulfil, and more than fulfil, the function of a real, tangible mirror. If she looks into her mirror, it shows her only what she herself has put into it—namely, her own beauty and her own estimate of it. If she looks into her lover's eyes, she will find her beauty more accurately portrayed, for she will see reflected there something of what her beauty means to him, and that, for all her own pride in it, is much more than what it means to her. If the modern reader should feel once again that all this is too fanciful, it can only be repeated that to one steeped in the traditions of the ghazal all such overtones readily suggest themselves.

This proud assertion of the lover, in words and in deeds, that his love makes no demands of her, and that it is for her own sake that she should accept it, is his most effective plea; and if he is patient and bears steadfastly all the tests to which his mistress puts him, the day may come when she shows signs of returning his love. She still likes to use her beauty to inflame him, while yet denying him access to her; but now there is an occasional hint that she not only recognises his devotion, but likes him for it. His first reaction is surprise:

پوچھا تھا راہ جاتے کہیں ان نے میرکو

آتا ہے اس کی بات کا اب تک عجب مجھے

As she went on her way she asked about me
And I am lost in wonder at it still.   (I.196.3)

He begins to realise how infinite are her attractions:

چشمک غمزہ عشوہ کرشمہ آن انداز و ناز و ادا

حسن سوائے حسن ظاہر میرے بہت ہیں یار کے بیچ

Her sidelong glance, imperious airs, her charm and grace and poise and
  pride—
Not just the beauty of her form, but how much beauty more beside!
    (V.556.16)

خندۂ و چشمک و حرف و سخن زیر لبی

کہے جو ایک دو افسوں ہوں دلدار کے پاس

Her smile, her glance, the way she talks, the murmur barely heard—
Not one or two the spells she casts, but past all reckoning.   (II.273.8)

She asks him what he wants of her. He thinks to himself:

دل میرے دلبروں سے چاہا کرے ہر کیا کیا

کچھ انتہا نہیں ہے عاشق کی آرزو کو

What does my heart *not* want of my beloved ?
For, Mir, a lover's longings have no end.   (IV.507.11)

And he answers her frankly:

کیا کہیئے کیا رکھیں ہیں ہم تجھ سے یار خواہش

یک جان و صد تمنّا یک دل ہزار خواہش

My love, I cannot tell the tale of all the things I want of you.
A hundred longings fill my soul, a thousand yearnings throng my heart.
(II.275.3)

But to desire is not to ask, still less to demand; and he is anxious to re-
assure her that the smallest sign of her regard would be precious to him.
And so he says:

صبر کہاں جو تم کو کہیئے لگ کے گلے سے سو جاؤ

بولو نہ بولو بیٹھو نہ بیٹھو کھڑے کھڑے ٹک ہو جاؤ

"Sleep in my arms!"—no, these are words I cannot find the strength to
say.
You need not speak; you need not stop; just pause as you pass by this way.
(IV.511.7)

بہار آئی گل پھول سر جوڑے نکلے

رہیں باغ میں کاش اس رنگ ہم تو

The spring has come, the flowers bloom cheek by cheek—
Would you and I might stand thus in the garden!   (VI.659.5)

یک نگہ ایک چشمک ایک سخن

اس میں بھی تم کو ہے تامّل سا

One glance, one kindly look, one word I ask—
But even so I see you hesitant.   (II.227.2)

ایک دو بات کبھو ہم سے کہو یا نہ کہو

قدر کیا اپنی ہمیں اس لیے تکرار نہیں

Speak to me now and then—or do not speak.
I know my worth. How can I press you to?   (III.415.21)

گر مجھ کب دیکھتے ہو پر دیکھو

آرزو ہے کہ تم ادھر دیکھو

I cannot think that you could look at me
Yet I will wish that you would look at me.   (I.124.22)

He does not even ask her to be kind to him alone:

کون کہتا ہے نہ غیروں پہ تم امداد کرو

ہم فراموش ہووں کو بھی کبھو یاد کرو

I do not ask you not to favour others
But only to remember me sometimes.   (I.130.14)

If she is moved by these appeals, there now comes a stage when, for
her, the emotional stress is at its most unbearable. She wants his love, and
wants to give him hers in return; but she cannot feel the complete certainty which she so desperately needs: she cannot *know* whether it will be
worth the price she must pay, whether she can trust him to be true to the
very end, or whether she can herself find the strength which the trials of
love will demand of her; and the closer she comes to committing herself,
the more likely she is to draw back in sudden panic before it is too late.
In such a state of mind every spontaneous impulse tends for the time
being to govern her, so that at one moment she will surrender to love,
and at the next draw back in fear; at one moment swear to be true forever, and at the next go back on her promise and determine to have
nothing more to do with her lover. These violent alternations of feeling
may persist over a long period, for as long, in fact, as the slightest

possibility of retreat remains to her. Thomas Hardy, in his novel *Under the Greenwood Tree*, set in rural England about a century ago, has portrayed in the character of Fancy Day a girl who resembles in many ways the heroine of the Urdu ghazal. He shows at the climax of the story how in her impulsiveness and uncertainty Fancy takes a step which amounts to complete betrayal of her lover, and which could mar her own happiness for life. But so well has Hardy portrayed her that the reader understands why she does it, and does not withdraw his sympathy from her.[16] With the heroine of the ghazal most of the background is left to the reader's imagination, but if he can understand Fancy Day, he can understand also how the girl in Mughal India, faced with alternatives so much more complex and so much more drastic than Fancy was, could act as she did.

The effort to attain to imaginative sympathy with her is all the more necessary, because in the ghazal we see her not directly but through the eyes of her lover. To him her conduct necessarily appears more perverse and her cruelties more capricious than ever, and even though he understands something of the state of mind which causes it, he cannot help expressing the misery it makes him feel, and protesting against it:

ملنا نہ ملنا ٹھہرے تو دل بھی اپنا ٹھہرے

اقرار ہے ہمیشہ انکار ہے ہمیشہ

Make up your mind to one thing;
    my heart is restless always.
Always you say you love me;
    always you keep me from you.   (VI.661.15)

But very often there is an implicit sympathy for her position and a note of humour to relax the tension:

ہے عشق میں صحبت مرے خوباں کی عجب کچھ

اقرار سے بے زاری ہیں انکار سے ناخوش

Strange is the loving converse which my mistress holds with me.
My pledge of love earns her disgust—denial her displeasure!
    (IV.486.8)

[16] *Under the Greenwood Tree*, Pt. IV, Chap. 6.

کیا کریں نیچی نظر کرنے سے غصّہ کھائے وہ

اور مجلس میں جو رہیئے دیکھ تو شرمائے وہ

What must I do? I lower my gaze from her and she is angry
And if I gaze only on her, she blushes and feels shy.   (III.435.5)

جو چپکے ہوں کہے چپکے ہو کیوں تم

کہو جو کچھ تمھارا مدّعا ہے

سخن کریئے تو ہو دے حرف زن یوں

بس اب منھ موند لے میں نے سنا ہے

If I am quiet she aks me, "Why so quiet?
Speak up if you have anything to say!"
And if I speak she quickly interrupts me,
"Now hold your tongue! I'll hear no more today!"
                                          (II.355.23–24)

When she deliberately ignores him, he tells her with mock naivete:

وجہ بیگانگی نہیں معلوم

تم جہاں کے ہو واں کے ہم بھی ہیں

I cannot see why you should act the stranger,
For you and I sprang from a common source.   (III.413.11)

They sit together, not knowing what to say to each other, until at last she
asks him why he does not say something. He answers with a straight face:

ہم تو تمھارے حسن کی حیرت سے ہیں خموش

تم ہم سے کوئی کرتے نہیں بات کیا سبب

I sit in silent wonder at your beauty.
And you? What is it that has struck *you* dumb?   (V.549.4)

As they grow more intimate and his occasional boldness provokes her anger, this playing the simpleton is often his way of disarming her:

بوسہ لبوں کا مانگتے ہی منہ بگڑ گیا
کیا اتنی میری بات کا تم کو برا لگا

I ask you for a kiss and you get angry.
Why should a little thing like this upset you?   (II.216.4)

بوسہ لبوں کا مانگتے ہی تم بگڑ گئے
بہتیری باتیں ہوتی ہیں اخلاص پیار میں

Such anger? Just because I want to kiss you on the lips?
But things like this keep happening all the time when you're in love.

(III.420.1)

آنکھیں غصے میں ہو گئیں ہیں لال
سر کو چھاتی پہ رکھ کے خواب کر دو

Your wrath has made your eyes all tired and bloodshot
Come, lay your head upon my breast and sleep.   (VI.658.18)

But whether he can placate her or not, whether he understands her or not, no matter how irrational and unpredictable in her ways she is at this stage, he simply cannot help loving her:

دیر بد عہد وہ جو یار آیا
دور سے دیکھتے ہی پیار آیا

Time after time she broke her word, but when she came at last
I saw her from afar and knew: to see her was to love her.

(VI.632.8)

As she inclines more and more towards him, he can hope that she will surrender herself completely to love and that all the barriers which for so long she has raised against him will be gone:

لطف سے لبریز ہے اس کام جاں کا سب بدن

مختلط ہو جائے ہم سے جو کبھو تو ہائے وہ

Joy of my life, her body overflows with all delights.
Ah for the day when she will come and sleep in my embrace!

(III.435.8)

چاہتا ہے جی کہ ہم تو ایک جا تنہا ملیں

نازِ بے جا بھی نہ ہو وے کم نگاہی بھی نہ ہو

I want to be alone with you—just you and I together
Where haughty airs and distant looks no longer come between us.

(I.135.6)

گرمیاں متصل رہیں باہم

نے تساہل ہوئے نے تغافل ہو

Let us love one another all the time—
No feigned reluctance, no indifference.   (II.311.8)

And that stage is reached—but not without a long conflict between shame and love. At first her shyness makes him desire her all the more:

ہوتا ہے شوق وصل کا انکار سے زیاد

کب تجھ سے دل اٹھاتے ہیں تیری نہیں سے ہم

You think your ''No!'' can ever cool my love for you? Not so.
My longing to possess you burns more strong because of it.

(II.289.21)

اقرار میں کہاں ہے انکار کی سی خوبی
ہوتا ہے شوقِ غالب اس کی نہیں نہیں پہ

Her sweet reluctance fires me with a keener love for her,
And her resistance gives a joy compliance cannot give.

(VI.644.5)

Yet as it continues, it puzzles him:

راتوں پاس گلے لگ سوتے ننگے ہو کر ہے یہ عجب
دن کو بے پردہ نہیں ملتے ہم سے شرماتے ہیں ہنوز

We pass the long nights naked in each other's arms. How strange
That in the daytime still she shyly veils her face from me.

(V.566.17)

At last she no longer feels any shyness when she is with him; and in her
simplicity and lack of all affectation, he finds her more irresistibly attractive than ever before:

ایک فقط ہے سادگی ترے بلائے جاں ہے تو
عشوہ کرشمہ کچھ نہیں آن نہیں ادا نہیں

You use no charms, no sidelong glance, no wayward airs to win me now—
Nothing but your simplicity—and this has won me heart and soul.

(I.110.3)

And though he has lost everything in loving her, he knows now that she
will respond to him fully when he says:

آج ہمارے گھر آیا تو کیا ہے یہاں جو نثار کریں
الّا کھینچ بغل میں تجھ کو دیر تلک ہم پیار کریں

Now you have come I've nothing left to offer you but this:
I'll draw you into my embrace and love you all day long.

(II.298.22)

Lines like these depict a stage where love has at length triumphed over every difficulty. But such lines are comparatively rare in ghazal poetry, for, unlike the masnavi, the ghazal is, in the main, the poetry of unrequited love. Both kinds of experience were abundant enough in real life, and at first sight it seems that both the masnavi and the ghazal present a false picture; for in all the masnavi stories, the girl, having once given her love, is constant to the end, while in the ghazal this never happens. The truth seems to be that here, once again, we are faced with a convention which we must simply accept, and that one poetic form alone was considered appropriate for the portrayal of each type of experience.

Be that as it may, the ghazal portrays in countless verses the picture of a girl cooling towards her lover and trying to break the ties that have bound them. As always, it expresses only what the lover feels when this happens; the motives of the girl's conduct are left to the imagination. They no doubt included everything which in universal human experience causes love to grow cold; but one must add to the picture all the strains imposed by the Mughal social setting. The need to maintain complete secrecy, and the ever-present fear of discovery and of the punishment that discovery would bring, put the whole relationship between them under tremendous stress. In general their meetings could only be infrequent, brief, and dangerous, and the atmosphere of strain would make for misunderstandings and quarrels which caused them both the most acute misery. Finally there was the feeling, especially on the woman's part, that her conduct was shameful and dishonourable. If, faced with all this, she felt that she could not go on, that is understandable. No doubt in real life the same situation led as often—perhaps more often—to a similar conclusion on his side, but the ghazal portrays only the constant lover. He sees her love for him dying out, until the days when she responded fully and freely to his love survive only as memories:

هر آن تھی سرگوشی یا بات نہیں گا ہے

اوقات ہے اک یہ بھی ہاک وہ بھی زمانہ تھا

We whispered to each other then; now you don't speak to me.
Well, those were other times, and now another age has dawned.

(III.375.13)

وصل میں اس کے روز و شب کیا خوب گزرتی تھی اپنی
ہجراں کا کچھ اور ہے ساماں اب وہ لیل و نہار نہیں

How happily the days would pass when she was with me day and night.
It is a different picture now: the nights and days are not the same.

(VI.653.21)

اب وہ ساماں نہیں ہے کہ وہ کام جان خلق
مغموم ہم کو دیکھ کے دوڑا لپٹ گیا

When I was sad she used to run and throw her arms about me—
She whom the whole world worshipped—but, alas, those days are gone.

(II.242.9)

But his memories are vivid, and they sustain him in his sorrow:

یہ بھی ساماں خوش ترکیبوں کا میرے نہ اپنے دل سے گیا
سوتے سے اٹھ کر آنکھیں ملی ہیں لی انگڑائی جمائیں ہیں

I loved to see her wake from sleep, and rub her eyes, and stretch and
yawn.
The beauty of this scene lives on unfading in my memory. (V.587.21)[17]

رہتے ہو تم آنکھوں میں بھرتے ہو تمہیں دل میں
مدت سے اگر چہ یہاں آتے ہو نہ جاتے ہو

---

[17] The original has not "her" but "them."

My eyes still see you; *you* live in my heart
Though years have passed since you would come and go.

روز آنے پہ نہیں نسبتِ عشقی موقوف

عمر بھر ایک ملاقات چلی جاتی ہے

(II.312.8)

The bond of love does not depend on seeing you each day;
You came but once, but you are with me still my whole life through.

(I.197.15)

As the days pass, he sees that the openness and confidence which once existed between them is dwindling, and that reserve is taking its place. Now when he speaks to her of what he feels for her, she does not want to hear him out:

سن سن کے درد دل کو بولا کر جاتے ہیں ہم

تو اپنی یہ کہانی بیٹھا ہوا کہا کر

I told the story of my heart: she listened for a while, and said
"I have to go. But you can stay; sit there, and go on with your tale."

(IV.482.13)

He tries to tell his story as though it were someone else's, hoping that perhaps her sympathies may be engaged before she realises that it is really of himself that he is speaking, and that then it will be too late for her to retreat; but this too fails:

اک شخص مجھی ساتھ تھا کہ تھا تجھ سے یہ عاشق

وہ اُس کی وفا کی پیشگی وہ اُس کی جوانی

یہ کہہ کے جو رو یا تو لگا کہنے نہ کہہ میر

سنتا نہیں میں ظلم رسیدوں کی کہانی

"There was a man like me loved one like you—[18]
Loyal and true and young and brave was he."
Tears came into my eyes. "Enough!" she said,
"I cannot bear these tales of cruelty."   (I.151.20–21)

Both verses describe an ambiguous situation, and express the uncertainty which the lover himself feels. Why will she not hear him out?
Perhaps because she is no longer interested in him; or perhaps because her
resolution to break with him is one which does violence to her own
feelings, and she cannot trust herself to uphold it if she thinks of the unhappiness it would cause him. In the situation described in the second
verse, it is her own conscience, as much as the tears in his eyes, which
tells her that the story is going to be a tragic one; and the reason *why* she
"cannot bear these tales of cruelty" is again left in doubt. Her lover is
again in the same uncertainty as when he first wooed her; he sees that
she wants him to believe she no longer loves him, but whether she really
has stopped loving him or whether it is fear impelling her, against her own
impulses and desires, to try and drive out love, he does not know.

While his hopes and his fears struggle with each other, he makes every
kind of approach that might move her. He complains jealously,

یا ساتھ غیر کے ہے تھیں ویسی بات چیت
سو سو طرح کے لطف ہیں اک اک سخن کے بیچ

یا پاس میرے لگتی ہے چپ ایسی آن کر
گویا زباں نہیں ہے تھارے دہن کے بیچ

You sit with *him*, and talk flows freely from you—
Kindness unending as the day is long
And when *I* come to you, you fall so silent,
That one would think that you had lost your tongue.
                                              (II.258.21–22)

[18] In the first line we follow a different reading from that of Āsi's text.

Or he appeals to her pity:

جب نام ترا ليجيے تب چشم بھر آوے
اس زندگی کرنے کو کہاں سے جگر آوے

Your name is spoken: tears come to my eyes.
Where shall I find the strength to live like this? (I.166.12)

گئی عمر میری ساری جیسے شمع باد کے بیچ
یہی رونا جلنا گلنا یہی اضطراب تجھ بن

The candle gutters in the draught, and my life too must waste away.
Like it I weep, and burn, and melt, and pine away parted from you.
(I.117.24)

Or he is gentle and persuasive:

ديرسے ہم کو بھول گئے ہو یاد کرو تو بہتر ہے
غم حرماں کا کب تک کھینچیں شاد کرو تو بہتر ہے

For many days you have not thought of me:
Recall me to your mind; that would be well.
How long must I bear separation from you?
Show me that you are kind; that would be well.
(IV.518.9)

Or he warns her that to spurn him will bring her unhappiness in days to come:

اب کرکے فراموش تو نا شاد کرو گے
پر ہم جو نہ ہوں گے تو بہت یاد کرو گے

Forget me now; and do not think how I shall bear the sorrow.
Today I die; it will be you who grieves for me tomorrow.
(I.169.11)

But more and more he finds that when he sees her, there is nothing he can say. He tries to persuade himself that it is because their meetings are too short:

دیر پچھ کھپتی تو کہتے بھی ملاقات کی بات
ملنا اپنا جو ہوا اُس سے سو وہ بات کی بات

Had there been time I would have told her what was in my heart
But when we met time was so short we could but meet to part.

(II.254.13)

Or that it is because he cannot catch her in the right mood:

بکالی سرکش نے چال ایسی کہ دیکھ حیرت سے رہ گئے ہم
دلوں میں کیا کیا ہمارے آیا کریں سو کیا بس چلا نہ اپنا

She walks in pride—so dread a sight I can but stand and stare.
Thoughts throng my mind—What of it, when I lack the strength to
  speak?   (VI.633.16)

کچھ کہنے کا مقام نہ تھا وہ دا ہوتا تو کہتے کچھ
آنا نہ آنا یکساں تھا واں ہوتے ادھر ہم گو آئے

I get no chance to plead my case to her;
Her mood is such it does not let me speak.
I go there, but what does it signify?
To go or not to go is all the same.   (V.603.24)

But he knows very well what the real reason is. Now that he fears he is going to lose her, his longing for her is so great that he cannot trust himself to speak:

جی میں تھا اُس سے ملئے تو کیا کیا نہ کہئے میر
پر جب ملے تو رہ گئے ناچار دیکھ کر

I told myself, "If we could meet I'd talk and talk to her."
But when I did, all I could do was gaze in silence at her.

(I.70.7)

He tells himself:

كہتے تو ہو یہ لوں کہتے یوں کہتے جو وہ آتا

یہ کہنے کی باتیں ہیں کچھ بھی نہ کہا جاتا

You tell yourself "I'd tell her this, and this, and this if she would come."
Yes, so you *tell* yourself, and yet when she is present you are dumb.

(II.237.2)

He sends word to her, and she does not even reply:

نہ کہا کچھ نہ آپھرا نہ ملا

کیا جواب ان مرے سوالوں کا

She sent no word, nor passed my way, nor let me come to her.
Why then do I petition her? She will not answer me.   (III.384.4)

But still he does not give up hope. Her indifference—apparent or real—
changes to anger; and for that very reason he feels that all is not yet lost,
for as he tells her:

ہوتے ہو بے دماغ تو دیکھو ہو تک ادھر

غصّہ ہی ہم پہ کاشکے اکثر رہا کرو

I rouse your wrath,—and when I do at least you glance this way.
If only I could make you angry with me all the time!   (II.316.18)

In other words, while he is still significant enough to her to be noticed,
no matter in what emotional context, there is still a basis on which he

may build some hope. So he still comes to her lane, not in the high hopes that others do, but hoping silently for some crumb of her attention:

میر صاحب بھی تمرے کوچے میں شب آتے ہیں ایک

جیسے دریوزہ گری کرنے گدا جاتے ہیں

> Mir Sahib too comes to your lane each night
> But as a beggar goes to beg for bread. (I.94.11)

He no longer even hopes for more than a minimum of human kindness from her; yet even that hope is vain:

اتنا کہا نہ ہم سے تم نے کبھو کہ آؤ

کاہے کو یوں کھڑے ہو وحشی سے بیٹھ جاؤ

> "Don't stand there all alone. Come and sit down."
> These words you could have said, but never did. (II.308.19)

کیا ہوتا جو پاس اپنے اے میر کبھوؤے آجاتے

عاشق تھے درویش تھے آخر بیکس بھی تھے تنہا تھے

> Once in a while if she had come, what harm would it have done her?
> I loved her, and was poor, and weak, and helpless and alone.
>
>   (IV.528.7)

And since even so modest a hope is not to be fulfilled, he consoles himself with the thought that even if it had been, it would not have amounted to evidence of any vestige of love on her side:

ہم تو عشق میں ناکس ٹھہرے کوئی نہ ادھر دیکھے گا

آنکھ اٹھا کر وہ دیکھے تو یہ بھی اس کی مروت ہے

> In love you are a failure, Mir—she will not look your way.
> And if she does, that is not love but common courtesy.
>
>   (V.608.14)

And if he has failed, he is in good company, for Farhād and Qais, the great lovers of Persian and Arabic legend, had fared no better:

فرہادوقیس ومیر یہ آوارگانِ عشق

یوں ہی گئے ہیں سب کی کہی ہی من کی من کے بیچ

Outcasts of love, Farhād and Qais and Mir roamed through the world;
And when they died their heart's desire died with them unfulfilled.[19]

(II.258.23)

Love has taught him the courage even to smile at his defeat:

دیکھا کروں تجھی کو منظور ہے تو یہ ہے

آنکھیں نہ کھولوں تجھ بن مقدور ہے تو یہ ہے

To keep my eyes on you, and you alone:
　　my one and only heart's desire is this.
To open them only if you are there:
　　the height to which I can aspire is this.　(I.190.7)

And after all what real difference does it make? Nothing can change the fact that he has learned to love. Nothing can stop him going on loving to the end, loving with undiminished intensity, no matter whether he can be with his beloved or is fated to live out his life parted from her, welcoming every trial, every hardship, every cruelty, in that it enables him to perfect his capacity to love, until his love is stronger than death and he is ready at any time to prove it so. Love has become a way of life for him, has developed all the potentialities which lay dormant in him, and

---

[19] Farhād, also called Kohkan "the mountain-digger," was, according to the Persian legend, in love with Shīrīn, the wife of Chosroes Parvez (d. 628), and the king promised her to him if he could dig a channel through solid rock. Contrary to the king's expectations, love gave him the power to complete the task, but the king sent him false news that Shīrīn was dead, and he died of a broken heart. As for Qais, he belongs to the stock of early Arabic legend. Qais was in love with Laila, but since he was unable to win her, he lost his senses and wandered through deserts and mountains, and hence was known as Majnūn, the madman. Both Farhād and Majnūn have become symbols of "absolute love," and their fate has been immortalized by the great Persian poet Nizāmī and by many other Persian and Indo-Muslim poets, from Amir Khosrau Dihlawī on. (A.S.)

has made him a real man. And for this no suffering is too great a price to pay. The man who has never loved is to be not envied but pitied. He tells his mistress:

ظلم و جور و جفا ستم بیداد

عشق میں تیرے ہم پہ کیا نہ ہوا

ہم تو ناکام ہی جہاں میں رہے

یہاں کبھو اپنا مدعا نہ ہوا

میرا افسوس وہ کہ جو کوئی

اُس کے دروازے کا گدا نہ ہوا

> Much have I suffered in my love for you—
> Cruelty, persecution, and much more
> And life-long deprivation of the joys
> I spent the years in endless yearning for.
> > Yet from my heart I pity any man
> > Who never stood a suppliant at your door.

$$(I, 54.7–10)$$

The man who has not loved appears in the ghazal in the stock character of the *nāsih*, or counsellor. He is portrayed as a man who thinks he understands the lover's point of view, sympathises with him, and wants to help him, but who in the last resort no more understands what love is about than do the lover's persecutors. The only difference between them and him is that what they try to do by violence, he tries to do by sweet reasonableness. But he lacks even the capacity to love, let alone the experience of it, and his advice is ludicrously irrelevant and ineffective. The lover's tone towards him ranges between angry sarcasm and good-humoured tolerance. Sometimes his advice is quoted without comment:

قدم تلک جو دیکھ کر رکھ میرے سر دل سے نکالے گا

پلک سے شوخ تر کانٹا ہے صحراۓ محبت کا

O Mir, be careful where you tread; their points can thrust right through
  your heart.
For sharper than her eyelashes are thorns that strew the path of love

(I.48.16)

—as though the lover did not know this even better than he! The
counsellor enlists the help of a bystander:

O you who sit and watch the people going by, take heed!
Tell Mir, if you should chance to see him passing in the street.
"Don't go into the desert-lands of love—Khizar himself,[20]
If he should wander off that way, turns back his straying feet."

(I.167.4–5)

Elsewhere, the counsellor's solemn advice is quite fatuous:

Love is a mortal sickness, Mir; keep clear of it if you would thrive.
Our ancestors, I understand, used not give their hearts away.

(V.613.15)

If the lover ignores this counsel, backed though it is by reference to such
excellent precedent, the counsellor puts it down to his youth and in-
experience, but thinks it his duty to warn him:

---

[20] Khizar is a legendary figure who appears to travellers who have lost their way and sets
them on the right path again.

اب تو جوانی کا نشہ ہے نہ خود تجھ کو رکھے گا
ہوش گیا پھر آوے گا تو دیر تلک پچھتاوے گا

You're young, of course, and drunk with love; the future is not clear to
   you.
Your senses will return one day; *then* see what you will have to rue.

(IV.467.2)

And so it goes on, with the counsellor ready at every stage with warnings
and good advice:

چھوڑ دو اس اوباش کا ملنا اور نہ سرکٹواؤ گے
چاہ رہو گے بہتیروں کو سر جو میرے سلامت ہے

Mir, give her up before your life is forfeit—
That way you'll live to love another day.   (V.621.18)

ضعف بہت ہے میرے تمھیں کچھ اس کی گلی میں مت جاؤ
صبر کرو کچھ اور بھی صاحب طاقت جی میں آنے دو

Mir, stay at home awhile until you're stronger—
You've worn yourself quite out in serving her.   (III.425.2)

And at last:

میر سدا بے حال رہو ہو مہر و وفا سب کرتے ہیں
تم نے عشق کیا سو صاحب کیا یہ اپنا حال کیا

To be good friends is very right and proper:
    You *loved*—and see the state it brought you to! (IV.466.7)

Mir replies to him quite plainly, and sometimes impatiently, but
without malice, preferring to make fun of him rather than rail at him:

You mock in vain to see me swoon under the stress of love.
Try loving for a day or two and you will understand! (II.310.16)

Friend, do you never stop to ask yourself
If lovers ever heeded what you say?
You think they hear your words? Let me tell you
They and their thoughts are miles and miles away.

(IV.509.5)

After all, he tells himself,

It does not cost me anything to listen
So I sit quiet and let him lecture on.
All my heart had to learn is learned already:
Poor fellow, let him give his good advice. (III.425.1)

Occasional verses make fun of the nondescript, respectable man in the
street, who is too lacking in imagination and too immersed in his own
petty affairs to notice the lover, or, if he does notice him, to ascribe
more than the most commonplace interpretation to what he sees. He

amuses himself by imagining what such a person might have said to him
had they both lived in the days of Farhād, or Kohkan, and Qais:

کوکہن ومجنوں یہ دولوں دشت دکوہ میں سرماریں

شوق نہیں ملنے کا ہم کو میرا ایسے آواروں سے

Both Qais and Kohkan roam about the deserts and the mountainsides.
Mir, I have not the least desire to mix with vagabonds like these.

(IV.514.25)

Mir, too, like Farhād and Majnūn, is reputed in some quarters to be
a man possessed by a great love; but such down-to-earth, stand-no-
nonsense people know better. One says to another:

ہوگا کسو دیوار کے سایہ میں پڑا میر

کیا ربط محبت سے اس آرام طلب کو

You'll find Mir lying in the shade of someone's wall:
What have such idle fellows got to do with love? (II.317.17)

The first line is an effective example of the idiom of the ghazal. At first
reading it conveys plainly enough the immediate impression that his
worldly-wise critics receive when they see him—that here is an idle
fellow who does not care where he lies so long as it is in the shade. But
to men of imagination and sympathy the words themselves suggest the
real situation. They know at once that the "someone" is his mistress,
and they know why he is there, for in the symbolism of the ghazal the
constancy of the lover is represented by the picture of him watching and
waiting constantly in her lane or outside her house. They begin to
realise, too, all the implications of the word "shade," for it has many in
addition to the obvious meaning. The cool shade is a pleasant concept in
English, but it is even more so in a country where the intensity of the
heat becomes almost unbearable in some seasons of the year, and in
Urdu a wide range of metaphorical use reflects this fact. For example,
when a child's father dies, leaving him helpless and unprotected, it is

said that he has been deprived of the "shadow" of his father, in which he could rest, protected from the heat and dust of life. In this verse it suggests two things: first, an ironical situation in which what appears to others to be a life of ease and comfort passed in the cool shade is in fact the life of the lover, with all its inevitable and never-ending suffering; but secondly, it suggests also a proud acceptance of all the pleasant connotations of shade as indeed applying to the life of the true lover, for with all its suffering, it is his unbreakable constancy in love which provides the whole meaning and content of his life and brings him a profound spiritual happiness.

The tone of the lover's rejoinder to his well-meaning critics is generally mild, but there are times when he loses all patience with them. He sees that in the long run there is nothing to choose between their attitude and that of those who are openly and uncompromisingly hostile to him; and he knows that if he were to live forever, he could never hope to change them. So he allows himself the pleasure of outraging them instead. To the counsellor's reproach that his love is a sin against religion, he replies:

Is my religion your concern? No, yours are other realms.
I, and my love, and what I do is foreign ground to you.

(III. 397.7)

—a reply that deliberately invites his critic to conclude that the lover's religion *is* love. He avows this quite openly, and indeed proudly, in other lines couched in terms which he knows will shock his adversaries. Thus he tells his mistress:

سجده اس آستاں کا نہ جس کو ہوا نصیب

وہ اپنے اعتقاد میں انسان ہی نہیں

The man who was not fated to bow down and worship you
In my belief has not attained the stature of a man. (I. 100.11)

The words imply, and are meant to imply, something which is anathema to the orthodox Muslim—namely, that to worship one's beloved is a better religion than to worship God; though as we shall see later, what the poet is in fact contrasting with true love is not true religion but the lifeless, formal worship of a falsely-conceived God, to which he believes that most of his fellow Muslims have fallen prey. The same contrast is made when he flouts the Muslim's intense abhorrence of idolatry to say of lovers like himself:

If Paradise itself were theirs they would not look at it—
Such bliss is the idolatry of gazing on her form.   (II.282.12)

The symbol of idolatry is only one of those commonly used in the ghazal to express the situation of the lover in his relationship with the ordinary, conventional man. Such a man looks upon love as a sort of madness, and the lover is proud to wear this ''madness'' as a badge of honour, distinguishing him from the much-prized sanity of the counsellor and the conventional citizen. His madness becomes the symbol of his complete possession by love, which so consumes him that material comforts, the social conventions, the cruelty of his beloved, and the bitter persecution of society are alike ineffective to turn him from his path. In his madness he loses all he has, lets his home fall into ruins, tears his clothes, and flees the cities and inhabited places to wander in the deserts, where the burning hot sands blister his feet and the great thorns tear at his body until it is all lacerated and bleeding, thus following the example of Qais, or Majnūn, who, in his madness, realized the reality of love. The desert becomes the symbol of the world in which he lives, his wounds the symbols of his sufferings at society's hands, and his deliberate choice of his lot and his rejoicing in it, the symbol of his deepest conviction that love is the highest ideal to which man can aspire.

But mostly the lover is less concerned with assailing the values of his adversaries than with proclaiming his own. He declares his faith that only the lover knows what it is really to live. The joy he finds in the anguish

of love's tortures, even though they reduce him to dust, is something
beyond the conception of the ordinary man. He speaks for all lovers
when he says:

اب بھی دماغ رفتہ ہمارا ہے عرش پر

گو آسماں نے خاک میں ہم کو ملادیا

And still we dwell enraptured in the stars
After our stars have ground us in the dust.   (II.214.2)

A life of trial is the only life worth living. To suffer endlessly for one's
love, and to triumph endlessly over suffering, gives meaning to life:

ہے عاشقی کے بیچ ستم دیکھنا ہی لطف

مر جانا آنکھیں موند کے یہ کچھ ہنر نہیں

In love, to face the torture open-eyed is purest joy.
To close your eyes and die is something anyone can do.

(II.300.5)

The supreme joy, however, is to lay down one's life for one's love; to
die like this is better than to live forever. Mir uses Muslim legend to
bring this home more effectively. There is a legend that Khizar and
Sikandar (Alexander the Great) set out in search of a spring from which
flowed the water of eternal life. They found it only after facing many
dangers and difficulties, and Sikandar died before he could drink of it; but
Khizar drank, and so never dies. Mir says:

اب حیات وہی نا جس پر خضر و سکندر مٹتے کے ہے

خاک سے ہم نے بھر او وہ چشمہ یہ بھی ہماری ہمت تھی

I found the water of eternal life
That Khizar and Sikandar strove to find.
I stopped it up until it ceased to flow.
In this you see the lover's high resolve.   (V.609.3)

The lover is of the same company as Isa (the Muslim name for Jesus) whom Muslims revere as one of the great Prophets, for,

اب جو عیسیٰ فلک پہ ہے وہ بھی

شوق میں برسوں خاک چھان گیا

If Isa lives in heaven, it is because
For years he roamed the desert lands of love.   (II.241.6)

But he is even more fortunate than Isa, who—since according to Muslim belief, Jesus did not die on the Cross, but was taken up, still living, into Paradise—never knew the joy of giving his life for love:

لذّت سے نہیں خالی جانوں کا کھپا جانا

کب خضر و میسحا نے مرنے کا مزا جانا

To spend your strength unstinting till your life is forfeit too—
This is a joy that Khizar and Masīhа never knew.   (II.211.15)

—Masīha meaning Christ, the Messiah. And he sums up in a striking metaphor the sustained, intense joy of the man who lives his life possessed by love. The tears of blood which, both in English and Urdu metaphor, one weeps when pain and suffering have reached their extreme, come, in the symbolism of Urdu poetry, from the heart, which constant anguish reduces to blood. And so, Mir says:

I passed my life in love's intoxication
Drunk with the rose-r~d wine of my heart's blood.

(I.207.21)

Verses like these express the spiritual exaltation of the man who has by constant self-discipline passed all the tests of love. He has a long road to travel before he can reach this goal. The path is the more difficult because his conception of love is not the ascetic one, which renounces love

once and for all at every level except the spiritual. He wants to win his
mistress physically too, to hold her in his arms and sleep with her, and
hope for this outcome never wholly deserts him. But he must combine
this hope with a clear understanding that it may never be fulfilled, and
with an ability to make his love sufficient in itself, so that its intensity and
sustaining power can bring him spiritual peace whatever may befall.

It is Mir's proud claim that he succeeded in this, and in *The Stages of
Love* we have already seen him as a man whose delight in all the physical
joys of love is frank and unashamed, and yet one who can also love, for
as long as he lives, a woman whom he expects never to see again. As he
puts it in one of his ghazals:

عشق میں وصل و جدائی سے نہیں کچھ گفتگو

قرب و بعد اس جا برابر ہے محبت چاہیئے

This is a realm where near and far are one;
With her or parted from her, you must love.　　(I.160.16)

To reach this ideal the lover needs a steady resolve to see things as they
are, and to acquire an imaginative foreknowledge of all the possible
situations of love so as to school himself beforehand to meet them. Mir
reproves the young lover who feels too keenly the early trials of love:

شکوۂ آبلہ ابھی سے میر

ہے پیارے ہنوز دلّی دور

Already you bewail your blistered feet?
"It's a long way to Delhi yet," my son　　(I.71.21)

—as the proverb goes. He tells him that tears should not be shed too
lightly:

ابتدائے عشق ہے روتا ہے کیا

آگے آگے دیکھیے ہوتا ہے کیا

Why do you weep ? Love's trials have just begun.
Keep back your tears; see what is yet to come.[21]   (I.29.11)

And he holds up his own example, stressing that one must see clearly
what the end will be and accept it without fear or equivocation even before one sets out on the long journey of love:

جب جی سے گزر سگۓ ہم اے میر
اس کوچے میں تب ہوا گزارا

I washed my hands of life, and only then
Could I set foot in my beloved's lane.   (III.382.16)

And he adds half-humorously:

درد سراب جو عشق کاہر گور تک ہی ساتھ
کچھ نیشہ ہی اور ہے اس کا خمار اور

You are in love: your head splits, and the pain is there for life.
Love's is a different drunkenness, a different aftermath. (III.397.13)

He warns him:

عشق میں گام اوّل اپنے جی ہے سے گزر نا پیش آیا
اس میداں میں رکھکے قدم کیا مرنے سے ڈر جاوینگے

At the first trial your life may be demanded.
If you're afraid, don't come into the field.   (IV.493.11)

But the first step, he tells him cheerfully, is the worst:

گزر جان سے اور ڈر کچھ نہیں
رہِ عشق میں پھر خطر کچھ نہیں

Just sacrifice your life, and fear is banished.
Go on your way; all danger will have vanished. (I.119.22)

21 The verse quoted is one traditionally attributed to Mīr, though Āsī says that in the correct version the first words are different (cf. I.29.11 and Āsī's note).

He stresses too that readiness to give one's life is not enough. Love is a skill which must be learned like any other:

In everything he does a man needs skill.
Even the art of sinning must be learned. (I.158.17)

The crises he will have to face are many and varied; he must learn how they may be overcome, and go on learning as long as he lives, and learning, above all, from his failures:

All my life through I learned the skills to pass the tests of love
And passed because my failures taught me how I must succeed.

(I.12.10)

Among the skills he must learn is that of perfect self-restraint, for nothing that he does must give any clue to the secret of his mistress' identity, and this means that while he may give vent to all the extravagance of his emotions when he is alone or with a trusted friend, in company where his mistress is present his conduct must be such that not even a shade of suspicion can arise. This is the severest test of his sense of honour and of his overriding regard for his mistress' good name:

I keep love's secret in my heart: none ever sees me shed a tear;
Heavy as the rain-bearing cloud I wander on year after year.

(II.230.9)

تالوگ بدگماں نہ ہوں آئے نہ اس کی اُور

ہم توکیا ہے عشق میں دوراز قیاس پاس

That no one might suspect her, I have never walked her way.
Such is the unimagined price I paid for loving her.   (II.274.4)

He imagines what people will say of him when he is dead:

مرتا تھا جس کی خاطر اس کی طرف نہ دیکھا

میرؔ ستم رسیدہ ظالم غیور کیا تھا

Dying to see his mistress, he never glanced towards her.
Truly a man of honour was Mir, her hapless victim. (IV.462.2)

And, as so often, he expresses an essentially serious point with a touch of
humour when he says,

غیرت سے نام اس کا آیا نہیں زباں پر

آگے خدا کے جب ہم محو دعا ہوئے ہیں

So jealous is my silent tongue to guard and keep her from all blame,
It calls on God to bless her, but will not tell even Him her name.
(VI.658 n.)

The same self-restraint is needed so that the lover may accept without
hesitation and without complaint everything that his mistress may see fit
to do. He tells her,

لطف و مہر و خشم و غضب ہم ہر صورت میں راضی ہیں

حق میں ہمارے کر گزر و بھی جو کچھ جانو بہتر تم

Kindness and love and anger and disdain are all alike acceptable to me.
Whatever you think fit to do to me, make up your mind and do it out of
hand.   (IV.493.23)

And if her cruelty destroys him, there is no ground for complaint in that. It is in the nature of beauty to be cruel, and she can no more help it than the rose can help the nightingale dying of love of her, or than the lightning can help striking the nest:

آتشِ رنگِ گل سے کیا کہیے

برق تھی آشِیان پر آئی

Burn in the red fire of the rose in silence—
Lightning must strike, and it has struck your nest. (I.141.25)

He sustains his resolution by attributing to some fault in himself every bitter experience for which at first sight she would seem to be to blame:

مجھی کو ملنے کا ڈھب کچھ نہ آیا

نہیں تقصیر اس ناآشِناکی

I did not know the way to bring her to me.
She never came, but it was not *her* fault. (VI.670.7)

میر صاحب ہی چوُکے اے بےعہد

ورنہ دینا تھا دل قسم سے کر

Mir was at fault in trusting to your promise:
He should have made you *swear* your love for him. (I.73.9)

He even tells himself that it is better they should not meet, in case he should fail in his duty towards her:

ہے فرق ہی میں خیر نہ کر آرزوئے وصل

مل بیٹھے جو اس سے تو شکوہ دراز ہو

Better that we should stay apart; so do not yearn to see her.
Meeting would be one long complaint against her cruelty.

(I.127.3)

If death overtakes him, and she has still not fulfilled her promise to come
to him, he reasons:

اس کے ایفائے عہد تک نہ جیے
عمر نے ہم سے بے وفائی کی

Life could not stay for her to keep her promise;
It was not she, but life that played me false.   (I.141.14)

If he sometimes allows himself, with a straight face, a mild joke at her
expense, this is not because his attitude has changed, but because he
hopes that his superficially unexceptionable statement may prompt some
feelings of guilt in her heart which will incline her to relent towards him.
So he replies indignantly to her suggestion that perhaps he has been complaining against her:

شکوہ کروں ہوں بخت کا اتنے غضبناک عتاں
مجھ کو خدا انخواستہ تم سے تو کچھ گلا نہیں

How *could* you, lovely one? 'Twas Fate that I complained against.
God grant I never see the day I murmur against you!   (I.109.23)

And he replies to hints from his friends that she has no intention of
meeting him:

جھوٹ ہر چند نہیں یار کی گفتار کے بیچ
دیر لیکن ہے قیامت ابھی دیدار کے بیچ

My mistress promised I should see her; and she does not lie.
Though I must wait till Doomsday, I shall see her by and by
        (II.258.25)

—an unanswerable argument, for every Muslim knows that on the last
day the whole of mankind will meet together on the great plain to hear
God's judgement.

He fully expects to die from the wounds her constant cruelty in-
flicts upon him—a situation portrayed in the conventional imagery of the
ghazal as the mistress striking off her lover's head with the sword of her
glance—and he accepts his fate with such calm composure that he can
joke even about this, telling himself:

تلوارکے تلے بھی ہیں آنکھیں تری اُدھر

تو اس ستم کا میرے سزاوار کیوں نہ ہو

The sword falls, Mir, and still you stare at her.
Is that not proof that you deserve to die?   (I.131.18)

Or he dies of love, and his friends debate whether or not this is tanta-
mount to murder at his mistress' hands. From beyond the grave he interrupts them impatiently:

خواہ ماراانھیں نے میرکو خواہ آپ موا

جلنے دو یارو جو ہونا تھا ہوامت پوچھو

Natural death or murder—what's the difference?
What had to be has been, friends. Let it pass.   (I.133.22)

He loved his mistress truly, and true love necessarily entailed unfailing
respect and reverence for her. He imagines the final proof: he has died in
her lane and turned to dust; yet when the dust is stirred by the passing
wind, it settles again at a respectful distance from his mistress' house.
His friends see it and reflect:

دُور بیٹھا غبارِ میر اس سے

عشق بن یہ ادب نہیں آتا

Mir's dust has settled at a distance from her;
Respect like this is only learned from love.   (I.31.21)

Superhuman restraint, absolute submission to his beloved's will, unfailing respect for her, and complete constancy—these are the qualities

which the lover must learn. Above all, constancy. Mir extols it in verse after verse, sometimes speaking directly of himself and sometimes quoting, so to speak, the testimony of others:

He went into her lane; then all was silent.
"Mir! Mir!" I shouted; but no answer came.   (I.26.23)

To those who warn him to come away before it is too late, he replies with grave humour:

It was *love's* strength that brought me to her lane:
Where shall *I* find the strength to go back home?   (I.84.5)[22]

Or he agrees pleasantly that it is sheer obstinacy that keeps him there:

Obstinate? That indeed I am—and to the last degree.
Once I sit down nothing this side of death will get me up.
(I.70.19)

In short, so constant is he that he cannot be bothered even to reply seriously to advice to change his ways, however sympathetic and well-intentioned it may be. He has determined his course, and "though the

[22] Cf. I.181.13.

sword-blows rain upon his head," he will not turn aside. For him the only swords and daggers that matter are those which his mistress wields:

چھِیں تِھیں جی میں سے پلکیں، لگیں تِھیں دل کو سے بھووِیں
یِہی شمشیرِ چلتی تھی، یِہی خنجرِ جہاں سامیں تھا

Her eyelashes pierce to my soul, her eyebrows strike me to the heart.
These are the scimitars that cut; these are the daggers that can wound.

(III.379.5)

Yet she too has no weapon in her armoury which he cannot withstand:

تیرے تیرِ نازکے جو یہ ہدف ہوئے ہیں ظالم
مگر آہنی تو سے ہیں جگرِ نیازمنداں

The arrows of your pride fly fast against the target of our breasts,
But iron breastplates are the hearts of those that pledge their love to you.

(I.99.6)

He knows the treatment he must expect of her, even though she herself should promise him something else:

کہتے تو ہیں کہ ہم بھی تمھیں چاہتے ہیں میر
پر اعتماد کس کو ہے خوباں کی چاہ پر

True, you have said, "And I love you too, Mir."
But who would trust a lovely woman's love?   (VI.643.9)

And so engrossed is he in his love that he simply does not feel anything else; pain and joy alike do not affect him:

خوش ہیں نہ گلِ تر سے نہ ہم خار سے ناخوش

The fresh-blown rose gives me no joy, its piercing thorn no pain.

(IV.486.6)

Whatever her treatment of him, his love is ever fresh, and he renews
every day of his life his vows to serve her:

دہ سرکشی سے گو متوجّہ نہ ہو ادھر

ہم عاجزانہ کرتے ہیں اس کو سلام روز

Each day she passes by, too proud even to glance my way:
I in humility bow low to greet her every day.

منظور بند گی نہیں میری تو کیا کروں

حاضر ہے اپنی اُورسے یوں تو غلام روز

My service is not pleasing to her; yet what can I do?—
Other than come and stand and wait to serve her every day.

(II.272.15, 17)

And he must serve her with all his strength:

عشق میں کیا دخل ہے نازک مزاجی کے تئیں

کوہکن کے طورسے جی تو ڑ کر محنت کر

In love there is no room for the unduly delicate:
Like Kohkan, toil with all your strength—yes, though your heart
    should burst   (III.427.15)

—a line which itself implies that you may well toil only to meet with
failure in the end, like Farhād Kohkan "the mountain-digger."

Love, and only love, gives him the courage and the strength to meet
the dangers in which love's realm abounds. That is why, when he meets
Khizar roaming in the deserts of love, he warns him that "this is a place
where lions roam" (VI.632.19) and expresses concern for his safety—
even though Khizar is immune to death.

بِلا جو عشق کے جنگل میں حضر میں نے کہا
کہ خوفِ شیر ہے مَخذم یاں کدھر آیا

He must be ready to face death itself at any time, and never to hesitate:

برسوں سے مری اس کی رہتی ہی ہی ہی صحبت
تیغ اُس کو اٹھانا تو سر مجھ کو جھکا جانا

For years together this has been the converse that we hold:
She lifts the sword to strike: I bow my neck without ado.

(II.212.4)

Not only ready to die, he is eager to show that he can, eager to win the
satisfaction of giving his all for love:

نظر میں آوے گا جب جی کا کھونا
ملے گا نیند بھر تب مجھ کو سونا

Let me once see my life is forfeit to you
And I shall sleep the sleep of peace at last.   (II.236.15)

For

جی دیتے ہیں مرنے پر سب شہرِ محبت میں
کچھ ساری خدائی اُسے یہ طور نیا دیکھا

Men of love's city give their lives to win the chance to die.
Search God's creation through and through: you will not find their like.

(II.228.12)

And though she is unrelenting to the last, this makes no difference.

وقتِ قتل آرزوئے دل جو لگے پوچھے لوگ
میں اشارت کی اُدھر اُن نے کہا مت پوچھو

Led out to die, the people asked me what was my last wish.
I glanced towards her; she replied, "Say nothing. Do not ask."

زیرِ شمشیرِ ستم میرے تڑپنا کیسا
سر بھی تسلیم محبت میں ہلایا نہ گیا

(I.133.21)

The sword of tyranny was falling, and I could not flinch.
I did not move my head—not even to avow my love.   (I.27.9)

And so the lover dies, reminding those who condole with him:

عشق جانا تھا مار رکھے گا
ابتدا میں تھی انتہا معلوم

I knew that love would take my life as forfeit.
When I began I knew how I would end.   (II.286.4)

کرنے سے کیا میرے جی صاحب ہم کو ہوش تھے کیا کرتے
جی سے ہاتھ اٹھائے گئے پر اس سے دل نہ اٹھائے گئے

I knew what I was doing when I chose to die; what could I do?
I washed my hands of life: I could not wash my heart of love for her.

(I.207.13)

For to die for love, to remain constantly in the beloved's lane until one
is reduced to dust, is the hallmark of the true lover:

آوارگانِ عشق کا پوچھا جو میں نشاں
مشتِ غبار لے کے صبا نے اڑا دیا

I asked the breeze, "Where shall I find the vagabonds of love?"
It gathered up a little dust and raised it in the air.   (I.54.22)

CHAPTER FIVE

Mir and the Lover's Way of Life

IT IS NOT DIFFICULT to see that this conception of love as a way of life is one which lends itself to a wide range of symbolic application, with the beloved as the symbol of a man's ideals in life and his constancy to her as the symbol of his constancy to those ideals. As might be expected in a medieval society, it was to the sphere of religion that this transference of the experiences and the value of earthly love was first made. Long before the Urdu poets adopted the ghazal form from the Persian, ghazal poetry was moving simultaneously on two levels, so that almost any line might be interpreted as an expression either of a man's love for his mistress or, in the mystic sense, of the worshipper's love for his God. Love was divided into two categories—*ishq i majāzi*, or symbolic love, and *ishq i haqīqi*, or real love—and it is again characteristic of the medieval mind that contrary to what a modern would expect, it was earthly love which was characterised as symbolic, and mystic love which was called real.

The idea that a man's passionate love for a woman and his love for his God are two closely parallel experiences has long been unfamiliar to the modern world, and it is not easily reacquired. In the modern West in particular, people are inhibited by the strong Protestant tradition, which tends to regard sexual love as sinful, or if not sinful, at least not religious, and for this and other reasons feels very uncomfortable with the symbolic identification of God with an irresistibly beautiful woman. They would do well to remember that it did not occur to their ancestors—not even to some of their Protestant ancestors—that there anything objectionable in the parallelism between sexual and divine love. Thus in the Bible, in the Song of Solomon, one finds that the chapter headings take the most sensuous descriptions of the beloved—her feet, her thighs, her belly, her navel, her breasts—as Christ's description of the graces of the Church. This treatment is not exceptional. J. M. Cohen in his *History of Western Literature* speaks of love poetry "translated *a lo divino* for pious reading, according to the strange custom of the time, with a divine lover carefully substituted on all occasions for an earthly one."[1] True, the ghazal symbolism is here reversed, and God is not the beloved but the lover. However, the ghazal symbolism is also commonly found. The most notable instance is in Dante's *Divine Comedy*, where the figure of Beatrice appears both as Dante's earthly beloved and on other occasions as the symbol of Christ.[2] Even the *Romance of the Rose*—that most celebrated of all medieval love poems—was read by some in the divine sense, with the rose as the symbol of Jesus.[3]

Once this symbolic identification of God with the mistress is accepted, the recurring parallels between earthly and divine love are not difficult to grasp. For the starting point of mysticism is that true religion is inconceivable without a direct and intimate relationship between man and his God, and that this relationship comes into being, like earthly love, through a process which is experienced with overwhelming intensity, and which in the last resort cannot be reasoned about. In both loves there is the same yearning for union with the beloved, the same striving for perfect constancy, the same unhesitating submission to the beloved's will—even where that will seems to be cruel and capricious—the same readiness to sacrifice even life itself where love demands that price. In the Urdu ghazal the parallel goes further, for it is taken for granted that the true lover of God will face persecution and martyrdom at the hands of the world as certainly as the true lover of an earthly mistress does. A good deal of history lies behind this assumption and provides the logic on which it is based.

It is not difficult to see that mysticism is potentially a doctrine subversive of the medieval order, and therefore deeply suspect to it. For if

---

[1] *History of Western Literature* (Harmondsworth, 1956), p. 139.
[2] Cf. Dante, *The Divine Comedy*, trans. Dorothy Sayers (Harmondsworth, 1949), I. 67–68.
[3] Cf. J. Huizinga, *The Waning of the Middle Ages* (Harmondsworth, 1955), pp. 119–120.

a man's one overriding aim in life is to draw ever closer to his God, then the great ones of this world are unimportant in his eyes; and the great ones of this world do not like those who do not think them great. If he relies upon his love of God to guide him, he does not need the guidance of learned divines and does not accept their pretensions to be in some special sense the guardians of true religion; and these spiritual pillars of the medieval order do not like this attitude any more than their temporal counterparts. Islamic mysticism has a wide range of expression, and it should not be thought that this potentially subversive trend in it was everywhere made explicit, still less that it was the dominant trend in Islamic mysticism as a whole. But in the convention of the Urdu ghazal it does dominate, and is not only made explicit but, like almost everything else in the ghazal, is carried to an extreme; and piecing together the lines of Mir's ghazals, one can trace the logic of its development.

To the mystic the essence of religion is man's love of God, a love as all-consuming as love for a beautiful mistress. Rituals of worship are of no significance as compared with it, and at this point the clash with orthodoxy begins. The "Five Pillars" of orthodox Islam—that is, the five fundamental duties of a Muslim—are faith in God and his Prophet, prayer (saying the five daily prayers, the words and postures of which are minutely prescribed), almsgiving (a fortieth of one's income, in money or in kind), fasting (especially the month-long fast of Ramzān), and the pilgrimage to Mecca. To the mystic the last four are good only if they are an aid to the expression of the worshipper's love for God; they are meaningless if they are performed as a mere ritual, and positively harmful if they give rise in the worshipper's heart to the Pharisee's satisfaction that he is "not as other men are." So Mir says:

$$مکّے گیا مدینے گیا کربلا گیا$$
$$جیسا گیا تھا ویسا ہی چل پھر کے آگیا$$

I went to Mecca, and Medina, and to Karbala⁴—
And what I was, I still remain now that I have returned.

(IV.464.14)

⁴ Places of Muslim pilgrimage.

And:

جگ سے کوئی آدمی ہو تو سارا عالم جگ ہی کرے
مکے سے آئے شیخ جی لیکن وے تو وہی ہیں خر کے خر

If pilgrimage could make a man a man
Then all the world might make the pilgrimage.
But *shaikh ji* [5] is just back, and look at him—
An ass he went: an ass he has returned.   (V.560.22)

Mir is equally contemptuous of the man who serves God in order that
at the last he may taste the delights of Paradise: the true lover of God
would see Paradise turned into Hell sooner than have the purity of his
love tainted with greed for reward:

حور و قصور و غلماں نہر و نعیم جنت
یہ کلہم جہنم مشتاق یار ہیں ہم

Houris and boys and palaces and streams of Paradise—
Cast every one of them to Hell, and I will love my Love.

(III.407.24)

This is already an Islam different in kind from that of the orthodox,
ritual worshipper. But the mystic takes a step beyond even this, and
declares that God is known in many forms and worshipped under different names by men of different creeds. The community of his worshippers includes all men—Muslims, Jews, Christians, Zoroastrians,
Hindus—whose hearts are filled with passionate love for Him, no matter
in what form or under what name they conceive of Him, and who
dedicate themselves wholly to doing His will. In this community differences of formal creed are of no account.

---

5 In the ghazal the shaikh is the type of the Pharisee. The root meaning of the word is "an
old man," but it comes to mean "a venerable old man," "an elder," and in the context of the
ghazal means the custodian of orthodox formalized Islam. Mir often sarcastically calls him
"Shaikh ji"—the ji being the Indian suffix of respectful address. He is the frequent target of
Mir's attacks, as we shall see.

کس کو کہتے ہیں نہیں میں جاتتا اسلام و کفر

دیر ہو یا کعبہ مطلب مجھ کو تیرے درسے ہے

What does it mean to me? Call me "believer," call me "infidel."
I seek His threshold, be it in the temple or the mosque.　　(II.366.3)

مقصود درد دل ہے نہ اسلام ہی نہ کفر

پھر ہر ہر گلے میں سبحہ و زنار کیوں نہ ہو

The bond of love is all—Islam and unbelief are nothing:
Take rosary *and* sacred cord and wear them on your neck.

(I.131.16)

The rosary is here the symbol of Islam, while the *zunnār*, the word here
translated "sacred cord," is a very comprehensive symbol. In an Indian
context it first suggests the sacred thread worn by the high caste Hindu,
but it is used also for the cord worn by Eastern Christians and by
Zoroastrians.

Just as the Muslim who truly loves his God is at one with the Hindu
who truly loves his, so, for all their detestation of each other, is the
Muslim shaikh at one with the Hindu Brahmin, for each sees himself as
the jealous guardian of what he conceives of as the true religion, but
what is in fact an empty ritual. In some verses the mosque and the
temple are seen as their special preserve, in which the lover of God therefore has no place:

شرکت شیخ و برہمن سے میر

کعبہ و دیر سے بھی جائیے گا

اپنی ڈیڑھا اینٹ کی جدی مسجد

کسی ویرانے میں بنائیے گا

Mir, quit the company of Shaikh and Brahmin
And mosque and temple too—leave them behind.
Lay one stone on another in the desert:
Worship your Love at your own humble shrine.

(I.39.8–10)

Desert, as we have seen, is an expressive word, and suggests all the connotations discussed in the previous chapter. Neither shaikh nor Brahmin is capable of seeing that

اس کے فروغِ حسن سے جھمکے ہر سب میں نور
شمعِ حرم ہو یا کہ دیا سومنات کا

It is the power of *His* beauty fills the world with light,
Be it the Ka'ba's candle or the lamp that lights Somnāth.[6]

(II.210.7)[7]

The idea of God's radiant beauty occurs again and again in Mir. God manifests himself in the universe as in a great mirror: He is immanent in all things, so that God *is* all things, and the true lover may adore Him in His handiwork:

لبریز جلوہ اس کا سارا جہاں ہے یعنی
ساری ہے وہ حقیقت جاوے نظر جہاں تک

The universe brims over with His radiance—
Nothing but He, look wheresoe'er you will.　　(VI.645.22)

ہے ماسوا کیا جو میر کہئے
آگاہ سارے اُس سے ہیں آگاہ

---

[6] Site of one of the most famous of Hindu temples, which was destroyed in 1025 by Maḥmūd of Ghazna.
[7] The original has not "Ka'ba" but simply "mosque."

جلوے ہیں اُس کے شانیں ہیں اُس کی

کیا روز کیا خور کیا رات کیا ماہ

ظاہر کہ باطن اوّل کہ آخر

اللہ اللہ اللہ اللہ

Tell me, what else exists but He?
To him who has the eyes to see
The day, the sun, the night, the moon
Show forth His forms, His Majesty.
Manifest, hidden, first and last
Is He, is He, is He, is He! (I.1'38.8–11)

And it follows that reverence for God's creation is as incumbent on the
true Muslim as is reverence for the Holy Quran, every verse of which is
His authentic word; for

آیات حق ہیں سالے یہ ذرّات کائنات

The atoms that compose the universe
Are verses written by the hand of God. (I.131.6)

The example of the universe itself shows man the way, for it is inspired with unceasing love and adoration of the Divine Beloved, its
Creator. The stars shine like the bright eyes of the lover gazing expectantly in the direction from which he expects his beloved to come.

دیکھیں ہیں راہ کس کی یارب کہ اختروں کی

رہتی ہیں باز آنکھیں چندیں ہزار ہر شب

Whose coming do they look for, O Lord? The stars, bright shining
Gaze on in all their thousands, wide-eyed, night after night.

(I.55.10)

The waves of the sea rise and fall like a lover repeatedly trying, and repeatedly failing, to draw his mistress into his embrace:

اٹھتی ہے موج ہر اک آغوش ہی کی صورت

دریا کو ہے یہ کس کا بوس و کنار خواہش

Its every wave is rising up as though to clasp its love;
Who is it whom the ocean thus seeks ever to embrace?

(II.275.9)

To love and to worship the beauty of the universe is to worship God, whose manifestation that beauty is:

عالم حسن ہے عجب عالم

چاہیے عشق اس بھی عالم سے

The world of beauty is a wondrous world;
A man must fall in love with that world too.   (V.614.25)

گل ہو، مہتاب ہو، آئینہ ہو، خورشید ہو میر

اپنا محبوب وہی ہے جو ادا رکھتا ہو

Whether it be the rose, the moon, the mirror, the bright sun—
Mir's love is for each thing in which the grace of beauty dwells.

(I.129.5)

The symbols of beauty are wine, the spring, youth, love—and the intensity of Mir's love for it is heightened by his ever-present consciousness that all these things pass quickly away. The very beauty that you see today springs from the soil of other beauties long since turned to dust: the rose grows from the dust of some beautiful woman; the nightingale in some way preserves the traces of some dead poet; and he who walks in the garden today thinks of these things and feels his joy tinged with sadness: [8]

جمشید جس نے وضع کیا جام، کیا ہوا

بے صحبتیں کہاں گئیں کیدھر بے نادُ نوش

جُز لالہ اُس کے جام سے پاتے نہیں نشاں

ہے کو کنار اس کی جگہ اسِ جو بدوش

جھومے ہے بید جلائے جوانان کے گسار

بالائے خم ہے خشت سر پیرے فروش

The great Jamshed who made the wine cup, where is he today?
Where are the revellers whom wine and music used to thrill?
His cup is gone—save that the tulip still preserves its shape.
Only the poppy's shoulder now supports its wine bowl still.
A fragment of the tavern-keeper's skull closes the vat.
The willows sway where slender youths once came to drink their fill.

(I.78.9–79.1)

And present beauty in its turn will quickly fade. Beauty is like the running water of a fast-flowing river, in which you may just dip your hand before it is gone from you forever.[9] All beautiful things are short-lived, and life is like them:

بوئے گل یا نوائے بلبل تھی

عمر افسوس کیا شتاب گئی

The rose's scent, the nightingale's sweet song
And life—alas! how soon they fade away! (IV.529.5)

---

[8] Allusions to IV.503.14 and I.50.5–6.
[9] Allusion to II.288.21.

And youth, the springtime of life, passes yet more quickly, like the flash
of light on a cup of wine.[10] The young lover tells his mistress:

مل وان دنوں ہم سے اک رات جانی
کہاں ہم، کہاں تم، کہاں پھر جوانی

My darling, come to me tonight: the days move on:
Tomorrow you, and I, and youth will all be gone. (V.608.1)

Enjoy beauty while you may and let all else go by the board:

سب مزے در کنار عالم کے
یار جب ہم کنار ہوتا ہے

I spurn all other joys the world can offer
When my beloved lies in my embrace.   (V.619.24)

Rejoice in the coming of spring, when the rosebuds, red as wine, appear
in the garden, and the green plants sway like drunkards. Soon the green
leaves come out on every branch, and the plants bend under the weight of
their flowers, and the breeze tugs, as it were, at your heart, as though to
draw you towards the rose garden; and you must respond and take your
flask of wine and go out.[11] And poetry crowns your enjoyment of it all:

عجب کچھ ہے گر میرے آوے میسر
گلابی شراب اور غزل اپنے ڈھب کی

What wonderful good fortune when you get
Both rose-red wine, and poetry like Mir's.   (I.143.25)

---

10 Allusion to I.40.2.
11 Allusions to II.334.23, IV.521.15, III.404.21.

The memories of these days last when they are gone beyond recall; and you remember how

مے گلگوں کی بوئے سے لبک میخانہ مہکتا تھا
لب ساغر پہ منھ رکھ رکھ کے ہر شیشہ بہکتا تھا

The fragrance of the rosy wine pervaded all the tavern;
The bottle babbled to the cup, his mouth upon her lip.

(680.3)

کیا لطف تھا کہ میکدے کی پشت بام پر
سوتے تھے مست چادرِ مہتاب تان کر

What days those were!—when I would drink and climb up to the tavern roof
And fall asleep, the white sheet of the moonlight over me.   (II.270.13)

That these beauties are short-lived is a lesson you find it hard to learn, for you do not want to believe it. Each year you hope that the rose will bloom a little longer, but such hopes are foolish self-deception:

کہا میں نے کتنا ہے گل کا ثبات
کلی نے یہ سُن کر تبسّم کیا

I asked how long the rose would bloom.
The rosebud heard my words and smiled.   (I.4.2)

The word "smiled," to repeat Olive Schreiner's words, "says more than it says." The rosebud smiles, first at the foolish hopes that lie behind so naive a question, and secondly because in smiling it answers the question. "To smile" is a regular metaphor for the blooming of a flower; the moment the bud blooms, it loses its existence as a bud; and its implication is that the rose itself will fade and pass out of existence as quickly and irrevocably. So learn the lesson while you are young; learn to treasure every moment of beauty that is given you; make the love of beauty your way of life, and it will not forsake you even in old age. In verses written quite late in his own life, Mir says:

مستی حُسن پرستی رِندی یہی عمل ہر مُدّت سے
پیر کبیر ہوئے تو کیا ہے چھوٹے ہیں معمول کوئی

Drinking, worshipping beauty, revelry—
These three have occupied me all my days.
I am an old, old man, but what of that?
After so long, I cannot change my ways.　　　(V.606.14)

قرار دل سے گیا ہیاب کی کر کے گھر میں نہ بیٹھے گا ہوں
بہار آئی جو اپنے جیتے تو سیر کرنے چلا کریں گے

I cannot sit down quietly to die.
Yes, even now my heart will not be still.
While I have breath, with each returning spring
I must go out—my eyes must look their fill.　　(IV.519.19)

The man who has learned this way of life will, to his last breath, be grateful for every crumb of beauty life still gives him. In the ghazal the lover's mistress is a falconer and he the hunted bird, who loves her the moment he sees her, and regrets only that he is dying and will never see her more. And yet

نگاہِ یاس بھی اس صیدافگن پر غنیمت ہے
نہایت تنگ ہے اے صیدِ بسمل دقت فرصت کا

Even the last despairing glance you cast towards the fowler
Is treasure: for, O dying bird, your time is short indeed.
　　　　　　　　　　　　　　　　　　　　(I.48.13)

A man can and should cultivate a capacity for the worship of beauty, but in the last resort the full awareness of the beauty of the universe,

which is the beauty of its Creator, comes to him as a revelation, and a
revelation of such power that he can do no other than surrender to it. It
becomes something so precious to him that he will give anything to make
it his own. Mir pictures it being offered for sale in the market place:
hermits leave their solitary life to come to bid for it; the shaikh offers for
it his robes—the essential symbols of his shaikhhood. All men's eyes are
on it: the rake comes from the tavern and the sober, pious worshipper
from the mosque,[12] and men are eager to buy it with their very lives.[13]
The man whose eyes have once been opened to see God's beauty in the
universe is drawn to Him as wholly and as irresistibly as a man who falls
in love at the first sight of a lovely woman. In many verses this parallel
between the earthly and the divine beloved is explicit, and the verses may
be interpreted in either sense or in both:

کس کی مسجد کیسے بت خانے کہاں کے شیخ و شاب

ایک گردش میں تری چشم سیے کے سب خراب

Mosque and temple, shaikh and Brahmin, old and young and grave and gay—
Turn your eyes of black on them and see them fall beneath your sway.

(I.56.13)

طرزِ نگاہ اس کی دل لے گئی سبھوں کے

کیا مومن و برہمن کیا گبر اور ترسا

The way she looks has conquered all men's hearts—
Muslims and Brahmins, Christians and Jews.[14]　　(II.212.22)

ہم ہوئے، تم ہوئے، کہ میر ہوئے

اُس کی زلفوں کے سب اسیر ہوئے

---

[12] Allusions to V.590.21, II.259.1, II.297.10, III.387.6–7.
[13] Allusion to IV.484.14.
[14] The original has not "Jews" but "Zoroastrians."

O

Yes, we and you and Mir are all her captives;
The beauty of her tresses binds us fast.   (I.172.1)

معلوم نہیں کیا ہے لبِ سرخ بتاں میں
اس آتشِ خاموش کا ہے شورِ جہاں میں

God knows what magic power her red lips hold;
Their still fire raises tumult in the world.   (II.308.10)

The worship of beauty is expressed symbolically in the language of
Hindu idolatry. The mistress (whether human or divine) is the idol; and
her house (the universe) is the temple in which the lover worships. And
it is this idolatry of beauty, and not Islam, which is the true religion:

دیکھی ہے جب سے اُس بتِ کافر کی شکل میر
جاتا نہیں ہے جی تنک اسلام کی طرف

Since first I saw the form of that sweet infidel, my idol
I cannot find it in my heart to contemplate Islam.   (II.278.12)

جو کفر جانتے تھے عشقِ بتاں کو وہ ہی
مسجد کے آگے آخر تشقہ لگا کے بیٹھے

The very men who thought it blasphemy to worship idols
Sit now before the mosque and put the caste mark on their brow.
                                                        (II.348.13)

These verses are deliberately calculated to outrage the narrowly orthodox, but their real intention is to assert as forcefully as possible that true
religion, including true Islam, demands the love and worship of beauty as

an aspect of the love and worship of God, a point which Mir makes in the paradoxical verse:

ہیں مسلمان ان بتوں سے ہمیں

عشق ہے لا الہ الا اللہ

True Musalman am I, for to these idols
I pledge my love. "There is no god but God." (III.432.20)

"There is no god but God" are, of course, the first words of the Muslim profession of faith. There could be no more forceful way of asserting that God and "these idols"—that is, God and beauty—are one and indivisible.

If all created things "declare the glory of God," none declares it so eloquently as man himself. To the Muslim, man is *ashraf ul makhlūqāt*, "the noblest of created things," greater even than the angels, for when God created Adam, He commanded the angels to bow down before him, and Satan (or Iblīs), the chief among them, was banished forever from God's presence because he refused to do so.[15] All men, Muslim or Hindu, fair-skinned or dark, rich or poor, learned or ignorant, are heirs to this greatness, and the humanism already implicit in the insistence on the oneness of all men who love God truly, whatever the form in which they worship Him, is made explicit in many verses. If the universe is a

[15] The story that the angels were ordered to prostrate before the new-created Adam, and that only Iblīs refused to do so, is told in the Qur'ān several times: 7.10, 17.63, 18.48, 20.115. It is one of the favourite stories of the mystics, who developed their anthropology and satanology out of it. The expression "the noblest of created things" does not occur in this exact wording in the Qur'ān. (A.S.)

As another classic proof of the greatness of man, Mir refers (as the great Persian poet Hāfiz had four centuries before him) to a verse in the thirty-third chapter of the Qur'ān which reads—in the translation of A. J. Arberry, *The Koran Interpreted* (London, 1955), II, 129: "We offered the trust to the heavens and the earth and the mountains, but they refused to carry it and were afraid of it; and man carried it." What "the trust" was is not made clear, but to the poets the essential point is that God entrusted to man a burden which the heavens and the earth and the mountains dared not accept from Him, and that he alone had the courage and the strength to sustain it. Cf. VI.613.25, I.34.1, III.442.22. (This trust has likewise been a favourite topic of the modernists. Iqbāl, for instance, explains it as the power of individuation, which is man's prerogative and danger—A.S.) A. E. Housman has a poem of remarkably similar content: cf. p. 230 of *Collected Poems* (Harmondsworth, 1956). Āsī's footnote (to p. 442) quotes the most famous verse of Hāfiz on this theme. It is love that gives man the strength to sustain this burden. Cf. III.370.7.

mirror, the lustre which gives it both its own beauty and its power to
reflect the beauty of God comes from man alone:

آدم خاکی سے عالم کو جلا ہے دینے

آئینہ تھا یہ ولے قابلِ دیدار نہ تھا

Man, formed of clay, gave lustre to this mirror:
None would have looked into it but for him.   (I.43.23)

آدمی سے مَلَک کو کیا نسبت

شانِ ارفع ہے میر انساں کی

What have the angels got to do with man?
The highest rank belongs to him alone.   (II.325.23)

Man was made from a handful of dust, but it is as though that dust were
something very rare and precious, gathered by years of searching and
sifting from ordinary dust:

مت سہل ہمیں جانو پھرتا ہے فلک برسوں

تب خاک کے پردے سے انساں نکلتے ہیں

Don't think us cheap: the heavens revolve for years
To bring forth man out of the veil of dust.   (I.98.22)

Such a creation as man is develops potentialities of its own:

ہیں مُشتِ خاک لیکن جو کچھ ہیں میرے ہم ہیں

مقدور سے زیادہ مقدور ہے ہمارا

Made from the clay—but what we are, we are.
Our power is greater than the power God gave us.
(I.28.23)

16 Cf. III.376.1.

And his aspirations are high as his origins are low:

گرچہ انسان ہیں زمیں سے ولے
ہیں دماغ ان کے آسمانوں پر

True, man was fashioned out of earth, and yet
His high resolve exalts him to the skies.   (VI.641.12)

Mir represents mankind when he says:

ہیں گدا میر بھی ولے دو جہاں
کرکے ایک ہی سوال لیتے ہیں

Mir is a beggar, yes; but when he begs
He asks for nothing less than the two worlds.   (III.419.21)

God created man, and found His creation good. But man himself cannot
be satisfied to be simply what God made him:

اب ایسے ہیں کہ صانع کے مزاج اوپر ہم پہنچے
جو خاطر خواہ اپنے ہم ہوئے ہوتے تو کیا ہوتے

Such as we are, God fashioned us close to His heart's desire:
If we had been what *we* had wished, what might we not have been!
(I.157.16)

The man who does not rebel against the role God planned for him is not
worthy of his human status:

الٰہی کیسے ہوتے ہیں جنھیں ہے بندگی خواہش
ہمیں تو شرم دامن گیر ہوتی ہے خدا ہوتے

Oh God, what sort of men are they who love to be Thy servants?
I would have been beset with shame even had I been God. (I.157.14)

This note of rebellion against God's will is heard recurrently in many forms. God himself exalted man above the angels. And yet man is now everywhere degraded and dishonoured, even by God himself, for nothing happens except by His will. There is a note of sarcasm in Mir's reflection on this:

خاک کو آدم کرکے اٹھایا جس کے دست قدرت نے

قدر نہیں کچھ اس بندے کی بھی خدا کی قدرت ہے

Adam rose from the dust, formed by His mighty hand
To serve Him; now none honours him. Such is God's might!

(V.608.19)

If this was the fate God had in store for him, why did He create him? Why does God's word, the Holy Quran, stress his exalted status? And, most cruel mockery of all, why does God predestine all his actions and then call him to account as though he had acted of his own free will?

آنکھیں کھلیں تو دیکھا جو کچھ نہ دیکھنا تھا

خواب عدم سے ہم کو کاہے کے تئیں جگایا

My eyelids opened, and I saw what none should have to see;
I slept in nonexistence: why did You awaken me? (II.249.24)

بہت سعی کیجیے تو مر رہیے میر

بس اپنا تو اتنا ہی مقدور ہے

The most that you can win is death at last.
Such is the power God has given you! (I.179.8)

خوف قیامت کا یہی ہے کہ میر

ہم کو جیا بار دگر چاہیے

If Mir fears Judgement Day it is because
He must rise up and start to live again.   (I.158.18)

ناحق ہم مجبوروں پر یہ تہمت ہے مختاری کی

چاہتے ہیں سو آپ کریں ہیں ہم کو عبث بدنام کیا

You call us free? You slander us unjustly.
Your will is done—and *we* must take the blame.   (I.4.10)

منھ نہ ہم جبریتوں کا کھلواؤ

کہنے کو اختیار سا ہے کچھ

All that we "free" men do is under duress;
Mind that You do not force us to speak out!   (II.322.22)

God's very self-sufficiency is a ground for suspicion and complaint:

خدا کو کام تو سونپے ہیں میں نے سب لیکن

رہے ہے خوف مجھے دھان کی بے نیازی کا

To God I have committed all my purposes—and yet
My heart misgives me; is He not a law unto Himself?

(I.53.6)

The same awareness of man's unique potentialities and of the unique
honour he should enjoy in God's universe dictates the relations that
should prevail between man and man. Mir believes that the essence of
true religion can be summed up in the commandment not to injure your
fellowmen, and that formal religion is unimportant by comparison:

در مسجد پہ حلقہ زن ہو تم

کہ رہو بیٹھ حنا نہ خمار

جی میں آوے سو کیجیو پیارے

ایک ہونا نہ درپے آزار

Go to the mosque; stand knocking at the door—
Live all your days with drunkards in their den—
Do anything you want to do, my friend,
But do not seek to harm your fellowmen.

$$(I.68.24;69,1)^{17}$$

کہتا ہے کون تجھ کو یہاں یہ نہ کر تو وہ کر

پر ہو سکے جو پیارے دل میں بھی تنگ جگہ کر

When have I said to you, "Do this!" or "Don't do that!" No, only try
To make more room within your heart: there is no other law, say I.

$$(I.70.21)$$

Many verses elaborate these general commandments. If you would obey
them, you must first change yourself, learning how to see "the fire that
stirs beneath the ruby"—that is, the potentialities that lie hidden beneath the surface in every man.[18] You must eradicate from your heart all
arrogance towards him, and bring in humility in its place:

جائے غیرت ہے خاکدانِ جہاں

تو کہاں منہ اٹھائے جاتا ہے

دیکھ سیلاب اس بیاباں کا

کیسا سر کو جھکائے جاتا ہے

Here in this world of dust look to your honour;
Head high in pride, you care not where you tread.
See how the flood, which makes this desert blossom
Moves ever on its path with lowered head. $$(II.353.8-9)$$

---

17 This verse is almost an Urdū version of a couplet of Hāfiẓ.
18 Allusion to III.445.11.

In Urdu the word for a humble, modest man means literally "like the dust," and Mir argues that to be "like the dust" is not to degrade oneself but merely to pay the dust the honour due to it, for it was from the dust that Adam, the ancestor of all mankind, was formed, and it is to the dust that all men one day return.[19] Pride and careless indifference can inflict inestimable harm:

وے لوگ تم نے ایک ہی شوخی میں کھو دیئے

پیدا کئے تھے چرخ نے جو خاک چھان کر

One wilful act of yours, and he is lost
Whom heaven had sifted all the earth to find.   (I.74.1)

The "yours" may refer to God, to a cruel mistress, or to any man who fails in due regard for his fellowman, but in every case the stress is on the preciousness of man, and the need to act carefully so as not to hurt him. For man's heart is like a phial of delicate glass, which a single thoughtless action can shatter beyond repair.[20] In his autobiography Mir recalls the words of a mystic he had heard in his childhood: "Never on any account give pain to any man's heart, or break this phial with the stone of cruelty; for in the heart of man the Divine Beloved sits enthroned, and it is His special abode."[21] And often in his poetry, when he wants to stress the need to refrain from every action which can cause man pain, he uses this same metaphor of the phial or sometimes of the wineglass filled with the wine of the heart's blood and as beautiful as it is fragile. Or else in metaphors, which become all the more vivid when one recalls the conditions of the age in which Mir lived, the heart is a splendid city or a beautiful building that only a ruthless enemy would destroy:[22]

دل وہ نگر نہیں کہ پھر آباد ہو سکے

پچھتاؤ گے سنو ہو یہ بستی اُجاڑ کر

The heart is not a city that can rise again from ruins.
Loot it, and—do you hear me?—you will live to rue the day.

(I.69.17)

19 Allusions to IV.497.6 and I.103.21.
20 Allusion to I.179.4.
21 Cf. *Zikr i Mir*, p. 39.
22 Allusions to I.179.4, I.176.23, I.137.2–4.

دل سے خوش طرح مکاں پھر بھی کہیں بنتے ہیں
اس عمارت کو تک اک دیکھ کے ڈھایا ہوتا

No palace ever built could match the heart for grace and beauty.
Had you but glanced at it, could you have razed it to the ground?

(II.233.5)

The ideal is so to develop your sensitivity that you feel another's pain as
though it were your own. Often Mir compares man in his distress to a
songbird imprisoned in a cage, and says:

جی کھنچ گیا اسیرِ قفس کی فغاں کی اور
تھی چوٹ اپنے دل کو گر قتارہم ہوئے

I heard the lamentation of the prisoner in his cage—
It was *my* heart that ached, and *I* that was held captive there.

(III.442.23)

If it were in his power, he would make all men happy:

میرے جنگل تمام بس جاوے
بن پڑتے ہم سے روزگار اے کاش

All the waste land would thrive and teem with life—
Alas! if only I controlled the means!   (IV.485.18)

If you can once fill your heart with the love of your fellowman, you
will inspire an equal love in his heart, and you will then see a miracle performed. For when love possesses it, that same heart which was once as
brittle as glass becomes so strong that no power can assail it. No longer
is it a fair palace defenceless against those who would destroy it. On the
contrary, when cities are destroyed, the building of the heart still stands:

یہ بنا رہتی سی آتی ہے نظر یہاں کچھ مجھے
اچھی ہے تعمیر دل کی اس خراب آباد میں

The building of the heart alone is raised on strong foundations;
The heart alone will stand when ruin overwhelms the town.

ثباتِ قصر و در و بام و خشت و گل کتنا

عمارتِ دلِ درویش کی رکھو بنیاد

(III.412.14)[23]

Palace and gate and roof and brick and clay—none of them last;
So make the humble heart the strong foundation of your house.

(III.394.7)

دل میں رہ دل میں کہ معمارِ قضا سے اب تک

ایسا مطبوع مکاں کوئی بنایا نہ گیا

Live in the heart; make it your home; for the Great Architect
Has never built a dwelling so acceptable as this. (I.27.13)

Verses like these depict the heart possessed by love as a power that stands immovable against every conceivable force. But it is something more than that; it is itself a force or irresistible power:

ماہیتِ دو عالم کھاتی پھرے ہے غوطے

یک قطرہ خون یہ دل طوفان ہے ہمارا

دل کہ اک قطرہ خوں نہیں بیش

ایک عالم کے سر بلا لایا

This heart which seems no greater than a single drop of blood
Is like a whirlwind mingling earth and heaven with its force.

(I.43.17; 33.16)

---

[23] Cf. V.591.10.

For the heart bears all, but conquers all. Physically small though it is, its capacities are as great as the ocean, as vast as the great expanses of the desert.[24] And this is why the heart, the seat of love, the throne of the Divine Beloved, the heart infinitely sensitive and yet infinitely strong, is man's surest guide in life:

طریقِ عشق میں ہے رہنما دل

پیمبرِ دل ہے، قبلۂ دل غلط دل

Love was our faith, this heart our guide along the path we trod;
This heart was our preceptor, this our Prophet, this our God
(VI.647.6)[25]

—"our Prophet" and "our God" because the bidding of the heart *is* the bidding of the Prophet and of God.

Yet the man who would follow its dictates implicitly clashes inevitably with the pillars of society and with the man of the world. To the kings and nobles the good man is he who submits to their authority and obeys their will. To the shaikh, who is always the ally of the powers that be, he is the man who reveres him and looks to him for spiritual guidance. And neither king nor shaikh looks kindly upon one who rules his life not by their commands but by the voice of God, which speaks to his heart and tells him that love—love of God and love of his neighbour—must be the sole force which guides him. Neither the wealth of kings nor the learning of divines impresses him; both are quite irrelevant to man's task in life:

حق کو دینے کو چاہیئے ہے کیا

یہاں نہ اسباب نے ہنر ہے شرط

What do you need to render what is due?
Nor wealth nor learning enters into it.   (II.276.11)

---

[24] Allusions to the ghazal in the fifth divan, pp. 579–580.
[25] Cf. III.405.10.

The clash with the man of the world is equally unavoidable. For the man of the world prides himself on his practical wisdom, on accepting the world as it is, on taking the view that high principles are all very well, but that a man has to make his way in the world, and in the practical business of life it is madness to bring principles into it. To this argument Mir replies, in effect, that if that way of life is sanity, then give him madness every time. For this madness is, once again, the madness of the lover, the way of life of the man so possessed by love for his mistress or his God or his ideals that he remains true to it no matter what men who lack the capacity to comprehend it may think of him or do to him. Such madness is a source of both joy and pride to him, for it teaches a wisdom incomparably higher than that produced in the hard heads of practical men, and any lapse into their sanity and good sense is something to regret:

خرد مندی ہوئی زنجیر ورنہ

گزرتی خوب تھی دیوانہ پن میں

Good sense has come to fetter me. Before that
I knew the joy of life, for I was mad.   (I.98.15)[26]

He knows as well as the man of the world that this is the way not to wordly success but to poverty and destitution. The world does not treat kindly those who do not conform to its ways; Fate does not befriend such men, and it is the height of simplicity to expect it to:

تجھ سے ہزاران نے بناکر دے بگاڑ

مت جان سادگی سے کہ ہے روزگار دوست

It made and marred a thousand such as you.
Don't be so simple: Fate is not your friend.   (III.389.14)

The heavens extend like a vast table, with the gold and silver plates of the sun and the moon set out upon it, and you might expect to receive royal hospitality there. You would be wrong, for "both these plates are

---

[26] Cf. VI.661.7 and II.300.19.

empty.''[27] But to the true lover his poverty is his badge of honour, the mark of his freedom and independence and determination to follow his own ideal. He is a *faqīr*—a word in which the senses of beggar and holy man are still closely associated in Urdu; he asks no man's favour, but trusts to God and to the generous impulses of his fellowmen to sustain him. And no status that the world can give a man can compare with his:

هو کوئی بادشاه کوئی یہاں وزیر ہو

اپنی بلا ـــــــ سے بیٹھا رہے جب فقیر ہو

> This may be king, and that be minister;
> What do I care? Am I not a faqīr?   (II. 3 1 2. 1 8)[28]

He owns nothing, so that when he lies down to sleep, he must pillow his head on his arm. That is why, Mir explains gravely, he cannot hold out his arm to beg; it has gone to sleep from the pressure of the head resting on it, and he cannot move it.[29]

Enough has already been said to show that "the religion of love," as Mir many times calls it[30] has its own commandments, and that these more often than not clash head-on with the commandments of orthodox Islam. It would be an understatement to say that no attempt is made to avoid this clash. The mysticism of the ghazal is the extreme, radical mysticism which the orthodox—the shaikh of the ghazal convention—abhorred, hated, and persecuted; and his loathing was most cordially returned. In the ceaseless warfare that followed, each side pushed its position to extremes. The mystic had started from the point that the prescribed Muslim duties of prayer, fasting, almsgiving, and pilgrimage were at best of limited value in helping the worshipper to cultivate the all-important love for God, and could be harmful if their ritual performance became a substitute for true religion and a source of self-righteousness. He now took the unequivocal view that they were always harmful, the source of bigotry and self-satisfaction, and nothing else; and not only must the mystic not perform them; he must openly flout them. Much the same is

---

27 Allusion to I.101.3.
28 Cf. I.43.7, VI.672.8, II.342.
29 Allusion to IV.521.16.
30 I.24.13, V.570.11.

true for the Muslim prohibition on wine. Wine is not the enemy of the true lover of God, but his helper, for it frees him from the crippling inhibitions of worldly wisdom and brings into play all the generous impulses of his heart. Moreover, intoxication with wine serves as a symbol of that intoxication with the love of God which is the mystic's aim, and thereby helps him to achieve that aim. Music and love—both of them disapproved by the orthodox—fulfill a similar function, helping him towards an ecstasy in which all consciousness of self is lost. Hence the mystic is not only a lover but also a *rind*—a word in which the senses of drunkard, happy-go-lucky, profligate, and rake are all present. He spends his time in the taverns just as the ''godly'' man spends his in the mosque; the deference which the godly man pays to the *imām*, or the man who leads the congregation in prayer, the *rind* pays to the tavern-keeper; what prayer and fasting and pious works are to the orthodox, wine and music and revelry are to him. So that if he goes into the mosque, it is by accident:

Worshippers in the mosque, it was an accident that brought me here.
My drunken feet have strayed this way: I trust you will forgive me!

(II.231.4)

In this setting the profligate's attacks upon his archenemy the shaikh are more good-natured than in other contexts—rough, it is true, but not bitter, as though he vaguely realises that after all it is not the shaikh's fault, poor fellow, that he is like he is:

Of course shaikh won't concede to us the beauty of our idols.
There's something to be said for him, poor fellow. He is blind.

(II.280.1)

And sometimes Mir feels that even the shaikh, if only he can once be cajoled or bullied into exposing his heart to the full influence of wine and beauty, may yet be saved. One of the few ghazals of Mir which possesses continuity of theme expresses this mood:

شیخ جی آؤ مصلّیٰ گرو جام کرو
جنسِ تقویٰ کے تئیں صرف مئے جام کرو

فرشِ مستاں کرو سجّادہُ بے تہ کے تئیں
مے کی تعظیم کرو شیشے کا اکرام کرو

دامنِ پاک کو آلودہ بادے سے رکھو
آپ کو منگجھوں کے قابلِ دشنام کرو

نیک نامی و تقاوَدست کو دعا جلدی کہو
دین و دل پیش کش سادہُ خود کام کرو

ننگ و ناموس سے اب گزرو جوانوں کی طرح
پر فشانی کرو اور ساقی سے ابرام کرو

اٹھ کھڑے ہو جو تھکے گر دنِ مینائے شراب
خدمتِ بادہ گساراں ہی سرانجام کرو

مطرب آ گر ہو کرے چنگ نوازی تو تم
پیرہنِ مستوں کی تقلید سے انعام کرو

سایۂ گل میں لب جوئے گلابی رکھو
ہاتھ میں جام کو لو آپ کو بدنام کرو

آہ تا چند رہو خانقہ و مسجدیں
ایک تو صبح گلستان میں بھی شام کرو

Shaikh, pawn your prayer mat—for its price you'll get a glass of wine or so;
Yes, sell the gear of piety so that the rose-red wine may flow.
Or else unroll your worthless mat for drunkards to recline upon.
Sing praises to almighty wine! All honour to the bottle show!
Let the wine stain your spotless robe! Pester the pretty serving boys!
They'll swear at you, and that will be a fresh delight for you to know!
Come on now, say a quick goodbye to good repute. Your heart and faith
Present as an unworthy gift to her in whom all beauties glow.
Yes, let your good name go to hell. Be like the lads, and spread your
  wings.
Shout to the *sāqi*, "Bring more wine!"—and scold him if he comes too
  slow.

Stand up! The flagon bows its head to serve the revellers. You too
Proffer your services. You too in token of respect bow low.
The harpist comes to play and sing. You've nothing to reward him with?
Then be like us: take off your shirt and give him that. He won't say no.
Under the rosebush in the shade set down the wine jar by the stream.
Go on, take up your glass and drink. Disgrace yourself with high and low.
Too long the mosque and monastery have stifled you. One day at least
Set out at dawn and spend the day in gardens where red roses grow.

(I.130)

Verses in the same mood call on the recluse and the ascetic to follow
suit.

Come on out, recluse! Leave your cell and see the green plants growing
And black clouds sent from Mecca swaying high above the taverns.

(V.559.3)

Come to the tavern, recluse, now, for joy has left the mosque.
The rain falls, and the breeze blows soft, and all your body glows.

(IV.525.23)

Do people lead the holy life when clouds sway overhead?
In days like these, ascetic, you should see if you can sin.

(I.71.5)

The reference to the swaying clouds sets the scene in the rainy season, when after weeks of parching heat, rain falls torrentially and every green thing grows luxuriantly, and an atmosphere of relief and joy infects everyone. This season, and the nights of the full moon, are regularly associated in Urdu poetry with wine drinking, and the invitation to drink is therefore unmistakably implied. The tone of both verses is mocking. Thus in the first the point is stressed that the rain clouds come from Mecca, the holy city towards which Muslims turn to pray—and they do indeed come from that direction—so that the recluse may be more disposed to listen to their message. But the mockery is quite good-natured. The profligate's exhortation to the ascetic to see if he can sin stems from two convictions: first, that what the orthodox regard as sin is not sin at all, and secondly that if, by giving full rein to his best impulses, he does sometimes commit the sins of excess, this is still a far better thing than to live as the orthodox do, in mortal fear of sin, repressing every bold and generous instinct:

To save their souls they kill themselves with care.
A Paradise like that can go to Hell!   (III.419.7)

To lead such a life in the hope of heavenly reward is in any case unworthy of the true lover of God, who loves without any thought of benefit to himself. But is is also an insult to God in that it casts doubts upon His infinite mercy.[31] To mortify the flesh is to starve the soul as well and to do violence to the nature which God gave you. So Mir reassures his companions:

ہوا ہے اہلِ مساجد پہ کام از بس تنگ
نہ شب کو جاگتے رہنے کا اضطراب کرو

---

[31] Allusion to V.605.17.

خدا کریم ہے اس کے کرم سے رکھ کر چشم

دراز کھینچو کسو، میکدے میں خواب کرو

The people of the mosques are near to desperation. Why should you
Distress yourself to be like them and watch and pray throughout the
  night?
For God is merciful; His mercy is the hope to which we look.
Go to the tavern, lie full length, and sleep at ease till morning's light.

(IV.507.3–4)

ہم مذنبوں میں صرف کرم سے ہے گفتگو

مذکور و ذکر یہاں نہیں صوم و صلوات کا

It is God's mercy that we sinners speak of;
Fasting and prayer are never mentioned here.

(II.210.10)[32]

In other images the point is driven home that it is the profligate and not
the shaikh who finds favour in God's sight. Thus it is he who is chosen to
lead the worshippers in prayer:

پھر میر آج مسجدِ جامع کے تھے امام

داغِ شراب دھوتے تھے کل جانماز کا

Again today in the great mosque Mir led the worshippers—
He who but yesterday had washed the wine stains from his prayer mat.

(II.218.1)

Or, in another picture, the humblest of those who frequent the tavern is
worthy to be the guardian of the holy city of Mecca:

شریف کتر رہا ہے تمام عمر اے شیخ

یہ میرا ب جو گدا ہے شراب خانے کا

He has been all his life Sharīf of Mecca, shaikh—
This Mir who begs today outside the tavern door. (I.37.12)

If in this sort of context the shaikh is attacked with a sort of rough good humour, elsewhere the tone is bitter and contemptuous. For if the shaikh persecutes the mystic as a heretic and blasphemer, the mystic counter-attacks with charges of worldliness, self-seeking, and hypocrisy.[33] In his eyes the shaikh is a man whose guiding principles are derived not from the religion he professes but from a despicable worldly wisdom which teaches him to avoid unpopularity and shun conflict with the great and powerful, or an even more despicable greed for wordly power which makes him identify his interest with theirs. He is quick enough to fulminate against others for real or imagined lapses from religious duty, but in secret he himself does not observe even the plainest and most unambiguous commands of Islam, like the prohibition on wine. True, one cannot often prove that he sins, but sin he does, and not in moderation. The shaikh is to Mir what the Holy Willies and the "unco guid" are to his spiritual brother and younger contemporary, Robert Burns; and like Burns, he attacks them with ridicule, bawdy, and invective. The shaikh boasts of his other-worldliness, but God knows what pleasures he secretly prays for:

کاہے کو آۓ پوٹ کوئی دل پہ شیخ کے
اس ملہوس نے اپنے تئیں تو بچالیا

Shaikh never knew the ache of love. How could he ?
He took good care to feel no more than lust. (II.246.21)

His pretensions and those of his Pharisee friends to enjoy the privilege of a special closeness to God contrast glaringly with his utter insensitivity to what afflicts the hearts of God's servants, his fellowmen:

بندے کے درد دل کو کوئی نہیں پہچتا
ہر ایک بے حقیقت یہاں ہے خدا رسیدہ

They cannot feel the grief that wounds His servant's heart,
Yet every worthless fellow here "communes with God." (II.321.4)

---

33 Allusion to II.304.13.

For the sympathetic study of the human heart he substitutes the study of
his books, until all hope of humanising him is gone:

کب اس عمر میں آدمی شیخ ہوگا

کتابیں رکھیں ساتھ گو ایک خربار

What if he owns a donkey-load of books ?
Shaikh has got past the age to be a man.   (I.69.13)

The implied comparison is clear, and is sustained in other verses. Mir
pictures him with the staff which he always carries as the mark of his
authority, and comments:

بن عصا شیخ یک قدم نہ رکھے

راہ چلتا نہیں یہ خر بے چوب

Shaikh cannot walk a step without his staff—
An ass that needs the rod to make him go.   (I.57.3)

Give him wine and he at once reveals his true nature:

کچھ کم نہیں ہیں شعبدہ بازوں سے ہمے گسار

دارِ و پلا کے شیخ کو آدم سے خر کیا

Our revellers are quite a match for any conjurer;
They gave shaikh wine, and turned him from a man into an ass.
                                                  (I.30.15)

Yes, he is an ass, and should be used as one:

قصدِ حج ہے تو شیخ کو لے چل

کعبہ جانے کو یہ بھی خر ہے شرط

You're going to make the Pilgrimage ? Then take the shaikh along;
If you're to reach the Kaba, you must take an ass with you.
                                                  (II.276.9)

His pretensions to insight and understanding are ridiculed, and Mir combines sarcasm on this score with a neat compliment to himself:

میر صاحب کا ہر سخن ہے رمز

بے حقیقت ہے شیخ کیا سمجھے

Mir's every word has meaning beyond meaning—
More than a worthless shaikh can understand.   (II. 349. 10)

شیخ تونے خوب سمجھا میر کو

واہ وا لے بے حقیقت واہ واہ

Yes, shaikh, you understand Mir perfectly!
Bravo! you worthless dolt! Bravo! bravo!   (II. 320.8)

Sometimes the shaikh's associate, the *vāiz*, or preacher, comes under fire. He is treated with the same sarcasm:

ہم نے یہ مانا کہ واعظ ہیں ملک

آدمی ہونا بہت مشکل ہے میاں

I grant you, sir, the preacher is an angel.
To be a man, now—that's more difficult.   (II. 306.6)

The comparison with the angels, who never fail in serving God, is here turned against the preacher by recalling how God commanded the angels to bow down before man. And another verse makes the same point. However angelic the preacher may be, he hardly qualifies for the honoured status of man:

برسوں تئیں جب ہم نے تردد کئے ہیں تب

پہنچایا ہے آدم تئیں واعظ کے نسب کو

I worked at it for years, and only then
Could trace his lineage back to Father Adam.   (II. 317. 12)

Sometimes the tone is more serious:

شیخؔ کی تو نماز پر مت جا

بوجھ سر کا سا ڈال آتا ہے

Shaikh says his prayers? Don't be deceived by that.
Prayer is a load he lowers from his head.³⁴   (I.178.1)

The more serious tone of a verse such as this brings one back to the essential basis of the conflict between the mystic and the shaikh. To the mystic the essence of religion is to love God with all your heart and soul and to love your neighbour as yourself. If you live by this religion, all other commandments are superseded; you may—indeed, you must—give full rein to every generous impulse within you, to everything which stimulates love and adoration; and if this sometimes leads you to excess, you can trust implicitly in God's infinite mercy to forgive you. The shaikh by contrast cannot even comprehend the meaning of loving God; to him religion means to obey Him, and this obedience he interprets in the narrowest sense, of formal compliance with prescribed rituals. He calls God "the Compassionate, the Merciful," but his whole attitude shows that in practice he conceives of Him as a ruthless, implacable tyrant. Because he observes the forms of religion, he exalts himself above his fellowmen; narrowness, intolerance, bigotry, and pride dominate his outlook, and he is as zealous in the condemnation and persecution of his fellows as he should be in love for them. And all too often he is a hypocrite, false even to that apology for a religion which he himself professes, and dominated by the lusts of the world.

Between him and the mystic, therefore, it is war to the end, and because the world and all its powers are on the shaikh's side, the prospect for the mystic is life-long persecution and, in the end, martyrdom. Where it is war to the end, any attempt to mitigate the harshness of the struggle is pointless. On the contrary, any word or action of the mystic that wounds the shaikh is a victory over him. Hence the ridicule and

³⁴ In India loads are commonly carried on the head. The shaikh says his prayers not because devotion to God impels him to, but as an onerous duty that has to be discharged. The metaphor suggests also the ritual of Muslim prayer, in which one of the required postures is to lower one's forehead to the ground.

vituperation; hence the open violation of the prescribed ordinances of formal Islam; and hence the formulation of mystic doctrines in terms deliberately intended to outrage the orthodox. The type of the true mystic, in the eyes of the ghazal poet, is Mansūr al Hallāj,[35] who was crucified by the orthodox in A.D. 922 for crying out, "Anā'l Haqq Anā'l Haqq"—"I am God! I am God!"—words which to the mystic express his sense of the complete merging of the individual soul with the Divine Beloved, but which to the orthodox are unspeakable blasphemy. Mansūr used to urge the absolute duty of standing by right, whatever the circumstances, by saying that he must take Satan as his model—Satan, who stood his ground and refused to bow down to Adam, even though this involved defiance of God's direct command, punished by the loss for ever of his pre-eminent position among the angels and by expulsion from heaven. Mir's position, and that of the ghazal poets in general, is Mansūr's position, and he takes it for granted that he will share Mansūr's fate.

You must have heard what happened to Mansūr—
Here, if you speak the truth,[36] they crucify you. (I.114.15)

And thus the parallel is completed between earthly and divine love. Persecution and perhaps death await alike the man who is constant in his love for his mistress and him who is constant in his love for his God and his ideals.

It has already been emphasised that the mystic extremism which the convention of the ghazal reflects was only one of the many forms that

---

[35] Husain ibn Mansūr al Hallāj, the Woolcarder—mostly called after his father's name "Mansūr," the "Victorious"—to whose fascinating personality the French orientalist L. Massignon has devoted fifty years of study, has been transformed, especially in the Indo-Pak environment, into the typical symbol of suffering love; but since he declared openly, "I am the absolute Truth," he was accused of having disclosed the Divine secret—hence the stress laid by mystics upon "hiding the secret, concealing the name." Cf. A. J. Arberry, *Sufism* (London, 1950), pp. 59–60; A. Schimmel, "The Martyr-Mystic Hallāj in Sindhī Folk-Poetry," *Numen*, IX (1963), 3. (A.S.)

[36] This is a play on words. Here Mir uses the word *haqq* in the sense of "the truth." But it is the same word as Mansūr used in his cry "Anā'l Haqq!" which there means "God."

mysticism took, and certainly not the dominant one in Islamic mysticism as a whole. The identification of the ghazal poet with the mystic is a conventional and not a literal one; and so is the identification of mysticism as a whole with the radical, extremist brand of it which the ghazal presents. The actual historical picture is rather different. It shows that the earlier mystics, far from attacking orthodox usages, were most particular to observe them, and while orthodoxy always distrusted the mystic approach, it did not yet persecute it. Later mystics, of whom Mansūr al Hallāj is the type, clashed sharply with the orthodox and seem to have made no attempt to avoid doing so. Mansūr can hardly have failed to realise how blasphemous his teachings must have sounded to orthodox ears. Others were not less bold in their doctrines, but increasingly felt the need to conceal them from the uninitiated, speaking of their mystic experience only to those who had prepared themselves to receive and understand it. A further parallel here arises with the situation of the lover; like him, the mystic lover violates the code of love if he allows the secret of his love to become known to a hostile society. If Mansūr sinned, said later mystics, this was where his sin lay, and Mir is making the same point when he writes:

اِکوں کی کھال کھینچی اِیکوں کو دار کھینچا

اسرارِ عاشقی کا پچھتا ــــــ ئے یار کہہ کر

Some they impaled upon the stake, and some they
took and flayed alive.
No lover yet betrayed the secrets of his love but
had to die. (I.71.4)

After Mansūr came men who approach more closely the position that the ghazal describes. One of them was the Persian Abu Sa'īd,[37] who would not permit his disciples to make the pilgrimage to Mecca and taught that the true mystic had no need to keep the commandments of orthodox Islam. But the extreme position which the ghazal portrays, the position of men who—deliberately, ostentatiously, and with intention to

---

[37] Abū Sa'īd ibn Abi'l-Khair (967–1049), one of the leading mystics of his time, lived in Nīshāpūr. A number of mystical quatrains have wrongly been attributed to him. Cf. R. A. Nicholson, *Studies in Islamic Mysticism* (Cambridge, 1921). (A.S.)

provoke the hatred of the orthodox—violated the law of Islam and the conventions of Islamic society, was probably never that of more than a small minority. In any case, long before Mir's day the bitter persecution of the mystics had ceased. If orthodoxy never wholly lost its distrust of mysticism, it had nevertheless come to accept it as a legitimate approach to God, provided that the commands and prohibitions of orthodox Islam were also observed; and the mystics on their side, whatever they might say or do within their own closed circle, were quite content to show these outward signs of conformity. What survived in the ghazal tradition were the types of the protagonists of the earlier struggle and the portrayal of all their practices, used as the symbols of something wider. Just as the ghazal adopts the language of Hindu idolatry as a striking way of asserting the worship of God through the worship of beauty, and the complete incompatibility of such worship with a soulless, ritualised "Islam," so too it adopts the language of mystic extremism as the most vivid way of asserting the spirit of mysticism as a whole.

But the gap between symbolic expression and literal reality may be even greater than this. The fact that the conventions of the ghazal prescribed the theme of love (in both the literal and the mystic senses) compelled every ghazal poet to present himself as a lover and a mystic, and we have to assess in each case from such factual knowledge as we possess to what extent he really was either. In an age when poetry was one of the polite accomplishments, the answer was quite often, "Not to any extent at all," for the rules of the ghazal, both in regard to form and theme, are so detailed, and its stock of traditional symbols and allusions so vast, that anyone who had the technical competence could make a ghazal out of them; and ghazals were written by men who show no sign of ever having been in love either with a woman or with their God.

But this is not the case with Mir. We know, both from his own masnavis and from external sources, that he had experienced love and had undergone the inevitable social persecution which this involved and which in his case actually drove him mad. But we know also that his mistress was not the cold, cruel mistress of his ghazals but, on the contrary, one who responded fully and tenderly to his love; and we may therefore legitimately conclude that the cruel mistress of the ghazals is the symbol of something else. To say that she stands for God, the Divine Beloved, would convey too narrow an impression to the modern reader.

In the terminology of the ghazal "real love"—that is, divine love—embraces not only the love of God in the sense in which the modern understands it, but a man's complete dedication to his ideals in life, ideals which he will serve to the end, no matter what suffering this may bring down upon him. The medieval man did not distinguish between the service of God and the service of his ideals, for he saw his ideals as prescribed for him by God and his devotion to them as an integral part of his devotion to God. But the modern distinction is relevant to an understanding of Mir, the more so because Mir was not himself a mystic, although he was deeply influenced by mysticism.

We can estimate the extent of its influence fairly accurately, mainly from his own direct testimony, which is to be found in a short work that he wrote in Persian prose entitled *Zikr i Mir* (An Account of Mir). This is generally referred to as his autobiography, and indeed it is difficult to know what else to call it, though it is not what we understand by the term today, for Mir himself rarely comes into the foreground in it. Nowhere in the book does Mir claim to be a mystic, though he tells us that his father was, and the book begins with an account of his father and of the other mystics who were intimately associated with him. It continues with a very brief narrative of Mir's own experiences from the time of his father's death, during his boyhood, to the establishment of his reputation as a poet, and then goes on to tell the story of the decline of the Empire over a period of forty years—from 1748 to 1788—bringing in occasional references to the way in which the course of events affected his own fortunes. The quotations from Mir in Chapter 1 were taken from this book.

It is significant that the first part of the book, which covers little more than ten years out of the total span of about sixty, occupies more than a third of the whole. It consists, in the main, of stories of his father, of his father's young disciple Amanullah, whom Mir called "uncle," and of their mystic associates, and it is abundantly clear that their teachings made a life-long impression upon him. They treated him as a child mature beyond his years, and he has vivid memories of the things they said to him or to others in his presence. Scholars dispute over the extent to which the incidents he relates can be regarded as reliable, but whether they are reliable or not, they testify to Mir's deep interest in mysticism and show what aspects of it most strongly appealed to him. Chief among these was the mystics' stress on the all-pervading force of love. Mir quotes his father's words to him, urging him to love and to learn that love is the supreme force in the universe. And years later he begins one of his masnavis (*The Flame of Love*) [38] not with the lines in praise of God and the Prophet which convention prescribed, but with a hymn to love which virtually reproduces in Urdu verse these same words that his father had spoken to him. "Love brought forth light out of the darkness," it begins.

Without love God could not have made Himself manifest. Love alone drives on the work of the world: without it the world would cease to move, and the heavens to revolve. It is love that gave heat to the sun, love that scarred the heart of the moon. Love can set fire to water. It is love for the candle's flame that draws the moth to burn to death, and that same flame of love that melts the candle away. It is love that opens the delicate mouths of the rosebuds to blossom in a smile, love that moves the rose to unfold her beauty before the nightingale, and love for the rose that inspires the nightingale's sweet, lamenting song. . . . It is love that sets man's heart aflame, that heart which, without love, is no better than a stone. It is love that inspires him to heroic deeds, love that makes him bow his neck gladly to receive the death blow from his beloved's sword, love that makes possible those things that, without love, man could not even conceive of. The whole firmament is filled with love, and earth and sky are brimming over with it.

The introduction to his own love story, *The Stages of Love*, is on similar lines, and his own experience must have strengthened his conviction of the truth of his father's words. He took also from the mystics their belief in the holiness of beauty, their humanism, their refusal to compromise their principles for the sake of worldly advancement, and their proud self-dedication to the highest ideals of life. The verses in praise of wine and extolling the man who violates the formal commandments of Islam seem, however, to be purely symbolic, for there is no evidence that Mir, so far as the externals of daily life were concerned, was in any marked way different from the average Muslim of his day.

Whatever Mir believed in, he believed in passionately, and he sought to express his beliefs in his poetry. He seems to have decided to devote himself to poetry from quite an early age, and indications in his autobiography suggest that he had already made his name by the mid-1740s—

---

[38] *Kulliyāt*, pp. 890–891.

that is, in his early twenties. His verse shows that one aspect of his humanism was his keen awareness that present generations inherit the achievements of men who have lived before them, that every man "builds his house with the clay of a hundred vanished forms" [39] or with the clay of men "whose mark is still to be seen on earth." [40] And with this goes the awareness that he too must make his contribution to mankind:

What should I say if anyone should ask me:
"What did *you* do while you were in the world?"

(I.202.13)

Though Mir revered the mystics he did not follow those among them who withdrew from the world to live in solitary contemplation of God. He remembers how his father's young disciple, his "uncle" Amānullah, had shut himself up to devote himself to study and contemplation, and how when a year had gone by, his father had told him that he must return to live his life among other men. [41] And he writes:

You must live in the world, where griefs and joys beset you—
And live to such effect that men may not forget you. (III.428.10)

Time is short, and death comes every day to thousands:

کارواں در کارواں یاں سے چلے جاتے ہیں لوگ

ہر طرف اس خاکداں میں دیکھتے ہیں گرد گرد

Caravan after caravan moves off to leave this world.
On every side you see their dust that rises in the air.

(III.394.18)

[39] Allusion to I.70.16.
[40] Allusion to II.264.12.
[41] Cf. *Zikr i Mīr*, p. 19.

You cannot afford to delay in doing what it lies in your power to do. Man's life is like a spark which flies up in the air and is gone; [42] all the more reason then why he should make good use of the short time allotted to him:

جہاں میں دیر نہیں لگتی آنکھیں مندتے تیر
تمھیں توچاہیئے ہر کام میں شتاب کرو

Time does not wait: too soon your eyes will close, Mir.
All that you have to do you must do quickly.   (IV.507.5)

ہے لب بام آفتاب عمر
کرلے سو کیا ہے میرے دن تھوڑا

The sun of life sinks fast behind the roof.
Do what you have to do, Mir; night comes on.

(III.382.6)

Mir knew what he had to do, and it is characteristic of him that he could write with ironic understatement of what was in fact the most important thing in his life:

کچھ نہیں تو شعر ہی کی فکر کر
آئے ہیں جو یہاں تو کچھ کر کے جائیے

If nothing else, you can at least write poetry.
Now that you've come, do something while you're here.

(II.352.8)

Despite the fact that Urdu poetry was still in its infancy in northern India, Mir set himself ambitious aims. In a short work written before he was thirty, he defines *rekhta* (as Urdu poetry was called in his day) as "poetry on the Persian model, written in the language of . . . Delhi," [43] and goes on to describe his own practice in Urdu poetry in terms which

---

[42] Allusion to I.113.13.
[43] *Nikāt ush Shu'arā*, pp. 1, 187.

make it clear that he aimed to bring Urdu verse to the same pitch of
technical accomplishment as several centuries of development had produced in Persian. True, he enjoyed two great advantages: first, that the
whole literary heritage of Persian lay ready to hand, and secondly, that
he worked within a general trend towards supplanting Persian by Urdu as
the medium of poetry. The work just referred to is a brief account of his
contemporaries in Urdu poetry, and no less than 103 are spoken of in it.
Nevertheless, in this development Mir and Sauda—or "Mir and Mirza"—
were early recognised as being head and shoulders above the rest, and it
is remarkable in how short a time Urdu poetry developed to maturity in
their hands.

As we have said, Mir's main attention was devoted to the ghazal. In the
most recent edition of his collected verse, his six *dīvāns*, or collections of
ghazals, occupy 808 of the 1344 pages, and the first (and earliest) dīvān
contains some of the best. In general he works with apparent ease within
its somewhat strict conventions, but he also has no hesitation in breaking
them occasionally where he feels the need to do so. For example, two
ghazals on the same page in his first dīvān (I.50) consist of only three
couplets each (as against the generally prescribed minimum of five),
while at the other extreme, there is one in his second dīvān of no less
than thirty-two (where the most liberal of the prosodists allow only
seventeen), and that too with a single theme running throughout
(II.264–268). In another ghazal of exceptional length—nineteen couplets
—he anticipates criticism with a joke:

My ghazal's a qasīda? Well, what of it?
Is it not written on the theme of love?   (I.193.4)

The words imply several arguments. If one takes rhyme scheme as the
salient characteristic of a particular form of verse, the ghazal and the
qasīda differ only in length, so that a ghazal which exceeds its prescribed
length does indeed become a qasīda. Mir therefore admits the charge,
and then goes on to justify what he has done. His poem is "on the theme
of love," he says; and this implies, first, that the main requirement of the

ghazal has thus been fulfilled; secondly, that because the themes of love are so inexhaustible, it is not always proper to curtail them by imposing an arbitrary and inflexible limit on the length of the poem; and thirdly, that the qasīda is by definition a poem of praise, and what could be more fitting than to write one in praise of love, the thing which beyond all others is most precious to the ghazal poet?

He allows himself a similar freedom with the laws of metre. Urdu metre, being based upon the Arab-Persian system, resembles that of the ancient classical languages, Sanskrit, Greek, and Latin, in that it is primarily based upon quantity.[44] But long and short syllables are some-what differently defined. In Urdu a short syllable consists of an initial short vowel, or a single consonant followed by a short vowel, while a long syllable consists of an initial long vowel, consonant-long vowel, or con-sonant-short vowel-consonant. The pattern of longs and shorts in a line determines the metre, and these patterns are, to modern ways of thinking, very rigidly prescribed. Thus if a poet selects for a poem the metre: ˘ — — | ˘ — — | ˘ — — | ˘ — (the metre of Mir Hasan's *Enchanting Story*), every line of that poem must reproduce this pattern exactly, without the sort of variation which is permitted, for example, in the Greek and Latin hexameter, where in many positions two shorts may be used as a variant of one long. Moreover, the Urdu poet is not, in general, permitted—as the ancient poets were—to run together all the words of the line for the purpose of scansion: every word must scan separately. In practice these restrictions are less severe than they might seem, because in Urdu the laws of quantity are modified by what one may call the "beat" of the rhythm. The effect of this is that many, though not all, consonant-long vowel units may, according to the poet's convenience, be scanned short, provided that they are not in a position where the beat of the rhythm also falls. In addition, there are a few metres, out of a very large total, that permit a measure of variation. That which Mir adopted for his own love story, *The Stages of Love*, is perhaps the commonest of this small group. Its basic pattern is — ˘ — — | ˘ — ˘ — | — — , but a short may replace the first long of the first foot; two shorts may replace the first long of the last foot; and other variations as well sometimes occur.

---

[44] The traditional science of prosody does not treat of the metre in these terms. But cf. R. Russell, "Some Problems of the Treatment of Urdu Metre," *Journal of the Royal Asiatic Society* (April 1960), pp. 48–58.

This much freedom was available to every Urdu poet, but Mir claims more than the general share. Thus, where it suits him, he will use colloquial Delhi pronunciations as the basis of his scansion, while elsewhere he uses the generally accepted ones. He also has a favourite metre in which the role of the musical beat is much more marked than in most, and the range of permissible variations much greater than the writers of textbooks on metre find comfortable. Its basic line consists of fifteen long syllables, with the beat falling on the first, third, fifth, and so on. But in any of the even syllables (second, fourth, sixth, etc.) except the eighth, which immediately precedes the caesura, two shorts may replace a single long. The effect is strikingly beautiful, and Mir seems to have grown increasingly fond of it in his later years, for in his fifth and sixth dīvāns it occurs again and again.[45]

But ghazals which break the accepted canons—whether of metre or length or form or theme—are exceptional in his work. He chose the ghazal form as his main medium because he felt it to be suited to his needs, because the themes that convention prescribed for it were precisely those on which he wanted to write, and because its intense and personal tone accorded well with his own temperament. The ghazal allowed him the unrestrained freedom to speak the truth about love and life as he saw it, and to attack the enemies of that truth in the sharpest terms. Society tolerated such frankness in poetry alone, and it was a freedom that Mir treasured:

عجب ہوتے ہیں شاعر بھی میں اس فرقے کا عاشق ہوں

کہ بے دھڑکے بھری مجلس میں یہ اسرار کہتے ہیں

What wondrous people poets are! They are the men I love;
In full assembly they speak out all that is in their hearts.   (I.113.3)

اسرارِ دل کے کہتے ہیں پیر و جوان میں

مطلق نہیں ہے بند ہماری زبان میں

I speak the secrets of my heart to old and young alike;
My voice is free and unrestrained; and none can curb my tongue.

(VI.652.25)

[45] The ghazal given in the Appendix below is in this metre.

The great strength of his work lay in the fact that it told of things which he really felt with all his being. But he knew also that intensity of feeling alone was not enough; this was the raw material of poetry, but a mastery of the poet's craft was also needed before it could be made into a finished product, and he worked hard to acquire it. He wrote in his autobiography: "I exerted myself to the utmost in practising it [Urdu poetry], and the day soon came when the poets of Delhi acknowledged my mastery, and my verses became popular with high and low throughout the city."[46] His claims are borne out by a study of his verse, for some of his very best ghazals are in his first dīvān. In it he confidently prophesied the fame that he would win:

پڑھتے پھریں گے گلیوں میں ان ریختوں کو لوگ

مُدّت رہیں گی یاد یہ باتیں ہماریاں

Men will recite my verses as they walk the city's lanes;
For years to come my words will live on in their memory.

(I.96.23)

And more boldly still:

جانے کا نہیں شور سخن کا مرے ہرگز

تا حشر جہاں میں مرا دیوان رہے گا

My verse will live eternal dòwn the years;
As long as the world lasts, so will my fame.   (I.5.12)

By the time he was compiling his second dīvān, he could record with pride how justified his confidence had been, how his fame had spread from northern India into the Deccan, and how he had evolved his own thoroughly distinctive style:

شعر پڑھتے پھرتے ہیں سب میرے

اس قلمرو میں ہے ان کا دور آب

It is Mir's verses that you hear on all men's lips;
In these dominions it is he who reigns today.   (II.251.3)

[46] Zikr i Mīr, p. 67.

سرسبز ہند ہی میں نہیں کچھ یہ ریختہ

ہے دھوم میرے شعر کی سارے دکن کے بیچ

My poetry grows green not only in the northern plains.
In all the Deccan too the praises of my verse resound.

(II.258.17)

نہیں ملتا سخن اپنا کسو سے

ہماری گفتگو کا ڈھب جدا ہے

My verse is not like any other poet's—
The way I speak to you is all my own.　　(II.355.16)

And later still, in his fourth dīvān he boasts:

دور تک رسوا ہوا ہوں شہروں شہروں ملک ملک

میرے شعر و شاعری کا تذکرہ گھر گھر ہے اب

In every region, every city, far and wide my fame is known;
The beauty of my poetry is spoken of in every home　(IV.471.23)

—and this not only in the cities but "in the country towns and the
villages" as well (IV.475.18). Even if we allow for a measure of poetic
exaggeration here, the truth behind it remains substantial. A nineteenth-
century writer [47] tells us that Mir alone among Urdu poets had his verses
taken along by men going on a journey to present to their host on their
arrival.

It is worth attempting to illustrate some of the most notable aspects of
his craftsmanship, though some cannot be adequately conveyed by translation. The first is his command of language. He naturalised with complete success many of the turns of phrase of the Persian ghazal, but this
success is itself based upon the ease with which he made the speech of
Delhi the basis of his diction. He once said that the basis of his poetry was

---

[47] Āzād, *Āb i Ḥayāt*, p. 203.

"the steps of the Jama Masjid," [48] the great mosque in Delhi built a century earlier by the Emperor Shāhjahān. By this he meant that his language was that which the citizens of Delhi spoke when they conversed together on the steps of the great mosque; and he prided himself on his ability to use it poetically. His diction can be extremely simple, and yet extremely effective, exemplifying what in Persian and Urdu rhetoric is called "sahl i mumtana"—the forbiddingly simple. Ghālib, the greatest Urdu poet of the century following Mir's death, said that the term describes "the kind of writing which looks easy, but which you cannot match" [49]—the kind of line, for example, in which Mir describes how overwhelmingly beautiful his mistress' body appeared to him, saying that it was

قالبِ آرزو میں ڈھالا ہے

As though cast in the mould of my desire.   (921.9)

Or in which, writing years later, he describes his last parting from her:

یوں ہوا ان کے کوچے سے آنا

جیسے ہوو سے جہان سے جانا

It seemed that as I came out of her lane
I went my way leaving the world behind.   (927.21)

He describes the lover, dying to speak his love and yet unable to utter a word in his mistress' presence:

کیا کہیں کچھ کہا نہیں جاتا

اب تو چپ بھی رہا نہیں جاتا

What can I say to her? No words will come.
And yet unless I speak to her, I die.   (II.235.20)[50]

The lover, hoping desperately that his proud mistress will just glance his way, says:

---

[48] Cf. below, p. 265.
[49] Cf. Ghālib, 'Ūd i Hindī (Lucknow, 1941), p. 200.
[50] Which, however, differs slightly from the traditional version here translated.

گر چہ کب دیکھتے ہو پر دیکھو

آرزو ہے کہ تم ادھر دیکھو

I cannot think that you could look at me,
Yet I will wish that you would look at me.   (I.124.22)

Years after he has lost her he imagines himself telling her:

رہتے تو تم آنکھوں میں پھرتے ہو تمہیں دل میں

مدت سے اگر چہ یہاں آتے ہو نہ جاتے ہو

My eyes still see you; *you* live in my heart,
Though years have passed since you would come and go.

(II.312.8)

This extreme simplicity of diction often goes hand in hand with simplicity
of metre and form—used in short ghazals with a short unit line of eight to
ten syllables.[51]

His handling of the language is equally effective when he brings a
lighter touch to his themes. Many of his lines incorporate popular pro-
verbs and have a touch of humour about them:

شکوۂ آبلہ ابھی سے میر

ہے پیارے ہنوز دلّی دور

Already you complain of blistered feet?
"It's a long way to Delhi yet," my son.   (I.71.22)

کرے کیا کہ دل بھی تو مجبور ہے

زمیں سخت ہے آسماں دور ہے

What can I do? My heart is in her power.
"The earth is hard, the sky is far away."   (I.178.23)

51 Two examples of such ghazals were given above, pp. 128 and 175.

That is, my present lot is hard, but every alternative seems unattainable. Another time the lover justifies his way of life to a critic not directly but by pleading that he acts under constraint:

لاعلاجی ہے جو رہتی ہے مجھے آوارگی

کیجیے کیا میر صاحب بندگی بیچارگی

I roam about disgraced, but nothing can be done about it.
What is a man to do, Mir Sahib ? "Service is servitude."

(I.145.22)

That is, when a man serves someone else he cannot do as he likes, for he is not his own master. And the someone else is in this case, of course, his mistress (or, his God). In a verse where the context is left to be inferred someone says to Mir:

میر عمداً بھی کوئی مرتا ہے

جان ہے تو جہان ہے پیارے

No man goes to his death with open eyes, Mir.
"If you have life, then you have everything."   (I.180.9)

The speaker is probably the counsellor, the man who gives the lover well-meaning advice which common sense suggests to one who has no real inkling of what love is all about. And to those who know the ghazal and its values, the words themselves are enough to suggest their answer: that while other people do not adopt a course in life which they know will be fatal to them, the true lover does, and must, do precisely that.

Verses like these, in which Mir with such evident ease introduces the phrases of everyday speech, were and still are much appreciated. He makes similar use of the exclamations in Arabic which are still commonly used by Urdu speakers at solemn moments:

پیرِ مغاں سے بے اعتقادی

استغفراللہ استغفراللہ

The tavern-keeper is nothing to you?
May God forgive me! May God forgive me! (I.137.24)

"May God forgive me" is, in the Arabic phrase of the original, "astagh-firullāh!" It is used when someone has said or done something so shocking that only God can forgive it. Its use here conveys excellently the point of the verse: that if wine and all those associated with it are condemned by formal Islam, reverence for it and for those who dispense it is of the essence of true religion.

Mir sometimes uses even more homely idiom, though generally as something of a joke. One such instance is a verse in which he contrasts his own ill-fortune in love with the good luck of his rival, and which may be freely translated:

یہاں پلیتھن بکل گیا وہاں غیر

اپنی مکّی لگائے جاتا ہے

My rival is alright—he kneads the dough
—And I'm the flour he plonks it down upon. (II.353.4)

Here the colloquialism used in the original is so homely that the present-day Muslim housewife would understand it, where in many cases her husband would not.

Mir is fond of that expressive repetition of words which is one of the characteristics of Urdu idiom, and which conveys either emphasis or distribution in time or space, or both. Thus where he says that his fame is known "In every region, every city . . . every home," the literal translation of the Urdu original would be simply "region region, city city . . . home home." Only occasionally can one hope to convey anything like the full effect in English. In a line which may be taken equally well either in the literal or in the mystic sense he says:

جیسے نسیم ہر سحر تیری کروں ہوں جستجو

خانۂ بخانہ در بدر شہر بہ شہر کو بہ کو

I seek you like the morning breeze that with each dawn goes forth again
From house to house, from door to door, from town to town, from lane
to lane. (681.6)

Many other examples are quite untranslatable.

A similar liking for this style of expression is evident in the many verses where the whole force is achieved by piling word upon word:

هوش و صبر و خرد و دین و حواس و دل و تاب

اس کے اک آنے میں کیا کیا نہ گیامت پوچھو

She came but once, but do not ask what left me as she went:
My strength, and faith, and fortitude, and will, and heart and soul.

(I.133.19)

چشمک غمزه عشوه کرشمه آن انداز و ناز و ادا

Her sidelong glance, imperious airs, her charm and grace and poise and
pride   (V.556.16)

گئی عمر میری ساری جیسے شمع باد کے بیچ

یہی رونا جلنا گلنا یہی اضطراب تجھ بن

The candle gutters in the draught, and my life too must waste away.
Like it I weep, and burn, and melt, and pine away, parted from you.

(I.117.24)

ثبات قصر و در و بام و خشت و گل کتنا

عمارت دل درویش کی رکھو بنیاد

Palace and gate and roof and brick and clay—none of them last.
So make the humble heart the strong foundation of your house.

(III.394.7)

And in a verse which has nothing to do with the major themes of the

ghazal, but speaks directly of the plight of the people of Delhi during the
1760s and 1770s:

چور اُچکے سکھ مرہٹے شاہ و گدا زر خواہاں ہیں

چین میں ہیں جو کچھ نہیں رکھتے فقر ہی اک دولت ہے آب

Sikhs, Marāthas, thieves, pickpockets, beggars, kings—all prey on us.
Happy is he who has no wealth; this is the one true wealth today

(V.548.4)

—a verse in which the piling up of the words not only expresses the
multiplicity of demands to which the citizens of Delhi were subjected,
but also tacitly suggests that there is not much to choose between one and
another. It is worth noting incidentally that this verse occurs in Mir's
fifth dīvān, which consists of poems written long after he had left Delhi
forever to settle in Lucknow. It is one indication among many in his work
of how constantly he thought of the people of Delhi and how close a
kinship he felt with them. In the same dīvān it is of Delhi that he thinks
when he describes his sense of desolation:

Tears flow like rivers from my weeping eyes.
My heart, like Delhi city, lies in ruins now.   (V.621.6)

His intimate knowledge of the language of Delhi people, which has
already been discussed, is matched by a closeness to their lives and feelings, clearly evidenced in his use of simile and metaphor. Many of his
images are drawn from the experiences of invasion, pillage, and destruction, and to a Delhi audience he could have used none more meaningful.
Some have already been quoted; for example:

دل وہ نگر نہیں کہ پھر آباد ہو سکے

دیکھتا دُگے سُنو ہو یہ بَستی اُجاڑ کر

The heart is not a city that can rise again from ruins.
Loot it, and—do you hear me ?—you will live to rue the day.

(I.69.17)

دل سے خوش طرح مکاں پھر بھی کہیں بنتے ہیں
اِس عمارت کو ٹک اِک دیکھ کے ڈھایا ہوتا

No palace ever built could match the heart for grace and beauty :
Had you but glanced at it could you have razed it to the ground ?

(II.233.5)

But the images recur again and again :

خرابیِ دل کی کیا انبوہ درد و غم سے پوچھو ہو
وہی حالت ہے جیسے شہرِ لشکر لوٹ جاتا ہے

You ask me of the ruin of my heart by pain and grief :
It is a city looted by an army on the march.   (II.353.13)

شہرِ دل آہ عجب جائے تھی پر اِس کے گئے
ایسا اُجڑا کہ کسی طرح بسایا نہ گیا

The city of my heart—alas !—was once a wondrous sight.
Her going razed it to the ground ; none will live there again.

(I.27.18)

جل جل کے سب عمارتِ دل خاک ہو گئی
کیسے نگر کو آہ محبت نے دی ہے آگ

Burnt in the flames till every building was reduced to ashes—
How fair a city was the heart that love put to the fire ! (II.282.19)

In general his use of imagery is fresh and vivid. He sees beautiful women passing before him,

قامت لچکے ہے یوں ہوامیں

جس رنگ سے لچکتی پھولوں کی ڈالیاں ہیں

. . . their swaying walk as lovely
As flower-laden branches moved by the morning breezes.

(III.412.24)

He thinks of the radiance of his mistress' coming:

جس گھر میں تیرے جلوہ سے ہو چاندنی کا فرش

وہاں چادرِ مہتاب ہے مکڑی کا سا جالا

In that house where the moonlight of your radiance lies spread
The moonlight seems as lustreless as does the spider's web.

(I.39.16)

He recalls the days of his youth, when

لبِ ساغر پہ منہ رکھ رکھ کے ہر شیشہ بہکتا تھا

The bottle babbled to the cup, his mouth upon her lip.

(680.3)

کیا لطف تھا کہ مے کدے کی پشتِ بام پر

سوتے تھے مست چادرِ مہتاب تان کر

What days those were!—when I would drink and climb up to the tavern roof
And fall asleep, the white sheet of the moonlight over me. (II.270.13)

Or he describes the suppressed pain in his heart as the night of separation comes on:

شام سے کچھ بجھا سا رہتا ہے

دل ہوا ہے چراغ مفلس کا

Since evening fell, the flame within my heart
Burns dimly, as it were a poor man's lamp. (I.6.14)

In his masnavi *The River of Love* the small boat crossing the great river appears like the crescent moon upon the night sky (907.8).

کشتی اک آن کر ہوئی موجود

ہو فلک سے ہلال جیسے نمود

In the same poem the waves encircle the limbs of the drowning lover like fetters being clamped upon them (907.23).

موج زنجیر ہو گئی پا میں

In the ghazal the imagery is often the more striking because it is so condensed:

عمر بھر ہم رہے شرابی سے

دل پُرخوں کی اک گلابی سے

I passed my life in love's intoxication
Drunk with the rose-red wine of my heart's blood.

(I.207.21)

آتش رنگ گل سے کیا کہیے

برق تھی آشیان پر آئی

Burn in the red fire of the rose in silence:
Lightning must strike, and it has struck your nest.

(I.141.25)

میری تلوار چلتی ہے تو چلے
خوش خراموں کی چال ہے کچھ اور

Mir, *let* the bright sword flash—in dreadful beauty
A lovely woman's walk is something more.   (I.71.15)

Another metaphor, aptly suited to Mir's country and age, introduces
also the use of conceits—a further very characteristic feature of his
poetry and of ghazal poetry in general. In India a "wheaten" com-
plexion—that is, a skin-colouring like that of wheat ready for harvest—
is much admired. Mir laments the rarity of such beauty:

خوب رو اب نہیں ہیں گندم گوں
میرے ہندوستاں میں کال پڑا

One sees no longer faces fair as ripened wheat;
It seems that there is famine now in Hindustan.   (I.32.18)

The train of thought is clear: from a dearth of wheaten faces to a dearth
of real wheat and back again through the implied metaphorical use of this
image. Mir's verse is full of such verbal conceits, and they had a great
appeal for his audience. In one verse he says that the rose grows in the
garden, her skirt all the time held fast in the grasp of the nightingale, and
that the scene in the enclosed garden therefore foreshadows that of the
Day of Reckoning.[52] The central idea is that on the Last Day the cruel
mistress will have to answer to God for her cruelty to her lover. She is
here, as so often, symbolised by the rose, and her lover is the nightingale.
To grasp the skirt of someone's garment may mean one of two things: to
claim his protection against a threatening danger, or to demand redress
for a wrong he has done you. And the nightingale's grasp is here a metaphor for the calyx at the base of the flower, which, so to speak, holds the
flower in its hand. Once again, the English-speaking reader has to go well
back in his own literature to find parallels, back to the metaphysical poets
and beyond, who relished such conceits as much as Mir.

[52] Allusion to I.13.10.

One may concede that the use of conceits is not one of the essentials of great poetry, but in a form like the ghazal, where brevity is often essential, they sometimes serve a real purpose. Thus Mir writes:

عشق کا شور کوئی پُچھتا ہے

نالۂ عندلیب ہے گل بانگ

Do what you will, the lover's cry will yet be heard:
The nightingale's lament re-echoes everywhere.　(I.85.5)

The Urdu says: the nightingale's lament is a *gulbāng*, and the word has two meanings. First it *means* the song of the nightingale; and secondly, it means (to quote the standard Urdu-English dictionary) "fame, a loud shout, a war-cry." In addition *gul*, the first syllable of the word, means rose, and the Urdu reader relishes the suggestion it brings of the traditional association of nightingale and rose.

In other verses verbal conceit is only partly functional. The lover accused of stubborn persistence in his own ways replies, as though to justify himself:

نہ خود سر کیوں کہ ہم ہوں یار اپنا

خود آرا خود پسند و خود ستا تھا

Self-will is *my* trait—but then are not hers
Self-love, self-admiration, and self-praise?　(VI.627.19)

Here the play on the word "self" is the main thing in the couplet, and there is no real attempt at anything which could be called an argument. Similarly, in a much more complex example:

وصف خط و خال میں خوباں کے بیر

نامۂ اعمال سیہ کر گیا

Praise of the form and features of fair women, Mir,
Has blackened all the record of your deeds　(I.54.14)

—a verse of which one can be practically certain that it is intended as something of a joke. Among other things, the deliberately very obtrusive alliteration indicates this. (The translation parallels the alliteration of the original: *vasf i khat o khāl men khūbān ke, Mīr.*) In translation we do get the general sense. Mir is quoting, without comment, the words which an orthodox Muslim might address to him, telling him more in sorrow than in anger that to spend his life in praising beautiful women is to acquire a record which will tell against him when he is judged. But all the points that the verse makes can be brought out only by reference to the original. "The record of your deeds" translates an Urdu phrase which bears a technical meaning. Your "record of deeds" is the complete account of all your actions in life, kept by recording angels to be produced before God on Judgement Day. The words translated "has blackened" also bear two possible meanings: first, that which the English suggests, and secondly, to "blacken paper" by writing on it, but with the same suggestion of prolific output as the English phrase "to cover reams and reams of paper" gives. The first line also conceals double meanings. "Form and features" translates the Urdu *khat o khāl*. These are, formally speaking, two separate words linked by the Persian *o* (meaning "and"), but are regularly used as a single word meaning "physical appearance." Yet the meanings of the individual words are also relevant to the verse. Khat again has two meanings: first, a letter, or piece of writing, and secondly, the black line of down on the upper lip. And khāl means a mole (on a beautiful woman's face). So the "blackening of the record," which itself suggests two meanings, correlates also with the blackness of writing (khat in the first sense), the blackness of the line of down (khat in the second sense), and the blackness of the mole.

In other verses the verbal play fulfils practically no function at all, and is there for its own sake entirely. In the original of the verse:

اُڑ گئے خاک ہو کتنے ہی ترے کوچے سے

باز آتے نہیں پر تیرے ہوادار ہنوز

The wind has blown away the dust of men unnumbered from your lane;
Yet your true lovers are not daunted; men come to your threshold still

(I.76.7)

the Urdu word here translated "true lovers" is *havādār*; *dār* is a common suffix meaning "possessing," and *hava*, which in this context means "love," has the primary sense of "wind." In short, the word *havādār* is here used simply because its first element has a purely verbal connection with the image of the first line. And this is very frequently done.

But if verbal play of this kind does not often appeal strongly to the modern reader, there are lines where its use does add appreciably to the poetic effect, as in a verse which Mir wrote as a little poem on its own, and not as part of a ghazal:

تری زلف سیہ کی یاد میں آنسو جھمکتے ہیں

اندھیری رات ہے برسات ہے جگنو چمکتے ہیں

Your long black tresses come to mind and glistening teardrops dim my sight.
And all is dark; the rains have come; the fireflies glimmer in the night.
(681.4)

The season of the rains, when alone in the Indian year the clouds cover the sky and the nights are really dark, has the same romantic connotations as spring does in Europe. But the second line not only evokes the atmosphere with a few vivid strokes, it also suggests the elements which make up the first line, for the long black tresses of the beloved are regularly compared with the long black night, and tears with rain, while the glistening tears and the glimmering fireflies (the two Urdu words used are equally close) also suggest each other. This is surely the use of words at its best, where every connotation is relevant and brings its contribution to the vivid intensity of the picture.

These are just some of the technical skills which Mir brings to the making of his poetry. They help to give it the many-sidedness which he proudly claimed for it:

سہل ہے میر کا سمجھنا کیا

ہر سخن اُس کا اک مقام سے ہے

To understand Mir's meaning is no simple task:
Each at its level, meanings lie in every word.   (ll.367.14)

But this many-sidedness derives mainly from the very nature of the dominant themes of the ghazal. One cannot explain these themes without taking them one by one, but to an audience that has been acquainted with them almost from childhood, a verse that is capable of interpretation on several levels is at once comprehended as such and appreciated the more deeply for being so. In any given verse it is a matter for surmise which meaning or meanings the poet had in mind when he composed it, but there are many which, whatever the precise intention of the poet, fit aptly into a wide variety of different contexts. This would be true of scores of verses quoted in the last two chapters. To give but one instance, in the verse:

اڑ گئے خاک ہو کتنے ہی تِرے کوچے سے

باز آتے نہیں پر تیرے ہوادار ہنوز

The wind has blown away the dust of men unnumbered from your lane;
Yet your true lovers are not daunted: men come to your threshold still

(I.76.7)

the "you" referred to may be God or a human beloved or any ideal out of an almost infinite variety, in which a man believes so passionately that he will serve it even at the cost of his life. In the audience that hears such a verse recited, one will take it in one way, and one in another, according to the emotional and spiritual needs which each feels. The verse becomes the "little door that opens into an infinite hall where you may find what you please."

Much the same is true of the image of the cruel beloved, of whom Mir had no experience in literal reality. The image is the means of expressing the belief that true love is absolutely unselfish, giving its all without demanding the slightest return, and proof not only against indifference but even against hatred. In the mystic sense the cruel mistress is God—God who not only created all good but all evil too; God who may afflict His true servant with life-long pain and suffering, and yet whom His true servant loves with all his being. Or, in what one may call the quasi-mystic sense, she may symbolise a man's country or his people, whom he

R

labours all his life to serve, regardless of personal hardship, even though they never cease to despise and reject him, and crucify him in the end.[53]

Mir's pride in the many-sidedness of his poetry is thus a pride in his ability to develop all the potentialities of the ghazal—the verse form which he had chosen as the major medium of his expression. The capacity of its verses for simultaneous interpretation on several levels appealed to him, for he himself felt that every aspect of his experience of life was relevant to every other. Many of his verses make this clear: besides those in which the use of imagery links, for example, the suffering of his heart with the suffering of eighteenth-century Delhi, there are others in which his view of his age and his view of his mistress (in whatever sense) are brought into direct relationship:

زبانیں بدلتے ہیں ہر آن خوباں

یہ سب کچھ ہیں بگڑے زمانے کی باتیں

Fair women break their word from hour to hour—
These are all signs of our degenerate age.   (III.414.17)

وفا لوگ آپس میں کرتے تھے آگے

یہ رسم کہن آہ تم ـــنے اُٹھادی

People continued true to one another formerly.
This was the age-old custom—and now you have broken it.

(II.330.24)

[53] The range of possible identifications of "the beloved" is very wide. In sexual (albeit unfulfilled) love it may be a parda woman, a courtesan, or a boy. In the mystic or quasi-mystic sense it may be God or one's principles. In other human relations it may be a bosom friend. But it may also be a capricious, despotic king or noble—perhaps your patron—to whose service you are bound. For if the real beloved to whom you pledge your love and loyalty can be pictured as a cruel, capricious tyrant, symbol and reality may be reversed, and a cruel, capricious tyrant whom you must serve may be pictured as your beloved. There is no doubt that in the ghazal this is sometimes the case, and that the cruel mistress who slays her lovers with the sword of her proud glance stands for a real tyrant with a real sword. Thus the traditional story of Nādir Shāh's massacre in Delhi in 1739 (cf. above, p. 19) relates that when the massacre had continued for several hours, Niẓām ul Mulk went and stood silently before him, and when Nādir asked him what he wanted, replied by quoting a Persian verse: "Lay down your sword of pride, for none is left for you to slay / —Except you raise the dead to life that you may slay again." Nādir was touched, and gave orders for the killing to cease. Cf. Muḥammad Ḥusain Āzād, Qaṣaṣ i Hind, Pt. 2 (1872), (Lahore, 1961), p. 176.

But more than individual verses, his poetry as a whole makes clear his conception that not only are all aspects of his spiritual experience relevant to one another; they are all aspects of what is to him essentially the same experience, the experience of a man driven by the single spiritual force of love, manifesting itself simultaneously in love of women, love of God, love of his fellowmen, and love of a high ideal in life, as well as in the indomitable power to resist unbroken the persecution of the enemies of love in all these fields. It is this conception that unites all his poetry, makes it the expression of a single integral outlook, and gives it its powerful appeal.

CHAPTER SIX

Mir: The Man and His Age

WHERE A MAN'S POETRY proclaims high ideals of conduct, it is the tendency of some modern critics to compare his theory with his practice and criticise both the poetry and the poet if they find that the two do not correspond. This is perhaps not altogether fair, for the poet is not the whole man, and he may believe with all his heart in the ideals that his poetry declares, and yet lack the strength to bring his own life into conformity with them. Still Mir would have welcomed being judged in this way, and it is ironical that he usually had to face criticism from a standpoint which is almost the exact opposite of this. He found himself in a position where his poetry was universally praised, while his conduct was often disapproved; and yet that conduct was generally no more than the application in practice of the principles that his poetry upheld.

The fact is that the conventions of the ghazal worked in his favour in that they enabled him to speak "the secrets of his heart" with a voice that was "free and unrestrained"; [1] but they worked against him as well, because his hearers were all too ready to assume that his verse was no more than an accomplished handling of the conventional themes, and only to the more sensitive among them did it occur that in his case the poetry really meant what it said. To the rest it was "only poetry," and remained so even though he told them:

[1] Cf. above, p. 213.

مجھ کو شاعر نہ کہو میرؔ کہ صاحب میں نے
درد و غم کتنے کئے جمع تو دیوان کیا

Don't think me a mere poet—no, my verse
Is made of pain and grief more than you know.   (III.370.5)

And,

اس پردے میں غم دل کہتا ہے میراؔ اپنا
کیا شعر و شاعری ہے یارو شعارِ عاشق

Under this guise of poetry Mir speaks the sorrows of his heart.
What poetry it is, my friends!—this lover's way of life.   (II.279.1)

And,

کیا تھا ریختہ پردہ سخن کا
سو ٹھہرا ہے یہی اب فن ہمارا

Under this guise I spoke the message of my heart,
And all my practice now is to perfect this art.   (I.28.14)[2]

For these verses too could be taken to be "only poetry." He had to put
them into plain prose before people could see that he meant them—as
when he told a young nobleman who approached him with a request to
correct his verse: "Young sir, you are a noble and the son of a noble.
Practice horsemanship and archery and the handling of the lance. Poetry
is a task for men whose hearts have been seared by the fire of love and
pierced by the wounds of grief." [3] Whatever other men might think of
his attitude—and it was often resented and wrongly ascribed to arrogance
—Mir knew that the "pain and grief" of love, in all its senses, was the

---

[2] Cf. III.423.23 and III.388.10.
[3] Āzād, *Āb i Ḥayāt*, p. 215.

essential material of poetry, and that mere technical excellence could do nothing without it. At a distance of two hundred years most people can now see that he was right, and that his ghazals have outlived so many others precisely because they are the expression of an experience deeply and passionately felt.

What we know of his life [4]—and fragmentary though this knowledge is by modern standards, it is a good deal fuller than our knowledge of his contemporaries—shows how close was the relationship between his ideals and his practice. His capacity to suffer for his principles was put to the test while he was still a mere boy. His father had been married twice. By his first wife, a sister of the famous Persian scholar Khān i Ārzu, he had a son named Muhammad Hasan, and by the second, two sons, of whom Mir was the elder. Mir was clearly his father's favourite, and Muhammad Hasan bitterly resented this. When his father fell gravely ill, Mir was perhaps in his early teens. Despite treatment, his father's condition did not improve, and Mir describes in his autobiography how one day, sensing that death was near, he called his sons to his bedside and said: [5] "I am a faqīr,[6] and I own nothing. All I have is three hundred books. Bring them here and divide them between you." Muhammad Hasan said, "You know that I am a student, and that I spend most of my time on studies. What do my brothers want with these books? They will only tear them up to make kites and paper boats. It would be better to give them to me. But you must do as you please." His father replied, "You wear the cloak of unworldliness, but underneath it your nature is unchanged. You want to cheat these youngsters of their rights, and ill-treat them when I am dead. But remember that God is a jealous God, and befriends those who are jealous for their honour. I do not think that Muhammad Taqi [that is, Mir] will ever lay himself under obligation to you; and if you try to harm him, it will be he who will come off best. Men will never honour your name as they will this boy's. . . . People never trust a petty-minded man, and greed and jealousy will never reap

---

[4] The main sources for his life are *Zikr i Mīr* and his own poems, in which he often speaks more frankly than he does in prose. For *Zikr i Mīr* see above, p. 207. It is sometimes difficult to interpret, for though Mir has an excellent memory for the sequence of the events he describes, he does not date them. One has to refer throughout to Sarkar's *Fall of the Mughal Empire* to provide the dating.

[5] *Zikr i Mīr*, pp. 59–60.

[6] Cf. above, p. 194.

anything but contempt and disgrace. Very well then. Take the books and take good care of them.'' Then he turned to Mir and said, ''My son, I owe three hundred rupees to the money-lenders, and I want you to promise that you will not bury me until you have paid it. All my life I have been true to my principles, and I never yet cheated any man.'' Mir replied, ''These books, which are now my brother's, were all our wealth. How can I pay our debts now ?'' Tears came into his father's eyes, and he said, ''God will provide, never fear. Even now money is on the way. I wish I could live until it comes, but death is near, and time is short; and I cannot wait.'' Then he gave Mir his blessing and commended him to God's care, and after breathing a little longer, died.

Mir says that by God's grace he carried out his father's commands without having to be beholden to anyone, although his stepbrother openly refused to accept any responsibility for the settlement of his father's affairs. Then he handed over charge of the household to his younger brother and set out to find himself some means of earning a living. But he could find no livelihood in Agra, and so he set out for Delhi to try his fortunes there. Again he could find no one to help him for quite a while. At length, however, he won the ear of a nobleman named Khwāja Muhammad Bāsit, the nephew of the great noble Samsām ud Daula, to whom reference was made in Chapter 1.[7] Samsām ud Daula at this time held one of the highest offices in the Empire—that of Imperial Paymaster and Marshal of the Nobility—and through Muhammad Bāsit, Mir was now able to gain an introduction to him.[8]

Samsām ud Daula had known and reverenced Mir's father, and when he was told whose son Mir was, he ordered that the boy should, for his father's sake, be paid a daily stipend from his treasury. During the interview an incident occurred which is highly characteristic of Mir. He asked that the order for the payment of his stipend be put into writing so that no difficulty could arise when he went to receive it. Muhammad Bāsit, thinking perhaps that this down-to-earth request might offend the noble lord, intervened and said, ''This is not the proper time for the inkstand.'' At this Mir, as though he had not already gone quite far enough, began to laugh. Samsām ud Daula looked at him in astonishment and asked, ''What

[7] Above, p. 16.
[8] *Zikr i Mīr*, pp. 62–63.

is the matter? Why are you laughing?'' Mir replied: "I do not know what that means—'This is not the proper time for the inkstand.' If he had said 'The Navvāb cannot sign now,' or 'The inkstand-bearer is not here,' then I could have understood it. But this is a curious statement. The ink-stand is not a living thing that can observe times and occasions; it is a piece of wood, which any of your servants will fetch whenever you order him." At this Samsām ud Daula laughed too, and made out the written order there and then.

Mir's good fortune did not last long. About a year after this, in 1739, came the invasion of Nādir Shāh, and in the disastrous battle of Karnāl, Samsām ud Daula was mortally wounded. Thus Mir was again without support. Whether he had remained in Delhi up to this point we do not know for certain, but we do know that, either before or after Samsām ud Daula's death, he returned to Agra; and here he soon had more bitter and painful experiences to undergo. In his autobiography he says only that all his relatives and friends turned against him, so that, as his poetic prose puts it, "men who had once made the dust of my feet the adornment of their eyes" 9 made his life so unbearable that he felt obliged to leave the city and go once more to Delhi. 10 His poetry, in which convention allowed him the freedom to describe experiences which would not have been acceptable in prose, provides the key to the mystery, and we may deduce with near certainty that the love affair which his masnavi The Stages of Love describes was the occasion of his persecution. Sooner or later this hostility made itself felt even in Delhi. Mir stayed for a time with his stepbrother Muhammad Hasan's uncle, Khān i Ārzu, but one day a letter from Muhammad Hasan came condemning Mir roundly and asking Khān i Ārzu not to assist him in any way. Mir writes sarcastically that the old gentleman, despite his pretensions, was one for whom considerations of worldly wisdom were paramount, and for this reason he acted on his nephew's request. "I never asked him for anything," writes Mir, 11 "but still he persecuted me, and if I were to write of all I suffered at his hands, it would fill a book." It was the cumulative effect of all this that drove him mad; the account which he gives in his autobiography tallies with that which forms the theme of the masnavi Mir's Vision, already described.

9 Zikr i Mīr, p. 63.
10 He did not see Agra again for more than 20 years.
11 Zikr i Mīr, p. 64.

Thus Mir had indeed suffered "pain and grief more than you know" when he began to make his name as a poet; and it took him only a few years after he recovered his sanity to establish a reputation. Henceforth, for the rest of his long life, it was on his reputation as a poet that he depended for his livelihood. Most of his patrons were nobles highly placed in the imperial administration. The first was closely related to Qamar ud Dīn, Itimād ud Daula II, who was Vazīr of the Empire from 1724 to 1748. This man offended Mir, and he parted company with him. Soon after, he won the patronage of the eunuch Jāved Khān, who was all-powerful in the Empire from 1748 to 1752, when he was assassinated by his rival Safdar Jang. Mir, however, was taken under the wing of a noble close to Safdar Jang, until Safdar Jang's own downfall the following year again placed him in difficulties. It seems that for some years after this he was without any regular means of livelihood, until about 1757–1758, when Rāja Nāgar Mal, soon to become Deputy Vazīr of the Empire, became his patron. Except for a short break in 1760, Mir continued in his service for about fifteen years.

We can study more closely these twenty some odd years of Mir's life from the late 1740s to 1772, both in the histories of that period and in Mir's own brief account of them. A number of salient features emerge. The first is the ever-present insecurity which he must have felt, both from the repeated incursions of Abdāli from Afghanistan and from the armed strife between the different factions within India. His most powerful patron is assassinated; another is driven from Delhi after months of civil war; another time he himself is so distressed by conditions in Delhi that he wanders off on his own, "not knowing where he was going, but trusting in God to lead him." [12] So that if in 1772 he could look back on a period of twenty-five years during which he had rarely been without the patronage of an influential noble, it was nonetheless a period in which from day to day he had never felt secure.

The second striking thing is Mir's own close sense of involvement in the events of his day. His personal experience of Abdāli's invasions has already been described. [13] In addition, he tells us how he accompanied his first patron, Riyāyat Khān, in two campaigns in 1748, where he undertook a diplomatic mission of some importance on his behalf; how in 1750

[12] *Zikr i Mīr*, p. 90; cf. above, p. 33.
[13] Above, p. 32.

he suffered all the hardships of a forced retreat with Safdar Jang's defeated army after the fiasco of his military expedition to Rohilkhand and
Farrukhābād; and how in 1754 he was with the Emperor when he fled
before the forces of the Marāthas and of his own Vazīr Imād ul Mulk,
leaving his harem captive in their hands. But it is not only the events he
has personally experienced that remain clear in his mind. His autobiography gives the whole complicated story of the politics of imperial Delhi
during these years, for the most part crowding out all but the briefest
references to his own fortunes; and though he writes from memory many
years after most of these events had taken place, he is rarely at fault in the
account he gives. His belief that one must not withdraw from the life of
society, but "live in the world, where griefs and joys beset you,"[14] is
clearly one by which his own actions were guided.

Mir's attitude towards the great men upon whom he depended is also
worthy of note. He sees them in two roles, and judges them in each without reference to the other. As political figures, nearly all are judged
harshly, even scathingly. Thus Mir writes quite boldly of the eunuch
Jāved Khān that "[in 1748] the control of the Empire fell into his
hands,"[15] and by way of comment simply quotes a Persian verse to the
effect that power is perhaps a beggar that presents itself now at one man's
door, now at another's. Yet as a patron he found Jāved Khān generous,
and he praises him accordingly. Imād ul Mulk he considered in much the
same way. Mir describes the triumph of Imād and his associates with the
blunt words, "power came into the hands of worthless men,"[16] and
Imād's subsequent political crimes are related without any attempt at
palliation. But Mir also had dealings with him as a poet, and in this field
he found him a man of considerable accomplishments, and one who knew
the duties of a noble towards men of letters. And so a quite incidental
mention of him in connection with events that occurred in 1764–1765
prompts Mir to remark: "Despite his age he is still a unique figure in
these times, and has many accomplishments. He writes five or six styles
of script admirably, and composes good verse both in Persian and Urdu.
He is very good to me, and it has always been a great pleasure to visit

[14] Cf. above, p. 209.
[15] Zikr i Mīr, pp. 68–69.
[16] Zikr i Mīr, p. 74.

him." [17] A traditional, but quite credible, story of the two men shows that there was nothing in the nature of servility prompting this judgement. The story [18] is that one day Imād was sitting by the riverside amusing himself by watching the ducks and waterfowl. Mir happened to pass that way, and Imād called him across and proceeded to recite some qasīdas which he had composed. When he had finished, he asked Mir what he thought of them. "What need of my praise is there?" replied Mir. "See, every duck on the water is in ecstasy." Imād was much put out, as he clearly showed when he sent for Mir on the following day. When Mir entered, he found Imād seated, but there was no other seat in the room, and no carpet on the floor. Mir remained standing, expecting every moment that a chair or stool would be brought for him, but when none came, he understood that Imād expected him to stand in his presence. He at once folded his shawl, laid it on the floor, and sat down upon it. Imād then asked him to recite something. Mir recited this verse:

کل پاؤں ایک کاسۂ سر پر جو آگیا

ناگہ وہ استخوان شکستوں سے چور تھا

کہنے لگا کہ دیکھ کے چل راہ بے خبر

میں بھی کبھو کسو کا سر پُر غرور تھا

While walking yesterday I stumbled on a skull,
Which, as it crumbled into pieces, cried to me:
"O heedless one! Be careful where you set your feet!
I too was once the head of one as proud as you!"

There is nothing particularly outstanding about the verse, and the theme is the well-worn one that man should subdue his pride, remembering that death comes one day to level all men in the dust. The point of the verse is in the situation in which it was recited, and it would not be lost on Imād.

Mir himself relates an incident [19] of the period between 1753 and 1757, when he seems to have had no permanent security for his livelihood.

---

[17] *Zikr i Mīr*, p. 113.
[18] The story is quoted in Khwāja Aḥmad Fārūqī, *Mīr Taqī Mīr: Ḥayāt aur Shāʿirī* (Aligarh, 1954), pp. 291–292.
[19] *Zikr i Mīr*, p. 75.

He was sent for by Rāja Jugal Kishor, one of the wealthiest of the Delhi nobles and one who had held high office in a previous reign. He did Mir the honour of showing him his verses and requesting him to correct them. "I found," Mir writes, "that most of them were beyond correction, and scored them through." Such an action, which one of Mir's modern editors still finds shocking nearly two hundred years later, was not calculated to help him out of his material difficulties, but Mir would never allow such a consideration to weigh with him where he felt that his honour as a poet was concerned. And in fact the incident well illustrates the nature of the relationship between poet and patron that prevailed in Mir's day, for though Rāja Jugal Kishor must have been displeased, there was no breach in their relations. Only later did they part company, and Mir's account of the circumstances shows that for the noble it was a matter of honour to make adequate provision for a poet under his patronage, and a painful situation for him when he could not do so. At the time in question Mir was receiving so little support from him that he simply could not manage any longer on it, and one day in desperation he hinted this to him. "His face flushed with shame," writes Mir,[20] "and he replied, 'I am myself on the verge of poverty; otherwise I should not have been backward in helping you.'" One day shortly afterwards, Jugal Kishor visited Rāja Nāgar Mal and spoke to him about Mir. Later he told Mir to go and call upon Nāgar Mal. Mir did so, was kindly received, and was given to understand that permanent provision would be made for his support.

The fact that Mir lived for fifteen years under Nāgar Mal's patronage is the best testimony to his good opinion of him. There is little explicit comment on him in Mir's autobiography, but instances are given of his consideration not only for Mir but for the large numbers of others whom he took under his protection, and Mir's tone conveys the satisfaction he felt at this. There is also a notable absence of hostile comment on his political role. This could not have been a major one during the period of Mir's association with him, dominated as it was by the conflicts of far more powerful forces, but we know, partly from Mir and partly from other sources, that Nāgar Mal more than once mediated successfully between political rivals to avert armed clashes in which innocent people would have suffered, and there can be little doubt that this must have won him Mir's regard. All this notwithstanding, Mir was prepared to sever relations even with him when honour and self-respect seemed to demand it. The break came in 1771–1772, when the titular emperor Shāh Ālam, who had fled from Delhi thirteen years earlier to escape from the clutches of Imād ul Mulk and had ever since been a virtual captive—first of the ruler of Oudh and later of the British—decided to assert his right to return to the capital. Nāgar Mal, who had been living since 1761 in the Jāt kingdom, heard of this and sent Mir to smooth the way for him to join the imperial court. This Mir successfully did, but immediately after his return Nāgar Mal changed his mind and decided to throw in his lot instead with the Marāthas, who already occupied Delhi. Mir felt deeply humiliated, and though he accompanied Nāgar Mal on his journey to Delhi, as soon as they got there, he installed his wife and children in a suburb called Arabsarāi, and then parted company with him permanently.

He must have known how serious could be the consequences of the step he was taking. Nāgar Mal had been his mainstay for fifteen years, and for the last ten of them they had been away from Delhi. He was fifty years old, and had a wife and family to support. But the fact that Nāgar Mal had treated him dishonourably outweighed all these considerations, and though the next ten years were to prove some of the most difficult of his life, there is no indication in his writings that he ever regretted the course he took. He had long since determined not to submit to insult and dishonour—and long since realised what this resolve would cost him. He puts the point with wry exaggeration:

میرے صاحب زمانہ نازک ہے
دونوں ہاتھوں سے تھامے دستار

Mir Sahib, take care! The times are critical.
You need both hands to keep your turban on.[21]   (I.68.18)

The penalty Mir paid for such actions was not only material hardship and actual physical hunger; he had to endure also the disapproval of most of his contemporaries. It might be expected that though not themselves

---

[21] In the convention of Mughal society, to knock a man's turban off or to knock it crooked was a deadly insult.

prepared to make so drastic a sacrifice for their principles, they would at
any rate respect one who was. But this was not the case. They had lived
too long in an age when material self-interest was the overriding consideration guiding both the nobles and all those who depended upon
them. A man must make his way in life, and that meant that he must
change with every changing wind and not be too particular about principles. Poets were no exception: in their poetry they were lovers true
unto death, eternally constant to their "beloved"—that is, to their
mistress, to their God, to their ideals; but this was generally assumed to
be a mere literary convention. It was in vain that Mir told them that he
meant what he said. They could not understand that here was a poet who
really believed with all his heart in the values which his poetry expressed,
and did his best to practise them; and at a loss to comprehend the real
motives of his actions, they attributed them to stubborn, foolish pride.

Mir knew well enough what they thought of him. In one of his verses
he wryly addresses himself, as though in their words:

تری چال ٹیڑھی تری بات رُوکھی
تجھے میر سمجھا ہے یہاں کم کسوئے

Your ways are awkward, and your speech is blunt.
None of us really understands you, Mir.   (II.343.22)

But their attitude was a constant source of pain to him, and after his
break with Nāgar Mal, at the height of his difficulties, it was this, more
than any material privations, that he felt most keenly. This is made clear
in one of his most bitter poems, which must have been written at this
time. We know from his autobiography to what straits he had been reduced. For a while another noble, less wealthy than Nāgar Mal, made such
provision for him as he could, but a sudden change of political fortune
deprived his new patron of his sources of income, and Mir was left with
nothing. His autobiography says bluntly:[22] "I went out begging, calling at

[22] Ẕikr i Mīr, p. 122; the mukhammas on pp. 950–951 of the Kulliyāt. Khwāja Aḥmad Fārūqī
(Mīr Taqī Mīr, p. 172) wrongly associates this poem with Mīr's visit to Kāmā in 1760–1761.
The title given to the poem in the Kulliyāt is misleading, but Mīr was in Kāmā in 1771–1772 as
well as in 1760–1761, and it is to the later period that the poem belongs. The poem is actually
not about Kāmā at all, but about Mīr's experiences after his return from there to Delhi.

the door of every man of standing in the Emperor's camp; and because of my fame as a poet I was enabled to live somehow—as a dog or a cat might live.'' His poem gives a fuller account, describing how, weak with hunger, he made his way from one to another, with one hand on the wall to support himself; how he was rebuffed by men who had professed regard for him, and how he swallowed his pride to beg food and water from men whom in other circumstances he would have thought it beneath him to approach. He dwells bitterly on the lengths to which hunger forced him to go, and on the inhumanity with which he was treated, but these themes only lead up to the climax, and the poem ends with the words:

حالت تو یہ کہ مجھ کو غموں سے نہیں فراغ

دل سوزشِ دروُنی سے جلتا ہی جوں چراغ

سینہ تمام چاک ہے، سارا جگر ہے داغ

ہے نام مجلسوں میں مرا میرِؔ بے دماغ

از بسکہ کم دماغی نے پایا ہے اشتہار

Grief assails me without respite, and my torn and wounded heart burns, as though in a flame that burns within my breast: and where men gather together they call me ''Mir the arrogant''—so widespread has my name for pride become.

Mir was universally acclaimed as a great poet, but he often felt that he met with no more understanding here than he did in other fields. He lived in an age when poetry was one of the polite accomplishments—as indeed to a considerable extent it still is in circles where Urdu is the language of culture—and most cultured men aspired to write it. Men of the world found no difficulty in praising their verse, particularly where its author was a man of influence. Mir, on the other hand, found considerable difficulty, because poetry was his life, and since most of this verse was not poetry, he could not bring himself to speak as though it were. It is an accurate, though at the same time half-humorous, picture that he draws of himself listening to a poet reciting his verse at a mushāira:

بات اپنے ڈھب کی کوئی کرے وہ تو کچھ کہوں

بیٹھا خموش سامنے ہوں ہوں کروں ہوں میں

Once let him speak a worth-while line, and he shall hear my praise.
Till then I'll sit here silent, greeting every line with "H'm!"

(III.423.24)

People attributed his attitude to the worst motives, and in this field too thought him arrogant and overbearing.

It is ironical that this view is still quite widely held among modern Urdu critics, who do not seem to notice that their own judgements of eighteenth-century poets are generally quite in accord with his. Thus he and Sauda have always been recognised as the outstanding poets of their day, and it is surely no grave fault in Mir that he knew this to be a sound judgement, and said so. His assignment of the next place to the mystic poet Mir Dard would also be generally accepted as just by most modern critics. The judgement was not an arbitrary one, made on the spur of the moment. In his earliest collection of verse he had written:

کیا رہا ہے مشاعرے میں اب

لوگ کچھ جمع آن ہوتے ہیں

میر و مرزا رفیع و خواجہ میر

کتنے یہ اک جوان ہوتے ہیں

Though people still turn out to come to them
Mushāiras are dull affairs these days.
Mir, Sauda, Dard and just a handful more—
These stalwarts still deserve a poet's praise.

(I.110.13–15)

And according to a traditional story, which in essentials seems quite authentic, he repeated this judgement, with a significant modification, many years later.[23] "Who are the poets of today?" he was asked. He replied. "First, Sauda; next, your servant," and after a pause, "Mir Dard is half a poet." "And Mir Soz?" someone asked. Mir frowned and said, "Oh, is he a poet too?" "Well, after all," said the man, "he is the ustād of Navvāb Āsaf ud Daula." "Is that so?" said Mir drily, "Very well, then; make the total two and three quarters." We can only speculate what lay behind his assessment of Mir Dard as "half a poet," but it was certainly not arrogance or jealously, for we know that the two men liked and respected each other. Perhaps it was that Dard was one of the few Urdu poets who really were mystics, and Mir may have felt that his restriction of his poetry to mystic themes excluded him from the first rank of poets.

The latter part of the story illustrates perfectly the standards of judgement which his contemporaries applied and the contempt and ridicule with which Mir rejected them. To them the ustād of Āsaf ud Daula must be a great poet, because Āsaf ud Daula was a great man—ruler of Oudh and so one of the most powerful men in India. To Mir, as to us, this consideration is ludicrously irrelevant. (And we might add that nobody now thinks Soz a great poet.) He could indeed be scathing in his remarks about people who refused to recognise their limitations and imagined themselves to be the equals of Sauda and himself, and more than one of his comparatively few satirical poems are devoted to them. Once, during a prolonged absence from Delhi, he wrote of them:

The nightingale held pride of place for song, but he is captive now.
What wonder, then, if crows and kites should now aspire to sing like him?

(II.265.2)

[23] Āzād, *Āb i Ḥayāt*, p. 216. The story as Āzād gives it is not fully accurate, for he attributes it to the period when Mīr had settled in Lucknow. This cannot be correct, for the story implies that Saudā was still living. Yet he had died in 1781, a year before Mīr left Delhi for Lucknow.

And, more seriously:

بات بنانا مشکل سا ہے شعر سبھی یاں کہتے ہیں
فکرِ بلند سے یاروں کو اک ایسی غزل کہہ لانے دو

They won't find *saying* something all that easy.
As versifiers all of them are fine.
But let our friends show us their inspiration
By writing me a poem like this of mine.   (III.425.3)

This, however, is no proof of arrogance, particularly when one recalls
the satirical conventions of the age; and there is much weightier evidence
that points the other way. Thus throughout his life Mir acclaimed Sauda's
greatness in the warmest terms. He described him in *Nikāt ush Shu'ara* as
"outstanding among the poets of India . . . and fit to be acclaimed as
King of Poets."[24] More significant still in this connection in his unstinting praise of poets who never made a name for themselves but whose
work seemed to him to deserve it.

The truth is that Mir's "arrogance" sprang from a steadfast adherence
to principle which in his degenerate age the average man was incapable of
understanding, and from a keen and growing sense of spiritual loneliness.
The attitudes of men around him were not new to him. Again and again
in his verse he had lamented the change that had come over his country,
a change so complete and all-embracing that it was as though he were in-
habiting a different world and a different universe:

اس عہد کو نہ جاننے اگلا سا عہد میر
وہ دور اب نہیں وہ زمیں آسماں نہیں

This age is not like that which went before it:
The times have changed, the earth and sky have changed.
                                                    (II.290.16)

24 Pp. 32–33; cf. above, p. 56.

He feels that an air of desolation pervades everything:

جس جا کہ خس و خار کے اب ڈھیر لگے ہیں

یہاں ہم نے انہیں آنکھوں سے دیکھیں ہیں بہاریں

Here where the thorn grows, spreading over mounds of dust and ruins,
These eyes of mine once saw the gardens blooming in the spring.

(I.115.5)[25]

اڑتی ہے خاک شہر کی گلیوں میں اب جہاں

سونا لیا ہے گود میں بھر کر وہیں سے ہم

Here in this city where the dust drifts in deserted lanes
A man might come and fill his lap with gold in days gone by.

(II.289.25)

کل دیکھتے ہمارے بستے تھے گھر برابر

اب یہ کہیں کہیں جو دیوار و در رہے ہیں

These eyes saw only yesterday house after house
Where here and there a ruined wall or doorway stands.

(II.300.17)

The men who lived in these houses, the men whose achievements made
Mughal India great and prosperous, are gone, and no one remembers
them any more. Mir feels as though he had been present at a great assembly of talented men; just for a moment he had closed his eyes, and
when he opened them again they had vanished. All he can do is look at
the traces of their footprints in the dust, and weep for their loss. More
painful still, the people all around him have changed: he is living among
men to whom the old values mean nothing—values that have died with

the men who believed in them; and yearn for them as he will, he feels
that they are gone beyond recall.[26] These days men live to themselves,
loving no one, loyal to no one, grieving for no one, finding no warmth in
one another's company, lacking the most elementary sense of common
humanity:

کیا زمانہ تھا وہ جو گزرا میر
ہمدگر لوگ چاہ کرتے تھے

What days were those!—the days that are no more,
The days when people loved their fellowmen.   (VI.673.17)

عہد ہمارا تیرا ہے جس میں گم ہے مہر و وفا
اگلے زمانے میں تو یہی لوگوں کی رسم و عادت تھی

Ours is a dark age; men have lost all trace of love and loyalty.
In former days it was not so; these things were second nature then.
                                                    (IV.530.9)[27]

سو ملک پھرا لیکن پائی نہ وفا اک جا
جی کھا گئی ہے میرا اس جنس کی نایابی

Roaming from land to land I sought for loyalty.
Grief tears my heart; it is not to be found.   (I.142.14)

تو جہاں سے دل اٹھا یہاں نہیں رسم دردمندی
کسی نے بھی یوں نہ پوچھا ہوئے خاک یہاں ہزاراں

Live out your life away from men's society,
For men no longer feel that you are one of them.
Thousands and thousands here were laid low in the dust
And no one even asked what had become of them.   (I.94.1)

---

[26] Allusions to III.456.11, I.145.23, II.349.14.
[27] Cf. II.275.24.

کیا کیا عزیز دوست ملے میرے خاک میں
نادان یہاں کسو کا کسو کو بھی غم ہوا

Such friends I had—and one by one they died and turned to dust.
I am a fool—nobody grieves for anybody now. (I.26.3)

اب رسم ربط اٹھ ہی گئی ور نہ پیش ازیں
بیٹھے ہی رہتے تھے بہم احباب روز و شب

The custom now is quite extinct—and yet in days gone by
Friends would sit down and talk to one another night and day.
(I.55.22)

رسم اٹھ گئی دنیا سے اک بار مروت کی
کیا لوگ زمیں پر ہیں کیسا یہ سماں آیا

The cult of human decency has vanished from the world.
What men are these upon the earth! What times we live in now!
(IV.466.11)

You cannot talk to them about the things that make up the meaning of
life; they are creatures in human form, but they are not human. And the
worst among them are the great men, the nobles who set the tone for the
rest of society. Mir feels deeply the injustice of an age in which good men
suffer, while wealth and power go to those who show the least scruple in
fighting for them, and having won them, use them for their own selfish
advantage alone. Such men destroy the peace and prosperity of society,
while those whose skill and talent should be rewarded are ruined instead.[28]

---

[28] Allusions to I.113.18 and I.182.7.

Mir is at pains to dissociate himself from the rich and powerful, and to
express his sense of oneness with those who suffer hardship and distress:

کیا اہل دول سے ہے اے میر مجھے نسبت

یاں عجز و فقیری ہے واں ناز امیری ہے

What have you got to do, Mir, with men of wealth and substance?
On your side, all humility; on their side, boundless pride.

(III.439.6)

فرو آتا نہیں سر ناز سے ابکے امیروں کا

اگرچہ آسماں تک شور جاوے ہم فقیروں کا

The nobles are so proud, they will not bow their heads to listen
Though we, the poor and humble, shake the heavens with our cry.

(II.243.8)

نہ مل میر اب کے امیروں سے تو

ہوئے ہیں فقیر ان کی دولت سے ہم

Do not approach the great ones of the age, Mir;
It is their riches that have made us poor.   (II.289.16)[29]

Sometimes he expresses these themes with great bitterness, mingled with
a fierce pride that if he is denied the conditions of comfort due to a great
poet, at any rate his poverty clearly marks him off from a class of men
whom he despises:

گو تو بچے سے زمانے کی جہاں میں مجھ کو

جاہ و ثروت کا میسر سر و سامان نہ ہوا

---

[29] Cf. I.187.13 and Āsī's footnote.

شکر صد شکر کہ میں ذلّت و خواری کے سبب

کسی عنوان میں ہم چشمِ عزیزاں نہ ہوا

Although the fortunes of the age have not shown favour to me
So that the ways of wealth and grandeur could not be my ways,
Praise be to God that I am poor and mean—for none can class me
With the great ones whom men delight to honour in these days.

(I.46.1–2)

But he knows that it is their values and not his which prevail in the
cultured society in which he moves, and he joins with Sauda in the
conclusion that "we are living in a special kind of age" [30] in which everything is the reverse of what it should be, an age that rewards vice and
punishes virtue, an age that seems to think it a grave offence to possess any
talent or skill and therefore ruins talented men and allows worthless
people to prosper, an age in which a great poet can expect a life of
hardship, just as the bird that sings most sweetly knows for that very
reason that it is he who will be trapped and shut in a cage:

یہ زمانہ نہیں ایسا کہ کوئی زیست کرے

چاہتے ہیں جو بُرا اپنا بھلا کرتے ہیں

What man would want to live in times like these?
When doing good means wishing yourself ill.   (I.94.23)

صنّاع ہیں سب خوار ازاں جملہ ہوں میں بھی

ہے عیب بڑا اس میں جسے کچھ ہنر آوے

The craftsmen are all ruined now, and I am one of them.
It is a grievous sin to know your craft in times like these.

(I.167.3)

---

[30] Cf. above, p. 68.

گر زمزمہ یہی ہے کوئی دن تو ہم صفیر
اس فصل ہی میں ہم کو گرفتار دیکھنا

If I sing on like this, my friend, I know the day will come
This very spring when you will see me captive in the cage.

(I.48.3)

اسیری کا دیتا ہے مژدہ مجھے
مرا زمزمہ گاہ و بے گاہ کا

The song I sing, in season, out of season,
Heralds the news of my captivity.   (III.373.20)

The world itself is like a great cage:

زیر فلک رکا ہے اب جی بہت ہمارا
اس بے فضا قفس میں مطلق ہوا نہیں ہے

Pent in between the earth and sky, we stifle
In this cage where no breath of air can come.   (II.360.21)

A man may wander from place to place and find no peace:

کہیں ٹھہرنے کی جا یہاں دیکھی میں نے میر
چمن میں عالم امکاں کے جیسے آب پھرا

Here Mir could find no resting place; he must go on and on
Like running water flowing through the garden of the world.

(II.231.15)

Power and wealth are everything, and the man who has neither should
know better than to expect anyone to befriend him.

زور و زر کچھ نہ تھا تو بارے میر

کس بھروسے پہ آشنائی کی

Power and wealth were not at your command, Mir.
How could you, then, make anyone your friend?   (I.141.19)

پھرا میں صورت احوال ہر اک کو دکھا تا یہاں

مروّت قحط ہے آنکھیں نہیں کوئی ملاتا یہاں

I sought them one by one to show them how things stood with me.
Humanity is dead—not one would look me in the face.   (IV.505.22)

It is not enough that they are incapable of giving their love to him or to
any other man; none of them is prepared even to accept the love that
others offer him. Love, which was once treasured as precious beyond
anything else that life could offer, is not wanted any more:

ہر جنس کے خواہاں ہیں بازار جہاں میں

لیکن نہ ملا کوئی خریدار محبّت

Here in this market of the world all kinds of wares are in demand;
But one can find no purchaser: no one has come in search of love.

(I.58.17)

کوئی خواہاں نہیں محبّت کا

تو کہے جنس ناروا ہے عشق

Nobody here wants love; it seems they think
That it is tainted wares you offer them.   (II.279.10)[31]

---

[31] Cf. I.33.15 and I.90.24–25.

And if Mir's reaction is to withdraw into himself, then he is "proud," "unapproachable," "reserved." The rare exception, who treats Mir with a love and respect to which he can respond, is asked in astonishment:

You've been with Mir? How did you manage that?
—So proud and unapproachable a man!   (II.276.18)

And this is a reaction which he hears so often that Mir sometimes imagines half-humorously that living with one's fellowmen must have needed some special skill, known to past generations, but now lost:

In former days men knew the way to live with one another.
Alas! if only I had learned to master some such skill! (III. 380.23)

One is reminded of what Mark Rutherford wrote about himself:

I have been accused [of] secrecy and reserve. . . . People would ordinarily set it down to self-reliance, with no healthy need of intercourse. It was nothing of the kind. It was an excess of communicativeness, an eagerness to show what was most at my heart and to ascertain what was at the heart of those to whom I talked, which made me incapable of mere fencing and trifling and so often caused me to retreat into myself when I found an absolute absence of response. . . . Only when tempted by unmistakable sympathy could I be induced to express my real self.[32]

---

[32] Mark Rutherford, *Autobiography*, 13th ed. (London, n.d.), pp. 23–24; cf. also pp. 109–110. Others who have expressed this feeling about themselves are T. E. Lawrence and A. E. Housman; cf. John Sparrow's Introduction to Housman's *Collected Poems* (Harmondsworth, 1956), p. 16.

The words fit Mir's case exactly. Men's reaction to him makes him feel
as though he were a stranger in the land of his birth—

مسافر ہی رہے اکثر وطن میں

a foreign traveller in my own land. (I.98.14)

as though he and his countrymen did not speak the same language:

رہی نگفتہ مرے دل میں داستاں میری
نہ اس دیار میں سمجھا کوئی زبان میری

How could I tell my tale in this strange land?
I speak a tongue they do not understand (I.150.9) [33]

—a simile that occurs again and again in his verse.

There are times when he regrets that he ever devoted himself to
poetry:

ہر بحر میں اشعار کہے عمر کو کھویا
اس گوہرِ نایاب کی کچھ بات نہ پائی

I wrote in every metre, wasting all my years
Bringing up pearls for men who did not know their price.

(II.329.21)

پھر امت میر سرا اپنا گراں گوشوں کی مجلس میں
سنے کوئی تو کچھ کہیئے بھی اس کہنے کا کیا حاصل

Why bother, Mir, to speak to this assembly of the deaf?
One speaks to those who listen: what's the good of speaking here?

(III.405.20) [34]

---

33 Cf. III.420.5 and VI.655.17.
34 Cf. III.395.23–24.

And he reflects that these are men who love a poet's immature flights of "poetic fancy," but give him good cause to regret it if once they feel he is trying to tell them something:

بادلے سے جب تلک بکتے تھے سب کرتے تھے پیار

عقل کی باتیں کیاں کیا ہم ــــ سے نادانی ہوئی

I raved and ranted on, and so far everybody loved me.
I started talking sense—what folly I committed then!

(II.328.17)

He himself feels more and more the one survivor of a former race:[35]

کھا گیا اندوہ مجھ کو دوستانِ رفتہ کا

ڈھونڈھتا ہوں جی بہت پر اب انہیں پاؤں کہاں

My friends are dead and gone, and grief for them consumes my heart.
My soul seeks for them always, but where shall I find them now?

(III.409.21)

Men who knew the meaning of love and felt its torture with the same intensity as he are all dead. "Majnūn is gone from the desert and Farhād from the mountainside: the friends who brought some joy into my life are all dead."[36] And he tells himself that he should die too:

یارانِ رفتہ ایسے کیا دور ترگئے ہیں

ملک کرکے تیز گامی اس قافلے کو جاؤ

The dead friends that you mourn are not so very far ahead;
Quicken your pace a little; overtake the caravan. (II.319.15)[37]

---

[35] Allusion to I.136.20—21.
[36] Allusions to I.184.5,8,9; II. 234.24.
[37] Cf. IV.502.18.

Meanwhile, because he does not really belong to his own times and his contemporaries know it, they single him out for persecution, while they enjoy all the benefits that life has to give:

قسمت اس بزم میں لائی کہ جہاں کا ساقی

دے ہرے سب کو، ہمیں زہر ملاتا ہے میاں

Fate brought me here, into a gathering where the cupbearer
Brings wine to all—and pours a deadly poison in my cup.

(III.419.1) [38]

In these conditions it is, once again, the qualities of the lover—using the word in all the senses that it bears in the ghazal—that give a man the strength to live, and to live to some purpose. The lover, the true worshipper of God, the man who is true to his high ideals, expects misunderstanding and hostility and hardship, and he is proud to show that he can bear them without wavering in his devotion.

During the hard years that followed his return to Delhi in 1772, Mir needed all these qualities to sustain him. For ten years he lived on there, apparently without any sort of permanent provision for his support, and this part of his autobiography makes painful reading. At one point he writes, "For the last three years I have lived in the most straitened circumstances, for none is left in the world who could be my patron. I have put my trust in God, for it is He who gives us our daily bread, and keep to my own house. There are a few men left . . . whom I sometimes visit and whom I can depend upon to help me when they can, and I receive occasional gifts from people who admire me as a poet or respect me as a good and unworldly man. I am usually in debt, and I live in great poverty." [39]

He comforted himself with the thought that since he had nothing, he would at any rate be spared the attentions of all those who harrass wealthier men.

38. Cf. I.139.20-21.
39 *Zikr i Mīr* (Rāmpūr MS), ap. Khwāja Aḥmad Fārūqī, pp. 207–208. This passage does not occur in the published edition of *Zikr i Mīr*.

غم زمانہ سے فارغ ہیں مایہ باختگاں

قمارخانہٴ آفاق میں ہے ہاری ہی جیت

In times like these, those who have lost their all live free from care.
This is the sort of gambling house where only loss is gain.

(III.388.18)

He began to spend long periods in the seclusion of his own home. "Many times the Emperor sent for me, but I did not go. Abul Qāsim Khān . . . was very kind to me, and I occasionally used to visit him. From time to time the Emperor would send me something. I still write a line of poetry now and then, but that is all the world holds for me now." At another point he speaks with high praise of the Deputy Vazīr, Hasan Raza Khān, whom he describes as a good man, distinguished above all for his unstinting generosity. "Not only I, but many others, owe much to his kindness." [40]

As the years went by he made up his mind that he would leave Delhi as soon as opportunity offered. But as long as he had no money, this was out of the question, and it was not until 1782 that the opportunity came. In that year it was suggested to Āsaf ud Daula, who had succeeded Shuja ud Daula as ruler of Oudh in 1775, that he should send Mir enough money to cover the expenses of the journey and invite him to settle in Lucknow. Āsaf ud Daula did so, and Mir at once set out. There he was kindly received by Āsaf ud Daula in person, and fitting provision was made for all his needs. It is safe to say that nothing but the need to find conditions of comparative security in his declining years (he was now sixty years old) would have persuaded him to forsake Delhi. As it was, he was one of the last to go. Sauda, who was by no means the first poet of note to migrate elsewhere, had left twenty-five years earlier, and after Mir's departure only one poet of major importance—the mystic poet Mir Dard—was left there. One wonders how he would have fared if he had not left when he did, for in the same year, 1782, there was a severe famine in the Delhi district in which half of the total population died. [41]

---

[40] Zikr i Mīr, pp. 135 and 136.
[41] Spear, India, Pakistan and the West, p. 168. However, there seems to be some doubt whether this date is correct. The same author's Twilight of the Mughuls, p. 116, gives the date of the great famine as 1785.

Though almost all the famous poets of the day were now gathered in Lucknow, there is abundant evidence in Mir's poems of the deep regret he felt at leaving Delhi, the city which from his early youth had grown to be no less dear to him than Agra. Despite all the destruction, the city was still beautiful. To look at its lanes and side streets was like turning the pages in the album of a great painter, and wherever one looked, the scene that met one's eyes was itself a picture.[42] All the variety of the whole world was there:

ہفت اقلیم ہر گلی ہے کہیں

دلّی سے بھی دیار ہوتے ہیں

> The seven climes are in its every lane.
> Does Delhi have its equal anywhere?   (I.103.12)

The days of its greatest glory were past, but even now it seemed to him to preserve, more than any other place, the best values of Mughal India. It was the centre of the new Urdu poetry, the poetry which aspired to the heights already achieved by Persian, and the language of its people—"the language of the steps of the Jama Masjid"—was the raw material of that poetry. He felt a special warmth for the ordinary people of the capital and identified himself with them in their misfortunes:

متاع ہیں سب خوار ازاں جملہ ہوں میں بھی

> The craftsmen are all ruined now, and I am one of them.   (I.167.3)

He valued the appreciation with which they received his verse, and sometimes felt that they understood him better than the nobility did. He makes the point both in the innocent-seeming verse:

جیسی عزّت مرے دیواں کی امیروں میں ہوئی

ویسی ہی ان کی بھی ہوگی مرے دیوان کے بیچ

> I will write verses showing that I hold the great
> In that same honour as the great have held my verses[43]

(II.257.22)

[42] Allusion to I.146.19 and I.103.12.
[43] We have already seen the "honour" of the great that his verses express.

—and also quite directly, when he says:

شعر میرے ہیں سب خواص پسند
پر مجھے گفتگو عوام سے ہے

My verses are all liked by high society,
But it is to the people that I like to speak. (II.367.11)

In his autobiography, which was concluded six years after he had left Delhi forever, it is still political developments at Delhi which form the main thread of the narrative.

The traditional account of his arrival in Lucknow[44] well shows the intense pride in Delhi which he felt and which he was to continue to feel until his death. On the evening of his arrival he went to take part in a mushāira. He was not known by sight to those present, and the gathering of fashionable, modern young gentlemen, complacent in the conviction that they represented the finest product of the culture of the age, smiled at one another as they noted the newcomer's old-fashioned dress. All this was not lost on Mir, and when it was his turn to recite he rose and recited this verse:

ہم کو غریب جان کے ہنس ہنس پکار کے   کیا بود و باش پوچھو ہو پورب کے ساکنو!
رہتے تھے منتخب ہمی جہاں روزگار کے   دلی جو ایک شہر تھا عالم میں انتخاب
ہم رہنے والے ہیں اسی اجڑے دیار کے   اس کو فلک نے لوٹ کے ویران کر دیا

Why do you mock at me and ask yourselves
Where in the world I come from, easterners?
There was a city, famed throughout the world,
Where dwelt the chosen spirits of the age:
Delhi its name, fairest among the fair.
Fate looted it and laid it desolate,
And to that ravaged city I belong.

44 Āzād, *Āb i Ḥayāt*, p. 204.

After this his audience soon discovered who he was and hastened to make their apologies to him.

For some years after he had settled in Lucknow, a feeling of relief and thankfulness for his new-found security seems to have been uppermost in his mind, and in his autobiography, which takes us up to 1788, there is no indication that he was dissatisfied with his material position. Āsaf ud Daula gave him a stipend of three hundred rupees a month—considerably less than Sauda had received, if both figures are to be relied on, but more than that granted to most other poets, and, in any event, more than enough to provide for all his material needs.[45] In fact, Āsaf ud Daula is spoken of appreciatively in many passages. Mir accompanied him on hunting expeditions and wrote poems in which he gives an account of them. About one he writes in his autobiography,[46] "We went on a hunting expedition right to the foothills of the northern mountains [the Himalayas]. Although we experienced much hardship in covering so great a distance, we had never seen such game, or been in so lovely a setting or breathed such air. It was three months before we returned to the capital." He speaks highly of Āsaf ud Daula's skill as a poet, and seems to have felt it no burden in these years to fulfil his requests for the composition of particular poems.

But the words with which he ends his life story show that with all this he had not found peace in Lucknow. "The world is a place of strange vicissitudes," he writes.[47]

I have had eyes to see, and ears to hear, and what things have I not seen and heard! In this brief span of life this drop of blood which men call the heart has suffered all manner of blows, and is all bruised and bleeding. My temperament was unsuited to these times, and I no longer mix with people. I am sixty now, and old age is upon me.[48] I am generally ill, and for some time my eyes have been troubling me . . . . My failing powers, my sensitiveness, my weakness and grief and despondency, all tell me that my end is near, and the truth is that the times

---

[45] Cf. Khwāja Aḥmad Fārūqī, *Mīr Taqī Mīr*, p. 244. Saudā had been granted Rs.6,000 a year (according to accounts quoted by Shaikh Cānd in *Saudā*, pp. 61–62).
[46] *Ẕikr i Mīr*, p. 147.
[47] *Ẕikr i Mīr*, pp. 151–153.
[48] He was in fact more: perhaps 65 or 66.

are no longer fit to live in. It is time to withdraw from the world. I wish that I may come to a good end, but God's will must prevail.

The stylised, poetic prose which the fashion of the day dictated obscures to some extent the depth of feeling that lies beneath it, but his verse of this period—

"the guise in which he tells all that he has to tell" (II.365.24)—convinces one that he did indeed often feel that he had lived too long, and that death would be welcome. But another twenty-two years were to pass before his wish was to be realised, and as they dragged on, he came to feel an ever greater distaste for Lucknow and its whole atmosphere. For some years he seems to have received his stipend regularly and thus to have been free of any material worries. But he came more and more to feel that the treatment accorded to him was a mere formal rendering of what was conventionally due to a poet of his standing; for since Sauda's recent death in 1781, he was undisputedly the greatest Urdu poet living. His relations with Āsaf ud Daula himself became strained, and one day an incident occurred which led him virtually to sever his connection with the court.

The tradition is [49] that on one occasion Mir, at the request of Āsaf ud Daula, was reciting one of his ghazals. They were standing by a fishpond, and as Mir recited, the Navvāb was playing with the fish, touching them with the end of a stick which he held in his hand. After one or two lines Mir stopped. "Go on, Mir Sahib," said the Navvāb. "If Your Majesty will give me his attention, I will," replied Mir. The Navvāb replied casually, "Any worth-while line will compel my attention." Mir was so displeased at this incident that he stopped coming to the court. A few days later he was walking along the street when he saw the Navvāb's carriage coming towards him. The carriage stopped by him and the Navvāb said, "Mir Sahib, you seem to have forsaken me altogether. You never come to see me now." Mir replied brusquely, "This is no place to talk about it. Gentlemen don't discuss these things in the street." [50]

[49] Āzād, Āb i Ḥayāt, p. 205.
[50] Cited by Khwāja Ahmad Fārūqī, Mīr Taqī Mīr, p. 245.

This incident may well have made his breach with the court complete, though his stipend continued to be paid to him until Āsaf ud Daula's death in 1797 and, according to one authority, was still being paid three years later by Āsaf ud Daula's successor, Sa'ādat Ali Khān. But there seems to have come a time when even that ceased. At any rate the story is told[51] that one day Sa'ādat Ali Khān's carriage was passing through the streets and passed by a mosque near which Mir was sitting in a position overlooking the street. As the carriage drew level, everyone else stood up, but Mir remained seated. The poet Insha, a well-known younger contemporary of Mir, was in the Navvāb's immediate retinue, and the Navvāb turned to him and asked, "Insha, who is this man who is too proud to stand up?" Insha replied, "Sire, he is that proud pauper of whom we have often spoken to you. He is penniless, but see how proud he is! He has probably had nothing to eat all day." On his return Sa'ādat Ali despatched a palace servant to him with a ceremonial robe and a present of a thousand rupees. Mir would not take them. "I am not *so* poor," he said. "Give them to a mosque for charity." When this response was reported to Sa'ādat Ali, he was astounded. His courtiers explained the reason for Mir's reaction, and the Navvāb then instructed Insha to take the robe to Mir. Insha did so, urging him to accept it, if not for his own sake, then for the sake of his wife and family, adding, "It is a present from the ruling sovereign and you should accept it." Mir replied, "He is king of his own country, and I am king of mine. If a complete stranger had behaved as he has, it would have been understandable, and I would have had no cause to complain. But he knows who I am and what my present situation is. All this time he has shown complete indifference towards me, and then he sends some menial with a robe for me. I would rather stay poor and hungry than submit myself to such insult." Insha's eloquence persuaded him in the end to accept the gift, and thereafter he paid occasional visits to the court. But his relations with it remained tenuous for the rest of his life.

Mir's dissatisfaction was not only with the court. The cultural standards of Lucknow were changing, and in Mir's view changing very much for the worse. This was perhaps the inevitable result of the conditions of the time. When the eighteenth-century poets left Delhi in search of security

51 Āzād, *Āb i Ḥuyāt*, pp. 217–218.

elsewhere, it was natural that most of them should make for Oudh. It was remote enough from Delhi to escape involvement in the constant attacks of Afghans, Marāthas, Rohillas, Jāts, Sikhs, and others; and at the same time it was near enough for men to undertake the journey there—a perilous matter in those troubled times—more readily than they would have done to more distant centres. Oudh was one of the great powers in India, and after 1765 its security against attack by other Indian powers was further strengthened by alliance with the British, who were now felt to be a force to be reckoned with. The country was fertile and its rulers rich. Further, the rulers of Oudh consciously aspired to uphold in their dominions the values and traditions of Mughal India, including the tradition of generous patronage of literature and the arts. All these things attracted to their territories the emigrants from Delhi, and by the time Mir reached Lucknow, all the most famous poets had preceded him there. But Oudh was in fact a power already in decline. The British alliance had been imposed by force of arms, and though Shuja ud Daula seems to have tried to build up his resources with a view to ultimately reasserting his independence, the British saw to it that no such plan could be realised. When Āsaf ud Daula succeeded him, they imposed a new and more onerous treaty, and their inroads steadily increased until in 1856 Oudh was forcibly annexed to British territory.

Oudh's cultural decline was a logical consequence of this process. Whether from a sense of security in British "protection" or from a growing realisation that they were too firmly subordinated to British policies to play any independent role in Indian affairs, its rulers from Āsaf ud Daula onwards turned almost without exception to squandering their resources in all manner of ostentation. Their growing insignificance as political figures was matched by a growing self-conceit. Before Āsaf ud Daula's time they had been content to aim at continuing the best traditions of Mughal India; now they felt that Delhi's day was past, and that they could improve upon the old-fashioned ways of life which had been the standard there. One of Āsaf ud Daula's first acts was to move the capital from Faizābād to Lucknow, and here the change of cultural climate soon became very marked. Mir had a foretaste of it—if the traditional story is true—in the first mushāira he attended immediately after his arrival there.

There is no evidence that Mir grasped the causes of this cultural decadence, but he recognised it for what it was and reacted sharply against it. Lucknow had undertaken the task of (as it thought) giving polish and refinement to Urdu poetry. "Inelegant" words and loose grammar were henceforth to be excluded, and rules of diction, grammar, metre, and rhetoric were formulated to prevent the misguided from reverting to old, bad practices. Not all the work that Lucknow did in this respect was bad, but the spread of a literary taste which mistook technically accomplished versification for poetry was undoubtedly one of its results. Mir, who was now, since Sauda's death, undisputedly the greatest Urdu poet living, was angered by this presumption, and the stronger became Lucknow's conviction that Delhi's day was past and that Lucknow now set the standards, the more vigorously Mir asserted the contrary—that standard Urdu was the Urdu of Delhi, and the best models for poetry the work of the Delhi poets, including his own.

A traditional story of this period well illustrates the point.[52] On one occasion some prominent citizens of Lucknow went to call upon him, hoping to hear him recite his verses. The door was opened by an old maidservant, who, having enquired their business, went in, spread a piece of sacking on the floor, and asked them to be seated. She then prepared an ancient hookah for them to smoke and placed it before them, after which Mir came in. When the formalities of greeting were over, he was asked if he would recite. He was at first evasive, but being pressed, told them flatly that they would not understand his poetry. This of course they resented; but out of politeness they acknowledged their unworthiness, at the same time repeating their request. Mir again refused. At this one of them, unable to restrain his displeasure, said, "Come sir! We understand the poetry of Anvari and Khāqāni;[53] why should we not understand yours?" Mir replied, "Granted that you understand *them*; but there you have commentaries and vocabularies to help you; whereas one thing alone will help you to understand my verses—a knowledge of Urdu as you will hear it spoken on the steps of the Jama Masjid; and that knowledge you do not possess." He then recited one of his verses and said, "You will quote your books and tell me to give full weight to the *a* of *khayāl*, pointing out that in this line it is not taken into account. My answer to that is simply that I have used the word as the people of Delhi speak it."

52 *Ibid.*, p. 217.
53 Anvari (d. 1169–1170) is considered the greatest panegyrist of Iran in the Seljuqid period. Khāqāni (d. 1199) is thought to be his peer in the art of qaṣīda. (A.S.)

The great prophet of "correctness" in poetry was the Lucknow poet Nāsikh, a man whose writings are generally agreed to be practically devoid of any deep feeling. There is a tradition,[54] which may well be true, that when Nāsikh began to write verse, he approached Mir with a request to accept him as his shāgird, and that Mir refused.

If empty formalism was one aspect of the Lucknow trend in Urdu poetry, another was an increasing emphasis on themes of sexual pleasure. The poet Jurat was the most accomplished poet of these themes, and was very popular in Lucknow. There is a story[55] that Mir was once present at a mushāira where Jurat was reciting, and being so loudly applauded that at times it was difficult to hear what he was saying. Perhaps carried away by this applause, he approached Mir, and in language of the utmost deference, invited him to give his opinion. Mir frowned and made no reply. Jurat asked him a second time, and Mir made some noncommital remark. But Jurat would not be content with this, and pressed him further, whereupon Mir said, "The fact is that you can't write poetry; just stick to your kissing and slavering." This judgement could be interpreted as an expression of traditional puritanism, but the character of Mir's own verse speaks against such an interpretation. It is more likely that he is condemning the kind of love poetry in which most of what the word *love* implied for Mir was ignored and the concept of love was restricted to one of mere sexual enjoyment.

Mir's aversion to Lucknow grew more and more intense with the years, and one can trace the development of his feelings through the last three collections of his ghazals—the fourth, fifth, and sixth dīvāns—all of which were compiled after he had settled there. In the fourth he writes,

The ruins of Jahānābād were ten times better than Lucknow;
Oh, that I had stayed there to die—not come to live distracted here.
(IV.505.23)[56]

---

54 Āzād, *Āb i Ḥayāt*, p. 215.
55 *Ibid.*, pp. 237–238.
56 Cf. IV.463.7–8.

And in another verse, which does not mention Lucknow by name, he says that there is something wrong with a man who goes on living in a land that has no talented men.[57] The clear implication, that he still hoped even at this advanced age to find refuge in some more congenial place, is repeatedly made explicit in his fifth dīvān, compiled when, as one of his verses tells us, he had been living there "for years" (V.566.9). One whole ghazal in it is devoted to this theme. "Now I shall arise from here and go away; and never shall I come this way again," it begins (V.541.7). The city seems desolate, as though its human population had left it and the owls had moved into the empty city—so that "it is hard for a *man* [the word is deliberately emphasised] to live here any longer" (V.570.7). The word *owls* is deliberately and insultingly chosen, first because, as a bird that is commonly found in deserted ruins, it is a bird of ill-omen, and secondly because in colloquial Urdu it means a fool.

In the sixth dīvān this bitterness dies away. Rather, he laments his loneliness, which he feels more and more keenly as one by one his few remaining friends die, leaving him to long for death to release him from his imprisonment "within the four walls of the world." There is no more any sign that he still has hopes of leaving Lucknow, and in fact he never did.[58] Personal misfortunes added to the burden he had to bear. His health was failing and he was losing his sight. In three successive years he lost a son, a daughter, and his wife, to all of whom he had been deeply attached; and finally, he fell seriously ill with a painful disease of the bowels. But from this he never recovered, and in 1810, in his eighty-seventh or eighty-eighth year, he died.[59] In spite of all his afflictions, he had gone on writing poetry and attending mushāiras even in his last years. He writes:

I have no other work to occupy me now.
In season, out of season, I recite my verse.   (V.622.25)

---

[57] Allusion to IV.529.21–22.
[58] Allusions to VI.640.22 and VI.649.21.
[59] Cf. Āsī's account in the Introduction to his edition of the *Kulliyāt*, pp. 32ff.

He knows that his time is drawing to a close, but he claims proudly:

کوئی دُم رونق مجلس کی اور بھی ہر اس دم کے ساتھ

یعنی چراغ صبح سے ہیں ہم دم بھی اپنا غنیمت ہے

Some moments more this gathering gains lustre from my name.
Night passes, and the lamp burns low; yet men see by its flame.

(V.608.16)

One of the most striking features of his last dīvāns is the number of verses in which he continues to assert the same values that his poetry had proclaimed ever since he first made his name. Some of these are expressed in words almost identical with verses he had written many years earlier. One short poem in the last dīvān of all can fairly be described as his last testament as a poet.

باتیں ہماری یاد رہیں گی پھر باتیں ایسی نہ سُنیے گا

پڑھتے کسی کو سُنیے گا تو دیر تلک سر دُھنیے گا

سعی و تلاش بہت سی رہے گی، اس انداز کے کہنے کی

صحبت میں علما فضلا کی جا کر پڑھیے گنیے گا

دل کی تسلی جب کہ ہو گی گفت و شنود سے لوگوں کی

آگ بجھے گی غم کی بدن میں اس میں جلیے بجھنیے گا

گرم اشعار میر درد و نہ داغوں سے یہ بھر دیں گے

زرد رؤ شہر میں پھریے گا گلیوں میں گل چُنیے گا

A fairly free prose translation is: "Remember well my verse; you will not hear its like again. You will hear someone reciting it and long shake your head as you sit and wonder at it. If you would write as I did, long and earnestly must you seek. You must study in the company of men of learning and culture, and ponder what you learn from them. And when you have learned all you can from them, the fire of grief must kindle within you, and in that fire you must burn. Then the burning verses of Mir will sear all your heart, and you will roam pale and wan through the city.'' The original poem is a ghazal of four couplets, unusual not only because of its single, continuous theme but also because of its use of internal rhyme and the extreme freedom of its metre (VI.629.6). Its basic pattern is that of the fifteen long syllables (seven spondees and a single long at the end) of which he grew increasingly fond over the years.[60] But the variations are, in this poem, almost unlimited, with ‿‿ — as well as —‿‿ alternating with the basic — —, as though Mir were forcefully asserting the right that his mastery gave him to establish his own norms where he chose to do so. It deserves verse translation, but a comparable effect in English verse cannot be achieved. In short, his message is what it had been right from the start, that a poet must master his craft, but only if he speaks out of the deep pain of a passionate spiritual experience will he really be a poet.

Mir is buried in Lucknow. The graveyard in which he lies is a large one. Many of the tombs have through years of long neglect lost all distinguishing marks, and moreover, part of the cemetery was destroyed when the railway was built. At all events the site of Mir's grave is now unknown. One as accustomed as he was to indifference and neglect would perhaps not have minded too much, for he had long been convinced that he had raised his own memorial, and that it would be more lasting than any tomb. In one of his first poems he had claimed:

جاہے کا نہیں شورسخن کامرے ہرگز
تا حشر جہاں میں مرادیوان رہے گا

My verse endures eternal down the years:
As long as the world lasts, so will my fame. (I.5.12)

[60] Cf. above, p. 213.

And in one of his last he repeats the claim, more quietly, but just as confidently; for he knows that the poetry of his heart speaks to the hearts of his fellow men:

خاک کا پتلا ہے آدم جو کوئی اچھی کہے

عالمِ خاک میں برسوں تئیں وہ بات رہے

Man was first made of clay, and if the song you sing is good
This world of clay for years to come will listen to your voice.

(VI.675.5)

A Complete Ghazal of Mir

TRANSLATIONS of ghazals or of parts of ghazals have been given on pages 128, 148, 175, 177, and 196–197. That which is most nearly complete is that on pages 196–197, which omits only three couplets from the original poem of twelve. In the originals double rhyme has been used in every case, but only in the translation on page 128 have we found it possible to reproduce this feature in translation. In one important respect none of the ghazals translated is typical, for all of them possess a unity of theme or mood which the typical ghazal does not. We have found it impossible to reproduce in tolerable English verse, preserving the rhyme scheme of the original, any more fully typical Urdu ghazal than these. In default of this we give here a whole ghazal of Mir, followed by a full description and a literal prose translation with brief explanatory notes where these seem necessary.

الٹی ہوگئیں سب تدبیریں کچھ نہ دوا نے کام کیا ۔۔۔ دیکھا اس بیماریِ دل نے آخر کام تمام کیا

عہدِ جوانی رو رو کاٹا پیری میں لیں آنکھیں موند ۔۔۔ یعنی رات بہت تھے جاگے صبح ہوئی آرام کیا

حرف نہیں جاں بخشی میں اس کی خوبی اپنی قسمت کی ۔۔۔ ہم سے جو پہلے کہہ بھیجا سو مرنے کا پیغام کیا

ناحق ہم مجبوروں پر یہ تہمت ہے مختاری کی ۔۔۔ چاہتے ہیں سو آپ کریں ہیں ہم کو عبث بدنام کیا

بائکے ٹیڑھے تر چھے تیسکے سب کا تجھ کو امام کیا

کوسوں اُس کی اُور گئے پر سجدہ ہر ہر گام کیا

کوچے کے اس کے باشندوں نے سب کو ہیں سلام کیا

جُبّہ، خرقہ، کُرتا، ٹوپی، مستی میں الغام کیا

آنکھ مُندے پر اُن نے گو دیدار کو اپنے عام کیا

رات کو رد و صبح کیا یا دن کو جوں توں شام کیا

رُخ سے گل کو مول لیا، قامت سے سرو غلام کیا

بھولے اُس کے قول و قسم پر ہائے خیالِ خام کیا

استغنا کی جو گنی اُن نے جوں جوں میں ابرام کیا

سحر کیا، اعجاز کیا، جن لوگوں نے تجھ کو رام کیا

قشقہ کھینچا، دیر میں بیٹھا، کب کا ترکِ اسلام کیا

سلے رند و باش جہاں کے تجھ سے سجود میں رہتے ہیں

سرزدِ ہم سے بے ادنی تو وحشت میں بھی کم ہی ہوئی

کس کا کعبہ، کیسا قبلہ، کون حرم ہے، کیا احرام

شیخ جو ہے مسجد میں ننگا، رات کو تھا میخانے میں

کاش اب برقع مُنھ سے اٹھاۓ در نہ پھر کیا حاصل ہے

یاں کے سپید و سیاہ میں ہم کو دخل جو ہے سو اتنا ہے

صبح چمن میں اس کو کہیں تکلیف ہوا لے آئی تھی

ساعدے میں دونوں اُس کے ہاتھ میں لا کر چھوڑ دیے

کام ہوۓ ہیں سلے ضائع ہر ساعت کی سباحت سے

ایسے آہوۓ رم خوردہ کی وحشت کھونی مشکل تھی

میرے کے دین و مذہب کو اب پوچھتے کیا ہو اُن نے تو

The ghazal is from Mir's first dīvān.[1] It has fifteen couplets, and its themes include, among others, the life-long suffering which the lover must bear (couplets 1 and 2), God's injustice to man (4, 10), the poet's acknowledged pre-eminence among rakes and profligates—i.e., among mystics (5), the mystic's contempt for religious formalities and for those who uphold them (7, 8, 15), the great beauty of the beloved (11), and the beloved's timidity, elusiveness, fickleness, and inaccessibility (12, 13, 14). Thus there is no unity of theme in the ghazal as a whole; nor are the couplets on similar themes always grouped together.

[1] *Kulliyāt*, p. 4.

It is worth elaborating a little at this point the suggestion made earlier that the contrasting close unity of form and disunity of themes stems in great measure from the oral tradition of Urdu poetry. The ghazal was composed to be recited, not to be read, and where there was a prescribed line, fixing metre and rhyme for a whole succession of ghazals (cf. above, page 4), frequent variation of theme was a necessary measure to prevent monotony. Moreover, recitation with a pause after each couplet in order for the audience to react emphasised the completeness of each in a way which the printed page does not.

The rhyme scheme of the original is one syllable of qāfia (rhyme)—italicised in the transcription below—followed by three of radīf (end rhyme), thus:

First couplet:	*kām* (a)	kiya	A
	ta*mām* (a)	kiya	A
Second:	ānkhen	mūnd	B
	ā*rām* (a)	kiya	A
Third:	qismat	kī	C
	pai*ghām* (a)	kiya	A

and so on.

The metre is that described above, page 213—basically a line of fifteen longs (seven spondees followed by a single long syllable). There is a caesura after the fourth spondee, and the beat of the rhythm falls on the first, third, fifth, etc., syllables. But in the whole poem only one half-couplet (the first half of the fourth couplet) exemplifies this pattern:

nāhaq ham majbūron par yih tuhmat hai mukhtārī kī

Elsewhere two shorts may replace a long in any of the even syllables (second, fourth, sixth, etc.) except the eighth (which immediately precedes the caesura) and the fifteenth (the final syllable of the line). Thus the possibilities of variation are considerable. A full analysis gives the following figures:

| First foot: | 16 spondees; | 14 dactyls |
| Second foot: | 26 spondees; | 4 dactyls |

Third foot: 16 spondees;   14 dactyls
Fourth foot: 30 spondees;   0 dactyls
   (preceding the caesura)
Fifth foot: 16 spondees;   14 dactyls
Sixth foot: 24 spondees;   6 dactyls
Seventh foot: 12 spondees;   18 dactyls
Last single syllable always long.

It is noticeable that in the second, fourth, and sixth feet there is a heavy preponderance of spondees, and that it is in the first, third, fifth, and seventh feet that the dactyl most commonly replaces the spondee—in half the feet in question (60 out of a possible 120). This feature is emphasised by the fact that the rhyme-scheme necessarily produces the dactyl pattern in the seventh foot of every other half-couplet; but even if these feet are left out of account, 45 feet out of a possible 105 are dactyls.[2]

The first three couplets scan:

```
⎰ — — | — ∪ ∪ | — — | — — ‖ — ∪ ∪ | — — | — ∪ ∪ | —
⎱ — — | — — | — ∪ ∪ | — — ‖ — — | — ∪ ∪ | — ∪ ∪ | —
⎰ — ∪ ∪ | — — | — — | — — ‖ — — | — — | — — | —
⎱ — — | — ∪ ∪ | — — | — — ‖ — ∪ ∪ | — — | — ∪ ∪ | —
⎰ — ∪ ∪ | — — | — ∪ ∪ | — — ‖ — — | — — | — — | —
⎱ — ∪ ∪ | — — | — — | — — ‖ — — | — — | — ∪ ∪ | —.
```

The following is a literal translation of the ghazal. Each couplet is numbered and is followed by a brief explanation where necessary. Possible alternative interpretations are occasionally indicated, but these by no means exhaust the whole range of possible meanings:

1. All my plans have been overturned, and no medicine has had any effect. You see? This sickness of the heart [love] has killed me in the end [as I told you it would].

2. I passed the days of my youth in weeping, and in old age I closed my eyes. That is, I passed many nights in wakefulness, and when morning came I rested.

[2] However, in the first half of each couplet the seventh foot is a spondee in 12 cases out of 15.

There is a play on words here. The black hair of youth associated with the black nights, passed restlessly in the black despair of separation, contrasts with the white hair of old age, associated with the white light of dawn and peace and sleep.

3. I do not question her life-giving power. It is just the excellence of my fortune that the first message that she sent me was my sentence of death.

The beloved has power of life and death over her lover: one word from her can save him, and one word can kill him. It is his good fortune that her message, rejecting his love, is equivalent to sentence of death upon him. "Good fortune" may be ironical, or it could be literal, for it *is* good fortune to have the opportunity to die for one's love. The verse could also be interpreted in a mystic sense.

4. We act under constraint, and you slander us when you say we have free will. It is your will that is done, and we are blamed without cause.

A complaint against God.

5. All the rakes and profligates of the whole world bow down before you. The proud, the perverse, the awkward, the independent—all have acknowledged you their leader.

Mir addressing himself. He is the supreme profligate, the leader of all lovers of beauty—that is, of mystic worshippers of God.

6. If even in my distracted state I have been guilty of any want of respect [in daring to approach her], then it was little enough. For mile after mile as I made my way towards her, I fell down to worship her at every step.

Could be literal or mystical. The falling down perhaps also suggests the constant stumbling and falling as the lover makes his way through the thorns and briars of the wilderness of love.

7. What do we care for the Ka'ba, and the direction in which we should turn to pray, and the holy places and the robes of Pilgrimage? We who live in her lane have said farewell to all these things.

In the mystic sense. The constant lover never leaves the lane where his beloved lives. We who are constant in love for the Divine Beloved hold the formalities of religion as of no account.

8. If the shaikh stands naked in the mosque today it is because he spent the night drinking in the tavern, and in his drunkenness gave his cloak and gown and shirt and hat away.

Two points, perhaps. First a jeer at the shaikh's hypocrisy. And second, an expression of praise for the power of beauty, which even the shaikh cannot resist forever.

9. If only she would lift the veil from her face *now*. What will it profit me if when my eyes are closed [in death] she unveils herself for all to see?

Also could be taken in a mystic sense.

10. What can we do with the black and white of this world?[3] If anything, then only this, that we can see the [black] night out with constant weeping, and bear the toil of the [white] day until evening comes.

Perhaps a complaint to God, perhaps a more general lament on his sense of helplessness in the turbulent times in which he lived.

11. At morning in the garden she walked out to take the air. Her cheek made the rose her slave, and her graceful stature made the cypress her thrall.

So far did her cheek surpass the rose in beauty, and her stature the cypress in grace.

12. I held her silver-white wrists in my hands, but she swore [that she would come to me later], and I let them go. How raw and inexperienced I was to trust her word!

Not easily interpreted in a mystic sense.

13. Every moment I beseeched her, and this has brought all my efforts to nothing. Her proud indifference increased fourfold with every time I importuned her.

[3] I.e., what power have we to influence the course of events?

14. Such a timid, fleet gazelle does not easily lose her fear of man. Those who have tamed you have performed a wonder, as though by magic power.

Praise of his beloved's timid beauty, and envy of his successful rivals, who have won her favour when he could not.

15. Why do you ask at this late hour what Mir's religion is? He has drawn the caste mark on his forehead and sat down in the temple. He abandoned Islam long ago.

The worship of God through the worship of beauty, symbolised by Hindu idolatry.

BIBLIOGRAPHY
GLOSSARY
INDEX

BIBLIOGRAPHY

TEXTS OF THE POETRY

Saudā. *Kulliyāt*, ed. Mīr 'Abdur Rahmān Āhī. Delhi: Matba' i Muṣṭafā, A.H. 1272 (A.D. 1856). Later editions are unsatisfactory. No reliable text of the complete poetical works has yet been published.

Maṣnavī i Mīr Ḥasan, ed. 'Abdul Bārī Āsī. Lucknow: Newal Kishor, 1941.

Mīr Taqī Mīr, *Kulliyāt*, ed. 'Abdul Bārī Āsī. Lucknow: Newal Kishor, 1941. This edition is slightly less complete, but more accurate, than the later edition of 'Ibādat Barelavī.

WORKS ON THE POETS

Shaikh Cānd. *Saudā*. Aurangabad: Anjuman i Taraqqī i Urdū, 1936.

Mīr. *Zikr i Mīr*, ed. 'Abdul Ḥaq. Aurangabad: Anjuman i Taraqqī i Urdū, 1928.

Khwāja Ahmad Fārūqī. *Mīr Taqī Mīr: Ḥayāt aur Shā'irī*. Aligarh: Anjuman i Taraqqī i Urdū, 1954.

Qāzi 'Abdul Vadūd. Review of Fārūqī, *Mīr Taqī Mīr*, in two instalments in the periodical *Ma'āṣir*, Patna, August 1957 and January 1958.

Mahmūd Fārūqī. *Mīr Ḥasan aur khāndān ke dūsre shu'arā*. Lahore: Maktaba i Jadīd, 1953.

Muhammad Ḥusain Āzād. *Āb i Ḥayāt*, 14th printing. Lahore: Shaikh Mubārak 'Alī, n.d.

WORKS ON THE HISTORICAL SETTING

T. G. P. Spear. *India, Pakistan and the West*, 2nd ed. London: Oxford University Press, 1952.

Percival Spear. *Twilight of the Mughuls*. Cambridge University Press, 1951.

W. H. Moreland and Atul Chandra Chatterjee. *A Short History of India*, 3rd ed. London: Longmans, Green, 1953.

H. C. Rawlinson. *India: A Short Cultural History*. London: Cresset Press, 1952.

S. M. Edwardes and H. L. O. Garrett. *Mughal Rule in India*. London: Oxford University Press, 1930.

W. H. Moreland. *India at the Death of Akbar*. London: Macmillan, 1920.

William Irvine. *Later Mughals*, ed. Jadunath Sarkar. 2 vols. Calcutta: Sarkar, 1922.

Jadunath Sarkar. *Fall of the Mughal Empire*, 2nd ed. 4 vols. Calcutta: Sarkar, 1950.

SUGGESTIONS FOR FURTHER READING

Critical studies of Urdu literature, whether in Urdu or in English, tend to be unsatisfying. Old-style Urdu critics have followed the characteristically medieval tradition of evaluating poetry solely in terms of formal and technical accomplishment, without reference to the content of the poetry; and this tradition is still alive, though overshadowed now by more modern trends. Modern criticism came into existence a little less than a century ago, and was much influenced by nineteenth-century English writing—notably by Macaulay. This English influence unfortunately made its impact at a time when imaginative sympathy with medieval ways of thought and feeling was at a low ebb in Britain, and such lack of sympathy is still evident in both Urdu and English writings. There are three histories of Urdu literature in English:

T. Grahame Bailey. *Urdu Literature*. Calcutta: Association Press (Y.M.C.A.), 1932.

Ram Babu Saxena. *History of Urdu Literature*. Allahabad: Ram Narain Lal, 1927.

Muhammad Sadiq. *History of Urdu Literature*. London: Oxford University Press, 1964.

Bailey's is a very short sketch. Saxena's is fuller and more readable. Sadiq's is the best and fullest to be published so far.

The culture and literature of medieval and renaissance Europe has been studied with an insight and a sympathy not yet to be found in studies of Urdu. For this reason, and because the parallels with Urdu poetry are often strikingly close, it is worth while to read a number of them. Recommended are:

C. S. Lewis. *The Allegory of Love*. London: Oxford University Press paperback, 1958.

———— *The Discarded Image*. Cambridge University Press, 1964.

J. Huizinga. *The Waning of the Middle Ages*. Harmondsworth: Penguin, 1958.

J. M. Cohen. *A History of Western Literature*. Harmondsworth: Penguin, 1956. Chaps. 1–10.

J. B. Broadbent. *Poetic Love*. London: Chatto and Windus, 1964.

In other European languages are:

Joseph Garcin de Tassy. *Histoire de la littérature hindouie et hindoustanie.* 3 vols. Paris: Labitte, 1870–1871.

Alessandro Bausani. *Storia delle letterature del Pakistan.* Milan: Nuova Accademia Editrice, 1958. Chaps. 1 and 2 are relevant.

For those who know enough Urdu the best introductions to Urdu poetry are still Muhammad Husain Āzād's *Āb i Hayāt,* first published in 1879; and Alṭāf Husain Hālī's *Muqaddima She'r o Shā'irī,* first published in 1893. For a brief note on *Āb i Hayāt* see p. 7, n. 4. It is constantly being republished and is rarely out of print. Of Hālī's *Muqaddima* the first half is a general discussion of the canons of poetry, and leans heavily on Macaulay, but the second half, with all its limitations, is a good survey of the major forms of classical Urdu poetry. The edition of Vahīd Quraishī (Lahore: Maktaba Jadīd, 1953) reproduces the text of 1893, is excellently printed, and has many useful annotations.

A readable essay on Urdu love poetry is Firāq Gorakhpūrī, *Urdū kī 'Ishqiya Shā'irī* (Allahabad: Sangam Publishing House, 1945).

THE PERSIAN AND ISLAMIC BACKGROUND

Since Urdu poetry is in a direct line of descent from the Persian, works on Persian literature are also relevant to an understanding of Urdu; and Persian is much better served than Urdu by translations and interpretative studies. Some of the most important, together with some works on Islamic mysticism and on Islam in general, are:

E. G. Browne. *A Literary History of Persia.* 4 vols. Cambridge University Press, 1951. This is the classic survey.

A. J. Arberry. *Classical Persian Literature.* London: Allen and Unwin, 1958.

———— *Sufism: An Account of the Mystics of Islam.* London: Allen and Unwin, 1950.

———— *An Introduction to the History of Sufism.* London: Longmans, Green, 1942.

———— *Fifty Poems of Hafiz.* Cambridge University Press, 1947.

R. A. Nicholson. *The Mystics of Islam.* London: Bell, 1914.

———— *Studies in Islamic Mysticism.* Cambridge University Press, 1921.

———— ed., *Jalāluddīn Rūmī's Mathnawī.* 8 vols. London: Luzac, 1925–1940. Edition of the text, with translations and commentary.

G. C. Anawati and Louis Gardet. *Mystique musulmane.* Paris: Vrin, 1961.

H. Ritter. *Das Meer der Seele.* Leiden: Brill, 1955. This gives the fullest account of classical Persian mysticism and its love-symbolism, and should be studied by everyone who wants to understand Persian, Turkish, or Urdu mystical poetry.

For the literary symbolism see:
F. Rückert. *Grammatik, Poetik und Rhetorik der Perser, herausgegeben von W. Pertsch.*
  Gotha: Perthes, 1874. (Reprinted 1967).
A. Pagliaro and A. Bausani. *Storia della letteratura Persiana.* Milan: Nuova Accademia Editrice, 1960.
H. A. R. Gibb. *Muhammadanism.* London: Oxford University Press, 1949.
R. Hartmann. *Die Religion des Islam.* Berlin: Mittler, 1944.
I. Goldziher. *Vorlesungen über den Islam.* Heidelberg: Winter, 1923.

SPECIALISED WORKS IN URDU

Important new work in Urdu on the eighteenth-century poets has been published since this book was written, including the following:
Khalīq Anjum. *Mirzā Rafīʿ Saudā.* Aligarh: Anjuman i Taraqqī i Urdū, 1966.
  This comprehensive study should supersede the pioneering work of
  Shaikh Cānd.
Delhi College Magazine, Special Mir Number. Delhi, 1962–1963.
Vahīd Quraishī. *Mīr Ḥasan aur un kā zamāna.* Lahore: Istiqlāl Press, 1959.
It is to be hoped that Urdu scholars will soon give their attention to producing definitive texts of the poets' works. *Kalām i Saudā,* ed. Khūrshīdul Islām (Aligarh: Anjuman i Taraqqī i Urdū, 1965), is a reliable text of a comprehensive selection of Saudā's verse. A definitive text of the collected verse is currently being prepared by Shamsuddīn Ṣiddīqī.

GLOSSARY

burqa‘
A loose, flowing garment worn in the Indian subcontinent by Muslim women who observe *parda* (purdah.) It envelops the whole body, from the crown of the head (which supports the garment) to the feet. Lace network, or a strip of thinner cloth across the eyes, enables the wearer to see while remaining fully protected from others' eyes.

dīvān
A collection of ghazals.

faqīr
Literally, a beggar; but the word has religious connotations also, and signifies one who spurns all worldly possessions and trusts in God to provide for him through the charity of his fellow men.

ghazal
A short lyric poem consisting of couplets independent of one another in meaning, but bound by a strict unity of form, that is, a uniform metre and a rhyming scheme AA, BA, CA, DA, etc. The predominant theme is love, which may be either literal or figurative.

hakīm
A physician who practises the traditional Greek system of medicine as modified by the Arabs.

jāgīr
An assignment to a noble of the land revenue from one or more villages in lieu of salary.

kulliyāt
The collected verse of a poet.

masnavī
A lengthy poem in the rhyme scheme AA, BB, CC, etc. In Urdu it is generally a love story. The shorter masnavīs are generally realistic and tragic; the longer have a stronger element of fantasy and the story has a happy ending.

mukhammas
A poem of five-line stanzas, rhyming AAAAX.

mushā'ira	A gathering at which poets assemble to recite their verse.
navvāb	Literally, one who exercises deputed power; in general roughly equivalent to the British title of Lord.
parda (purdah)	The system of strict segregation of women traditionally practised by Muslims in India and Pakistan (cf. p. 98).
parī	A supernatural being with magic powers, in the form of a beautiful woman.
qaṣīda	A lengthy poem rhyming AA, BA, CA, etc.; generally a panegyric ode.
shāgird	A pupil, or apprentice. A young poet in his capacity of apprentice to his ustād.
shaikh	Literally, an old man; hence, an elder; hence, the pillar of orthodox religion, always represented in poetry as a hypocrite and a Pharisee.
takhalluṣ	The poet's pen-name, always introduced into the closing couplet of the ghazal.
tazkira	A short account of poets, giving for each entry brief biographical details and a few specimen verses.
ustād	Literally, teacher, or master; the poet of established reputation in his capacity of guide to his shāgirds.
vazīr	Minister, usually Chief Minister; the "Vizier" of the *Arabian Nights*.

INDEX